Practice Masters

Glencoe

Algebra

Concepts and Applications

Glencoe McGraw-Hill

New York, New York   Columbus, Ohio   Woodland Hills, California   Peoria, Illinois

Glencoe/McGraw-Hill

A Division of The ***McGraw-Hill*** *Companies*

Send all inquiries to:
The McGraw-Hill Companies
8787 Orion Place
Columbus, OH 43240-4027

ISBN: 0-07-821544-7

Algebra
Practice Masters

1 2 3 4 5 6 7 8 9 10 024 07 06 05 04 03 02 01 00

CONTENTS

NAME ______________________ DATE __________ PERIOD ______

Practice

Student Edition
Pages 4–7

Writing Expressions and Equations

Write an algebraic expression for each verbal expression.

1. the product of 6 and s

2. five less than t

3. g divided by 4

4. 13 increased by y

5. two more than the product of 7 and n

6. the quotient of c and nine decreased by 3

Write a verbal expression for each algebraic expression.

7. $r + 4$

8. $8s$

9. $\frac{t}{5}$

10. $3n - 2$

Write an equation for each sentence.

11. Thirteen decreased by n is equal to 9.

12. Three times g plus five equals 11.

13. Eight is the same as the quotient of 16 and x.

14. Four less than the product of 6 and t is 20.

Write a sentence for each equation.

15. $8 - p = 1$

16. $6x + 3 = 21$

17. $18 \div c = 9$

18. $\frac{2q}{4} = 3$

NAME ______________________ DATE __________ PERIOD ______

Practice

Student Edition
Pages 4–7

Writing Expressions and Equations

Write an algebraic expression for each verbal expression.

1. the product of 6 and s

6*s*

2. five less than t

***t* − 5**

3. g divided by 4

$\frac{g}{4}$

4. 13 increased by y

13 + *y*

5. two more than the product of 7 and n

7*n* + 2

6. the quotient of c and nine decreased by 3

(*c* ÷ 9) − 3

7–10. Sample answers are given.

Write a verbal expression for each algebraic expression.

7. $r + 4$ **the sum of *r* and 4**

8. $8s$ **the product of 8 and *s***

9. $\frac{t}{5}$ ***t* divided by 5**

10. $3n - 2$ **3 times *n* minus 2**

Write an equation for each sentence.

11. Thirteen decreased by n is equal to 9. $13 - n = 9$

12. Three times g plus five equals 11. $3g + 5 = 11$

13. Eight is the same as the quotient of 16 and x. $8 = \frac{16}{x}$

14. Four less than the product of 6 and t is 20. $6t - 4 = 20$

Write a sentence for each equation. **15–18. Sample answers are given.**

15. $8 - p = 1$ **8 decreased by *p* is equal to 1.**

16. $6x + 3 = 21$ **The product of 6 and *x* increased by 3 equals 21.**

17. $18 \div c = 9$ **The quotient of 18 and *c* is the same as 9.**

18. $\frac{2q}{4} = 3$ **Two times *q* divided by 4 is 3.**

NAME ______________________ DATE __________ PERIOD ______

Practice

Order of Operations

Find the value of each expression.

1. $16 \div 4 - 3$

2. $6 + 9 \cdot 2$

3. $3(8 - 4) \div 2$

4. $6 \cdot 2 \div 3 + 1$

5. $21 \div [7(12 - 9)]$

6. $\frac{7 + 5}{3 \cdot 2}$

Name the property of equality shown by each statement.

7. $4 + d = 4 + d$

8. If $\frac{y}{3} = 9$ and $y = 27$, then $\frac{27}{3} = 9$.

9. If $3c + 1 = 7$, then $7 = 3c + 1$.

10. If $8 - n = 3 + 1$ and $3 + 1 = 2 \cdot 2$, then $8 - n = 2 \cdot 2$.

Find the value of each expression. Identify the property used in each step.

11. $6(9 - 27 \div 3)$

12. $4(16 \div 16) + 3$

13. $5 + (3 - 6 \div 2)$

14. $8 \div 2 \cdot 7(9 - 8)$

Evaluate each algebraic expression if s = 5 and t = 3.

15. $3(2s - t)$

16. $\frac{4s}{t - 1}$

17. $s + 3t - 8$

18. $s - \frac{t}{3} \cdot 5$

19. $(s + t) - 2 \cdot 3$

20. $3s - 4t + 2$

1–2

NAME ________________ DATE ________ PERIOD ______

Practice

Student Edition
Pages 8–13

Order of Operations

Find the value of each expression.

1. $16 \div 4 - 3$ **1**

2. $6 + 9 \cdot 2$ **24**

3. $3(8 - 4) \div 2$ **6**

4. $6 \cdot 2 \div 3 + 1$ **5**

5. $21 \div [7(12 - 9)]$ **1**

6. $\frac{7 + 5}{3 \cdot 2}$ **2**

Name the property of equality shown by each statement.

7. $4 + d = 4 + d$ **Reflexive**

8. If $\frac{y}{3} = 9$ and $y = 27$, then $\frac{27}{3} = 9$. **Substitution**

9. If $3c + 1 = 7$, then $7 = 3c + 1$. **Symmetric**

10. If $8 - n = 3 + 1$ and $3 + 1 = 2 \cdot 2$, then $8 - n = 2 \cdot 2$. **Transitive**

Find the value of each expression. Identify the property used in each step.

11. $6(9 - 27 \div 3)$

= 6(9 − 9) Substitution
= 6(0) Substitution
= 0 Mult. Prop. of Zero

12. $4(16 \div 16) + 3$

= 4(1) + 3 Substitution
= 4 + 3 Multiplicative Identity
= 7 Substitution

13. $5 + (3 - 6 \div 2)$

= 5 + (3 − 3) Substitution
= 5 + (0) Substitution
= 5 Additive Identity

14. $8 \div 2 \cdot 7(9 - 8)$

= 8 ÷ 2 · 7(1) Substitution
= 4 · 7(1) Substitution
= 4 · 7 Multiplicative Identity
= 28 Substitution

Evaluate each algebraic expression if s = 5 and t = 3.

15. $3(2s - t)$ **21**

16. $\frac{4s}{t - 1}$ **10**

17. $s + 3t - 8$ **6**

18. $s - \frac{t}{3} \cdot 5$ **0**

19. $(s + t) - 2 \cdot 3$ **2**

20. $3s - 4t + 2$ **5**

1–3

NAME ______________________ DATE __________ PERIOD ______

Practice

Student Edition
Pages 14–18

Commutative and Associative Properties

Name the property shown by each statement.

1. $43 + 28 = 28 + 43$

2. $(9 + 5) + 4 = 9 + (5 + 4)$

3. $(8 \cdot 7) \cdot 11 = 8 \cdot (7 \cdot 11)$

4. $12 \cdot 3 \cdot 6 = 3 \cdot 12 \cdot 6$

5. $(b + 22) + 3 = b + (22 + 3)$

6. $c \cdot d = d \cdot c$

7. $2n + 13 = 13 + 2n$

8. $15 \cdot (2g) = (15 \cdot 2) \cdot g$

Simplify each expression. Identify the properties used in each step.

9. $(m + 7) + 2$

10. $4 \cdot x \cdot 8$

11. $12 + k + 5$

12. $(y \cdot 3) \cdot 12$

13. $13 \cdot (3h)$

14. $7 + 2q + 4$

15. $6n + (9 + 4) + 5$

16. $(7 + p + 22)(9 \div 9)$

17. State whether the statement *Subtraction of whole numbers is associative* is *true* or *false*. If false, provide a counterexample.

NAME ________________ DATE ________ PERIOD ______

Practice

Student Edition
Pages 14–18

Commutative and Associative Properties

Name the property shown by each statement.

1. $43 + 28 = 28 + 43$
Commutative (+)

2. $(9 + 5) + 4 = 9 + (5 + 4)$
Associative (+)

3. $(8 \cdot 7) \cdot 11 = 8 \cdot (7 \cdot 11)$
Associative (×)

4. $12 \cdot 3 \cdot 6 = 3 \cdot 12 \cdot 6$
Commutative (×)

5. $(b + 22) + 3 = b + (22 + 3)$
Associative (+)

6. $c \cdot d = d \cdot c$
Commutative (×)

7. $2n + 13 = 13 + 2n$
Commutative (+)

8. $15 \cdot (2g) = (15 \cdot 2) \cdot g$
Associative (×)

Simplify each expression. Identify the properties used in each step.

9. $(m + 7) + 2$
$= m + (7 + 2)$ **Associative (+)**
$= m + 9$ **Substitution**

10. $4 \cdot x \cdot 8$
$= 4 \cdot 8 \cdot x$ **Commutative (×)**
$= 32x$ **Substitution**

11. $12 + k + 5$
$= 12 + 5 + k$ **Commutative (+)**
$= 17 + k$ **Substitution**

12. $(y \cdot 3) \cdot 12$
$= y \cdot (3 \cdot 12)$ **Associative (×)**
$= y \cdot 36$ **Substitution**
$= 36y$ **Commutative (×)**

13. $13 \cdot (3h)$
$= (13 \cdot 3) \cdot h$ **Associative (×)**
$= 39h$ **Substitution**

14. $7 + 2q + 4$
$= 2q + 7 + 4$ **Commutative (+)**
$= 2q + 11$ **Substitution**

15. $6n + (9 + 4) + 5$
$= 6n + 9 + (4 + 5)$ **Associative (+)**
$= 6n + 9 + 9$ **Substitution**
$= 6n + 18$ **Substitution**

16. $(7 + p + 22)(9 \div 9)$
$= (7 + 22 + p)(9 \div 9)$ **Comm. (+)**
$= (29 + p)(9 \div 9)$ **Subs.**
$= (29 + p)(1)$ **Subs.**
$= 29 + p$ **Mult. Identity**

17. State whether the statement *Subtraction of whole numbers is associative* is *true* or *false*. If false, provide a counterexample.
false; Sample counterexample: $(7 - 2) - 1 \neq 7 - (2 - 1)$

1–4 Practice

NAME ______________________ DATE __________ PERIOD ______

Student Edition
Pages 19–23

Distributive Property

Simplify each expression.

1. $3t + 8t$

2. $7(w + 4)$

3. $8c + 11 - 6c$

4. $2(3n - n)$

5. $5(2r + 3)$

6. $4(6 - 2g)$

7. $15d - 9 + 2d$

8. $(7q + 2z) + (q + 5z)$

9. $24b - b$

10. $6 + 2rs - 5$

11. $9(f + g)$

12. $8x + 2y - 4x - y$

13. $(3a + 2)7$

14. $5(2m - p)$

15. $3(2 - k)$

16. $9(2n + 4)$

17. $12s - 4t + 7t - 3s$

18. $4(2a - 3b)$

19. $(5m + 5n) + (6m - 4n)$

20. $8 + 5z - 6 + z$

21. $2(4x + 3y)$

22. $(hg - 1)7$

23. $13st + 5 - 9st$

24. $8 + 2r + 9$

25. $w + 10 - 4 + 6w$

26. $3(6 + c - 4)$

27. $4(2f - g)$

28. $2 + 7q + 3r + q$

NAME ______________________________ DATE ____________ PERIOD ______

Practice

Student Edition
Pages 19–23

Distributive Property

Simplify each expression.

1. $3t + 8t$ **11*t***
2. $7(w + 4)$ **7*w* + 28**
3. $8c + 11 - 6c$ **2*c* + 11**
4. $2(3n - n)$ **4*n***
5. $5(2r + 3)$ **10*r* + 15**
6. $4(6 - 2g)$ **24 − 8*g***
7. $15d - 9 + 2d$ **17*d* − 9**
8. $(7q + 2z) + (q + 5z)$ **8*q* + 7*z***
9. $24b - b$ **23*b***
10. $6 + 2rs - 5$ **1 + 2*rs***
11. $9(f + g)$ **9*f* + 9*g***
12. $8x + 2y - 4x - y$ **4*x* + *y***
13. $(3a + 2)7$ **21*a* + 14**
14. $5(2m - p)$ **10*m* − 5*p***
15. $3(2 - k)$ **6 − 3*k***
16. $9(2n + 4)$ **18*n* + 36**
17. $12s - 4t + 7t - 3s$ **9*s* + 3*t***
18. $4(2a - 3b)$ **8*a* − 12*b***
19. $(5m + 5n) + (6m - 4n)$ **11*m* + *n***
20. $8 + 5z - 6 + z$ **2 + 6*z***
21. $2(4x + 3y)$ **8*x* + 6*y***
22. $(hg - 1)7$ **7*hg* − 7**
23. $13st + 5 - 9st$ **4*st* + 5**
24. $8 + 2r + 9$ **17 + 2*r***
25. $w + 10 - 4 + 6w$ **7*w* + 6**
26. $3(6 + c - 4)$ **6 + 3*c***
27. $4(2f - g)$ **8*f* − 4*g***
28. $2 + 7q + 3r + q$ **2 + 8*q* + 3*r***

1–5 NAME ______________________ DATE ________ PERIOD ______

Practice

Student Edition
Pages 24–29

A Plan for Problem Solving

Solve each problem. Use any strategy.

1. Tara read 19 science fiction and mystery novels in 6 months. She read 3 more science fiction novels than mystery novels. How many novels of each type did she read?

2. Gasoline costs $1.21 per gallon, tax included. Jaime paid $10.89 for the gasoline he put in his car. How many gallons of gasoline did he buy?

3. A coin-operated telephone at a mall requires 40 cents for a local call. It takes quarters, dimes, and nickels and does not give change. How many combinations of coins could be used to make a local call?

4. Together, Jason and Tyler did 147 sit-ups for the physical fitness test in gym. Jason did 11 fewer sit-ups than Tyler. How many sit-ups did each person do?

5. The perimeter P of a square can be found by using the formula $P = 4s$, where s is the length of a side of the square. What is the perimeter of a square with sides of length 19 cm?

6. Mrs. Hernandez wants to put a picture of each of her 3 grandchildren on a shelf above her desk. In how many ways can she line up the pictures?

7. Leona is 12 years old, and her sister Vicki is 2 years old. How old will each of them be when Leona is twice as old as Vicki?

8. Gunther paid for 6 CDs at a special 2-for-1 sale. The CDs that he got at the sale brought the total number of CDs in his collection to 42. How many CDs did he have before the sale?

9. Phil, Ron, and Felix live along a straight country road. Phil lives 3 miles from Ron and 4 miles from Felix. Felix lives closer to Ron than he does to Phil. How far from Ron does Felix live?

10. Gere has 3 times as many shirts with print patterns as he does shirts in solid colors. He has a total of 16 shirts. How many shirts in print patterns does he have?

NAME ______________________ DATE __________ PERIOD ______

Practice

A Plan for Problem Solving

Solve each problem. Use any strategy.

1. Tara read 19 science fiction and mystery novels in 6 months. She read 3 more science fiction novels than mystery novels. How many novels of each type did she read? **8 mystery novels, 11 science fiction novels**

2. Gasoline costs $1.21 per gallon, tax included. Jaime paid $10.89 for the gasoline he put in his car. How many gallons of gasoline did he buy? **9 gal**

3. A coin-operated telephone at a mall requires 40 cents for a local call. It takes quarters, dimes, and nickels and does not give change. How many combinations of coins could be used to make a local call? **7 combinations**

4. Together, Jason and Tyler did 147 sit-ups for the physical fitness test in gym. Jason did 11 fewer sit-ups than Tyler. How many sit-ups did each person do? **Jason, 68; Tyler, 79**

5. The perimeter P of a square can be found by using the formula $P = 4s$, where s is the length of a side of the square. What is the perimeter of a square with sides of length 19 cm? **76 cm**

6. Mrs. Hernandez wants to put a picture of each of her 3 grandchildren on a shelf above her desk. In how many ways can she line up the pictures? **6 ways**

7. Leona is 12 years old, and her sister Vicki is 2 years old. How old will each of them be when Leona is twice as old as Vicki? **Leona, 20; Vicki, 10**

8. Gunther paid for 6 CDs at a special 2-for-1 sale. The CDs that he got at the sale brought the total number of CDs in his collection to 42. How many CDs did he have before the sale? **30 CDs**

9. Phil, Ron, and Felix live along a straight country road. Phil lives 3 miles from Ron and 4 miles from Felix. Felix lives closer to Ron than he does to Phil. How far from Ron does Felix live? **1 mi**

10. Gere has 3 times as many shirts with print patterns as he does shirts in solid colors. He has a total of 16 shirts. How many shirts in print patterns does he have? **12 shirts**

NAME ______________________ DATE __________ PERIOD ______

Practice

Student Edition
Pages 32–37

Collecting Data

Determine whether each is a good sample. Describe what caused the bias in each poor sample. Explain.

1. Every third person leaving a music store is asked to name the type of music they prefer.

2. One hundred students at Cary High School are randomly chosen to find the percentage of people who vote in national elections.

3. Two out of 25 students chosen at random in a cafeteria lunch line are surveyed to find whether students prefer sandwiches or pizza for lunch.

Refer to the following chart.

Favorite Leisure Activity									
S	R	C	C	S	R	R	C	S	C
M	S	C	C	C	M	C	C	S	R
S	S	R	M	M	C	M	S	C	R

C = computer games, M = movies,
R = reading, S = sports

4. Make a frequency table to organize the data.
5. What is the most popular leisure activity?
6. How many more people chose sports over reading?
7. Does the information in the frequency table support the claim that most people do not get enough exercise? Explain.

Refer to the following chart.

Number of Breakfasts Eaten Per School Week									
0	5	3	2	0	2	1	3	4	2
5	1	3	2	1	3	1	3	4	1
0	2	3	5	5	2	3	4	1	3

8. Make a frequency table to organize the data.
9. How many students eat breakfast fewer than 3 times per week?
10. Should the school consider a campaign to encourage more students to eat breakfast at school? Explain.

NAME ______________________ DATE __________ PERIOD _____

Practice

Student Edition
Pages 32–37

Collecting Data

Determine whether each is a good sample. Describe what caused the bias in each poor sample. Explain.

1. Every third person leaving a music store is asked to name the type of music they prefer. **Yes; the sample is random, appears to be large enough, and music stores sell all types of music.**

2. One hundred students at Cary High School are randomly chosen to find the percentage of people who vote in national elections. **No; students at a high school are not old enough to vote in national elections.**

3. Two out of 25 students chosen at random in a cafeteria lunch line are surveyed to find whether students prefer sandwiches or pizza for lunch. **No; the sample is not large enough.**

Refer to the following chart.

Favorite Leisure Activity									
S	R	C	C	S	R	R	C	S	C
M	S	C	C	C	M	C	C	S	R
S	S	R	M	M	C	M	S	C	R

C = computer games, M = movies,
R = reading, S = sports

Favorite Leisure Activity		
Type	**Tally**	**Frequency**
Computer Games	卌 卌 I	11
Movies	卌	5
Reading	卌 I	6
Sports	卌 III	8

4. Make a frequency table to organize the data.

5. What is the most popular leisure activity? **computer games**

6. How many more people chose sports over reading? **2**

7. Does the information in the frequency table support the claim that most people do not get enough exercise? Explain.
Sample answer: Yes; 22 out of 30 people preferred leisure activities that involve sitting. However, sports are not the only form of exercise.

Refer to the following chart.

Number of Breakfasts Eaten Per School Week									
0	5	3	2	0	2	1	3	4	2
5	1	3	2	1	3	1	3	4	1
0	2	3	5	5	2	3	4	1	3

Break. per School Week		
Number	**Tally**	**Frequency**
0	III	3
1	卌 I	6
2	卌 I	6
3	卌 III	8
4	III	3
5	IIII	4

8. Make a frequency table to organize the data.

9. How many students eat breakfast fewer than 3 times per week? **15**

10. Should the school consider a campaign to encourage more students to eat breakfast at school? Explain.
Yes; only 4 students out of 30 eat breakfast every school day.

NAME ________________________ DATE __________ PERIOD ______

Practice

Student Edition
Pages 38–43

Displaying and Interpreting Data

Use the table below for Exercises 1–4.

Year	U.S. Population
1960	179.3 million
1970	203.3 million
1980	226.5 million
1990	248.7 million

1. Make a line graph of the data. Use the space provided at the right.
2. For which ten-year interval was population growth the greatest?
3. Describe the general trend in the population.
4. Predict the U.S. population for the year 2000.

Use the table at the right for Exercises 5–8. In each age group, 100 people were surveyed.

Country Music Listeners	
Age Group	**Number**
10–19	10
20–29	15
30–39	35
40–49	40
50–59	25

5. Make a histogram of the data.
6. Which age group listens to country music the least?
7. How many respondents in the 40–49 age group listen to country music?
8. Suppose most listeners for a radio station are in their twenties. Should the station play a lot of country music? Explain.

Refer to the stem-and-leaf plot at the right.

Algebra Test Scores

Stem	Leaf
5	6 7 7 8
6	1 4 9
7	3 3 4 5 5 7 8
8	1 3 3 3 6 9
9	0 1 2 4

7 | 5 = 75

9. What were the highest and lowest scores?
10. Which test score occurred most frequently?
11. In which 10-point interval did most of the students score?
12. How many students scored 75 or better?
13. How many students received a score less than 75?

1–7 NAME ______________________ DATE ________ PERIOD ________

Practice

Student Edition
Pages 38–43

Displaying and Interpreting Data

Use the table below for Exercises 1–4.

Year	U.S. Population
1960	179.3 million
1970	203.3 million
1980	226.5 million
1990	248.7 million

1. Make a line graph of the data. Use the space provided at the right.

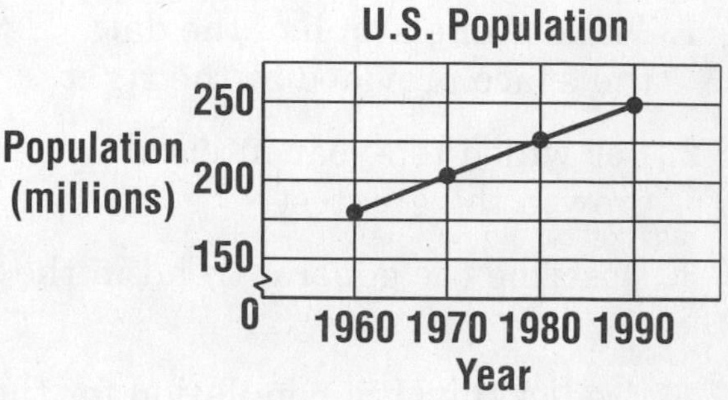

2. For which ten-year interval was population growth the greatest? **1960 to 1970**

3. Describe the general trend in the population. **steadily increasing every 10 years**

4. Predict the U.S. population for the year 2000. **Sample answer: 270 million**

Use the table at the right for Exercises 5–8. In each age group, 100 people were surveyed.

Country Music Listeners	
Age Group	**Number**
10–19	10
20–29	15
30–39	35
40–49	40
50–59	25

5. Make a histogram of the data.

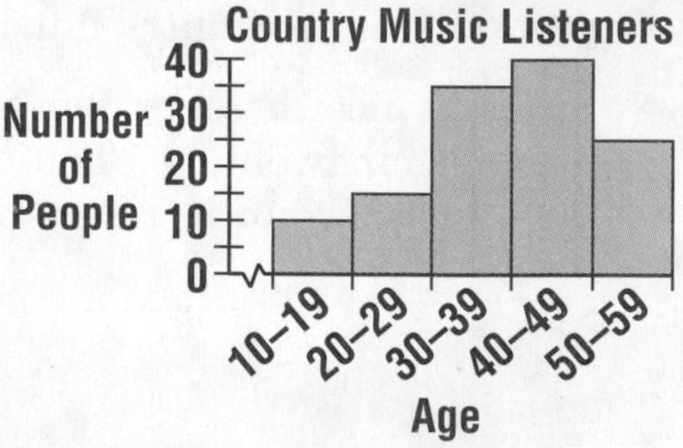

6. Which age group listens to country music the least? **10–19**

7. How many respondents in the 40–49 age group listen to country music? **40**

8. Suppose most listeners for a radio station are in their twenties. Should the station play a lot of country music? Explain. **Sample answer: No; most country music listeners are 30 or over.**

Refer to the stem-and-leaf plot at the right.

Algebra Test Scores

Stem	Leaf
5	6 7 7 8
6	1 4 9
7	3 3 4 5 5 7 8
8	1 3 3 3 6 9
9	0 1 2 4

7 | 5 = 75

9. What were the highest and lowest scores? **94 and 56**

10. Which test score occurred most frequently? **83**

11. In which 10-point interval did most of the students score? **70–80**

12. How many students scored 75 or better? **14**

13. How many students received a score less than 75? **10**

NAME ______________________ DATE __________ PERIOD ______

2–1 Practice

Student Edition
Pages 52–57

Graphing Integers on a Number Line

Name the coordinate of each point.

1. A
2. B
3. C
4. D
5. E
6. F

Graph each set of numbers on a number line.

7. $\{-5, 0, 2\}$

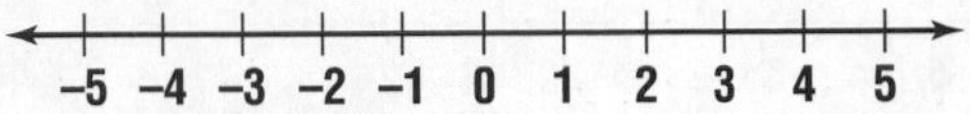

8. $\{4, -1, -2\}$

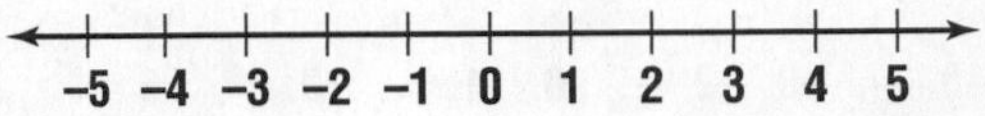

9. $\{3, -4, -3\}$

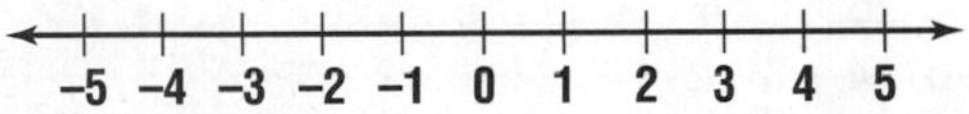

10. $\{-2, 5, 1\}$

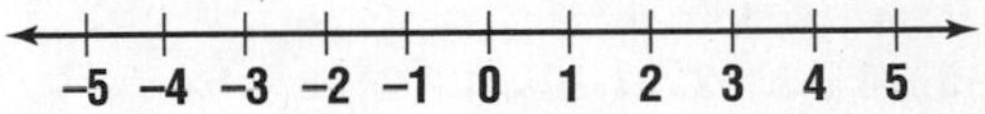

11. $\{2, -5, 0\}$

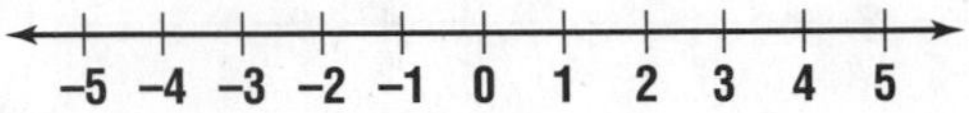

12. $\{-4, 3, -2, 4\}$

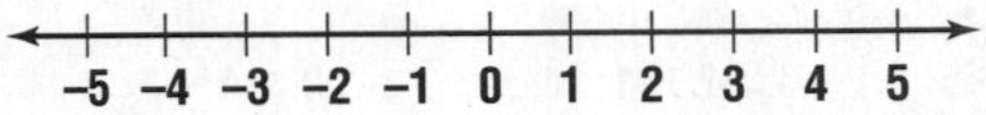

Write $<$ or $>$ in each blank to make a true sentence.

13. 7 ______ 9
14. 0 ______ −1
15. −2 ______ 2
16. 6 ______ −3
17. −4 ______ −5
18. −7 ______ −3
19. −8 ______ 0
20. −11 ______ 2
21. −5 ______ −6

Evaluate each expression.

22. $|-4|$
23. $|6|$
24. $|-3| + |1|$
25. $|9| - |-8|$
26. $|-7| - |-2|$
27. $|-8| + |11|$

Practice

Student Edition
Pages 52–57

Graphing Integers on a Number Line

Name the coordinate of each point.

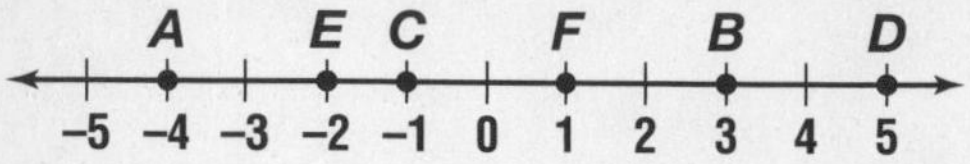

1. A **–4**
2. B **3**
3. C **–1**
4. D **5**
5. E **–2**
6. F **1**

Graph each set of numbers on a number line.

7. {–5, 0, 2}

8. {4, –1, –2}

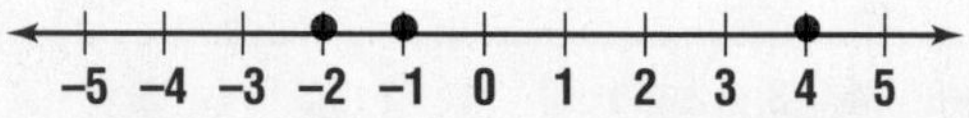

9. {3, –4, –3}

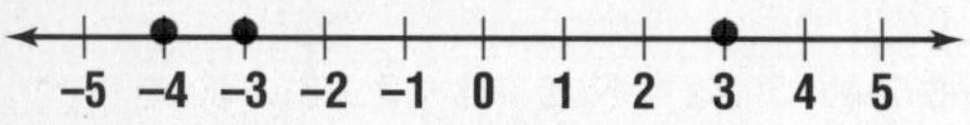

10. {–2, 5, 1}

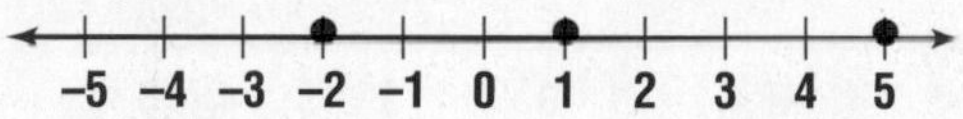

11. {2, –5, 0}

12. {–4, 3, –2, 4}

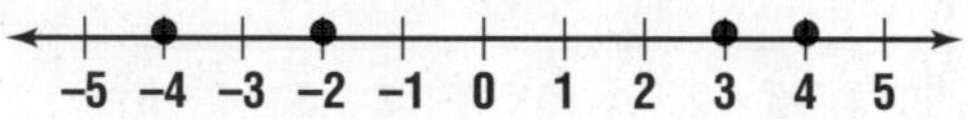

Write < or > in each blank to make a true sentence.

13. 7 ___<___ 9
14. 0 ___>___ –1
15. –2 ___<___ 2
16. 6 ___>___ –3
17. –4 ___>___ –5
18. –7 ___<___ –3
19. –8 ___<___ 0
20. –11 ___<___ 2
21. –5 ___>___ –6

Evaluate each expression.

22. $|-4|$ **4**
23. $|6|$ **6**
24. $|-3| + |1|$ **4**
25. $|9| - |-8|$ **1**
26. $|-7| - |-2|$ **5**
27. $|-8| + |11|$ **19**

NAME ______________________ DATE __________ PERIOD ______

Practice

The Coordinate Plane

Write the ordered pair that names each point.

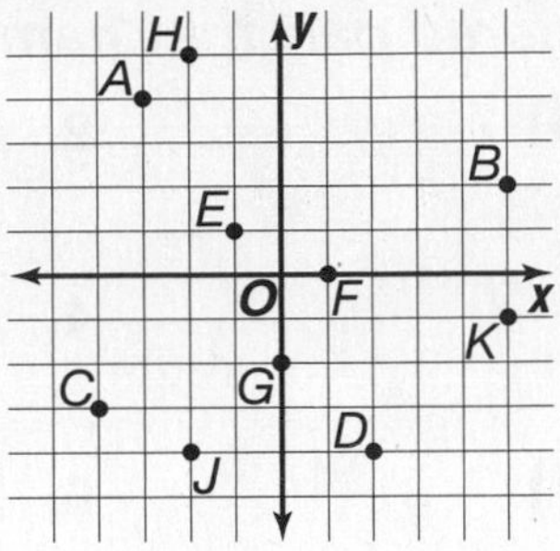

1. *A* **2.** *B*

3. *C* **4.** *D*

5. *E* **6.** *F*

7. *G* **8.** *H*

9. *J* **10.** *K*

Graph each point on the coordinate plane.

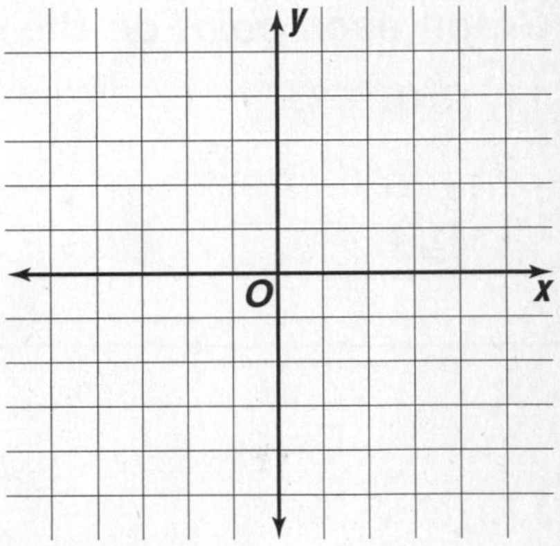

11. $K(0, -3)$ **12.** $L(-2, 3)$

13. $M(4, 4)$ **14.** $N(-3, 0)$

15. $P(-4, -1)$ **16.** $Q(1, -2)$

17. $R(-5, 5)$ **18.** $S(3, 2)$

19. $T(2, 1)$ **20.** $W(-1, -4)$

Name the quadrant in which each point is located.

21. (1, 9) **22.** (−2, −7)

23. (0, −1) **24.** (−4, 6)

25. (5, −3) **26.** (−3, 0)

27. (−1, −1) **28.** (6, −5)

29. (−8, 4) **30.** (−9, −2)

NAME ______________________ DATE __________ PERIOD ______

Practice

The Coordinate Plane

Write the ordered pair that names each point.

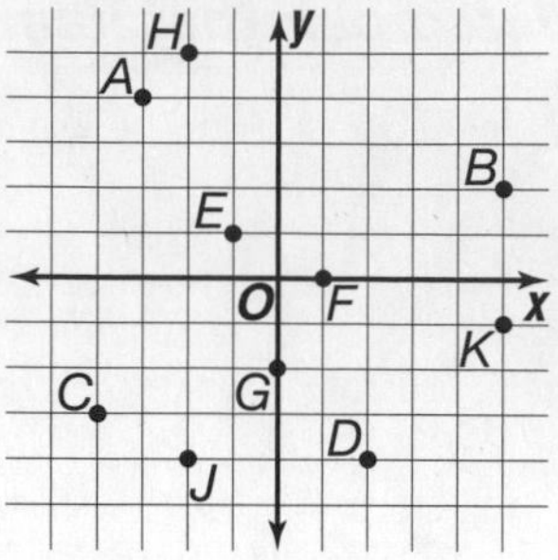

1. A **(−3, 4)**
2. B **(5, 2)**
3. C **(−4, −3)**
4. D **(2, −4)**
5. E **(−1, 1)**
6. F **(1, 0)**
7. G **(0, −2)**
8. H **(−2, 5)**
9. J **(−2, −4)**
10. K **(5, −1)**

Graph each point on the coordinate plane.

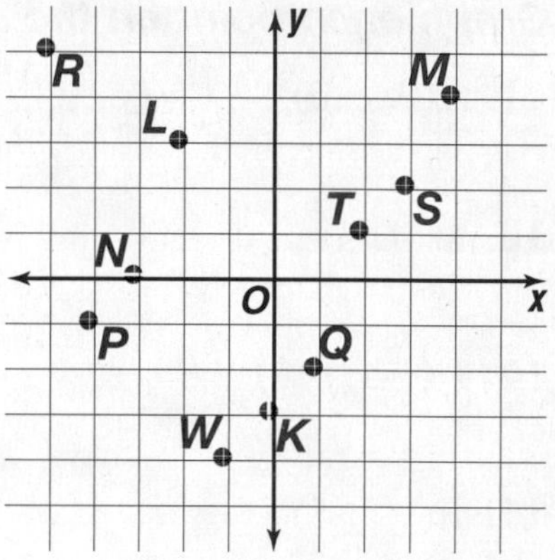

11. $K(0, -3)$
12. $L(-2, 3)$
13. $M(4, 4)$
14. $N(-3, 0)$
15. $P(-4, -1)$
16. $Q(1, -2)$
17. $R(-5, 5)$
18. $S(3, 2)$
19. $T(2, 1)$
20. $W(-1, -4)$

Name the quadrant in which each point is located.

21. (1, 9) **I**
22. (−2, −7) **III**
23. (0, −1) **none**
24. (−4, 6) **II**
25. (5, −3) **IV**
26. (−3, 0) **none**
27. (−1, −1) **III**
28. (6, −5) **IV**
29. (−8, 4) **II**
30. (−9, −2) **III**

NAME ______________________ DATE __________ PERIOD ______

Practice

Student Edition
Pages 64–69

Adding Integers

Find each sum.

1. $8 + 4$
2. $-3 + 5$
3. $9 + (-2)$
4. $-5 + 11$
5. $-7 + (-4)$
6. $12 + (-4)$
7. $-9 + 10$
8. $-4 + 4$
9. $2 + (-8)$
10. $17 + (-4)$
11. $-13 + 3$
12. $6 + (-7)$
13. $-8 + (-9)$
14. $-2 + 11$
15. $-9 + (-2)$
16. $-1 + 3$
17. $6 + (-5)$
18. $-11 + 7$
19. $-8 + (-8)$
20. $-6 + 3$
21. $2 + (-2)$
22. $7 + (-5) + 2$
23. $-4 + 8 + (-3)$
24. $-5 + (-5) + 5$

Simplify each expression.

25. $5a + (-3a)$
26. $-7y + 2y$
27. $-9m + (-4m)$
28. $-2z + (-4z)$
29. $8x + (-4x)$
30. $-10p + 5p$
31. $5b + (-2b)$
32. $-4s + 7s$
33. $2n + (-4n)$
34. $5a + (-6a) + 4a$
35. $-6x + 3x + (-5x)$
36. $7z + 2z + (-3z)$

NAME ______________________ DATE __________ PERIOD ______

Practice

Adding Integers

Find each sum.

1. $8 + 4$
12

2. $-3 + 5$
2

3. $9 + (-2)$
7

4. $-5 + 11$
6

5. $-7 + (-4)$
−11

6. $12 + (-4)$
8

7. $-9 + 10$
1

8. $-4 + 4$
0

9. $2 + (-8)$
−6

10. $17 + (-4)$
13

11. $-13 + 3$
−10

12. $6 + (-7)$
−1

13. $-8 + (-9)$
−17

14. $-2 + 11$
9

15. $-9 + (-2)$
−11

16. $-1 + 3$
2

17. $6 + (-5)$
1

18. $-11 + 7$
−4

19. $-8 + (-8)$
−16

20. $-6 + 3$
−3

21. $2 + (-2)$
0

22. $7 + (-5) + 2$
4

23. $-4 + 8 + (-3)$
1

24. $-5 + (-5) + 5$
−5

Simplify each expression.

25. $5a + (-3a)$
2*a*

26. $-7y + 2y$
−5*y*

27. $-9m + (-4m)$
−13*m*

28. $-2z + (-4z)$
−6*z*

29. $8x + (-4x)$
4*x*

30. $-10p + 5p$
−5*p*

31. $5b + (-2b)$
3*b*

32. $-4s + 7s$
3*s*

33. $2n + (-4n)$
−2*n*

34. $5a + (-6a) + 4a$
3*a*

35. $-6x + 3x + (-5x)$
−8*x*

36. $7z + 2z + (-3z)$
6*z*

2–4

NAME ______________________________ DATE __________ PERIOD ______

Practice

Student Edition
Pages 70–74

Subtracting Integers

Find each difference.

1. $9 - 3$ **2.** $-1 - 2$ **3.** $4 - (-5)$

4. $6 - (-1)$ **5.** $-7 - (-4)$ **6.** $8 - 10$

7. $-2 - 5$ **8.** $-6 - (-7)$ **9.** $2 - 8$

10. $-10 - (-2)$ **11.** $-4 - 6$ **12.** $5 - 3$

13. $-8 - (-4)$ **14.** $7 - 9$ **15.** $-9 - (-11)$

16. $-3 - 4$ **17.** $6 - (-5)$ **18.** $6 - 5$

Evaluate each expression if a = −1, b = 5, c = −2, and d = −4.

19. $b - c$ **20.** $a - b$ **21.** $c - d$

22. $a + c - d$ **23.** $a - b + c$ **24.** $a - c + d$

25. $b - c + d$ **26.** $b - c - d$ **27.** $a - b - c$

NAME ______________________________ DATE __________ PERIOD ______

Practice

Student Edition
Pages 70–74

Subtracting Integers

Find each difference.

1. $9 - 3$
6

2. $-1 - 2$
−3

3. $4 - (-5)$
9

4. $6 - (-1)$
7

5. $-7 - (-4)$
−3

6. $8 - 10$
−2

7. $-2 - 5$
−7

8. $-6 - (-7)$
1

9. $2 - 8$
−6

10. $-10 - (-2)$
−8

11. $-4 - 6$
−10

12. $5 - 3$
2

13. $-8 - (-4)$
−4

14. $7 - 9$
−2

15. $-9 - (-11)$
2

16. $-3 - 4$
−7

17. $6 - (-5)$
11

18. $6 - 5$
1

Evaluate each expression if a = −1, b = 5, c = −2, and d = −4.

19. $b - c$
7

20. $a - b$
−6

21. $c - d$
2

22. $a + c - d$
1

23. $a - b + c$
−8

24. $a - c + d$
−3

25. $b - c + d$
3

26. $b - c - d$
11

27. $a - b - c$
−4

NAME ______________________ DATE __________ PERIOD ______

Practice

Student Edition
Pages 75–79

Multiplying Integers

Find each product.

1. $3(-7)$
2. $-2(8)$
3. $4(5)$
4. $-7(-7)$
5. $-9(3)$
6. $8(-6)$
7. $6(2)$
8. $-5(-7)$
9. $2(-8)$
10. $-10(-2)$
11. $9(-8)$
12. $12(0)$
13. $-4(-4)(2)$
14. $7(-9)(-1)$
15. $-3(5)(2)$
16. $3(-4)(-2)(2)$
17. $6(-1)(2)(1)$
18. $-5(-3)(-2)(-1)$

Evaluate each expression if a = −3 and b = −5.

19. $-6b$
20. $8a$
21. $4ab$
22. $-3ab$
23. $-9a$
24. $-2ab$

Simplify each expression.

25. $5(-5y)$
26. $-7(-3b)$
27. $-3(6n)$
28. $(6a)(-2b)$
29. $(-4m)(-9n)$
30. $(-8x)(7y)$

NAME ______________________ DATE __________ PERIOD ______

2–5 Practice

Student Edition
Pages 75–79

Multiplying Integers

Find each product.

1. $3(-7)$
−21

2. $-2(8)$
−16

3. $4(5)$
20

4. $-7(-7)$
49

5. $-9(3)$
−27

6. $8(-6)$
−48

7. $6(2)$
12

8. $-5(-7)$
35

9. $2(-8)$
−16

10. $-10(-2)$
20

11. $9(-8)$
−72

12. $12(0)$
0

13. $-4(-4)(2)$
32

14. $7(-9)(-1)$
63

15. $-3(5)(2)$
−30

16. $3(-4)(-2)(2)$
48

17. $6(-1)(2)(1)$
−12

18. $-5(-3)(-2)(-1)$
30

Evaluate each expression if a = −3 and b = −5.

19. $-6b$
30

20. $8a$
−24

21. $4ab$
60

22. $-3ab$
−45

23. $-9a$
27

24. $-2ab$
−30

Simplify each expression.

25. $5(-5y)$
−25*y*

26. $-7(-3b)$
21*b*

27. $-3(6n)$
−18*n*

28. $(6a)(-2b)$
−12*ab*

29. $(-4m)(-9n)$
36*mn*

30. $(-8x)(7y)$
−56*xy*

Practice

Dividing Integers

Find each quotient.

1. $28 \div 7$
2. $-33 \div 3$
3. $42 \div (-6)$
4. $-81 \div (-9)$
5. $12 \div 4$
6. $72 \div (-9)$
7. $15 \div 15$
8. $-30 \div 5$
9. $-40 \div (-8)$
10. $56 \div (-7)$
11. $-21 \div (-3)$
12. $-64 \div 8$
13. $-8 \div 8$
14. $-22 \div (-2)$
15. $32 \div (-8)$
16. $-54 \div (-9)$
17. $60 \div (-6)$
18. $63 \div 9$
19. $-45 \div (-9)$
20. $-60 \div 5$
21. $24 \div (-3)$
22. $\frac{-12}{6}$
23. $\frac{40}{-10}$
24. $\frac{-45}{-9}$

Evaluate each expression if a = 4, b = −9, and c = −6.

25. $-48 \div a$
26. $b \div 3$
27. $9c \div b$
28. $\frac{ab}{c}$
29. $\frac{bc}{-6}$
30. $\frac{3c}{b}$
31. $\frac{12a}{c}$
32. $\frac{-4b}{a}$
33. $\frac{ac}{6}$

NAME ______________________ DATE __________ PERIOD ______

Practice

Dividing Integers

Find each quotient.

1. $28 \div 7$

   4

2. $-33 \div 3$

   −11

3. $42 \div (-6)$

   −7

4. $-81 \div (-9)$

   9

5. $12 \div 4$

   3

6. $72 \div (-9)$

   −8

7. $15 \div 15$

   1

8. $-30 \div 5$

   −6

9. $-40 \div (-8)$

   5

10. $56 \div (-7)$

    −8

11. $-21 \div (-3)$

    7

12. $-64 \div 8$

    −8

13. $-8 \div 8$

    −1

14. $-22 \div (-2)$

    11

15. $32 \div (-8)$

    −4

16. $-54 \div (-\ 9)$

    6

17. $60 \div (-6)$

    −10

18. $63 \div 9$

    7

19. $-45 \div (-9)$

    5

20. $-60 \div 5$

    −12

21. $24 \div (-3)$

    −8

22. $\frac{-12}{6}$

    −2

23. $\frac{40}{-10}$

    −4

24. $\frac{-45}{-9}$

    5

Evaluate each expression if a = 4, b = −9, and c = −6.

25. $-48 \div a$

    −12

26. $b \div 3$

    −3

27. $9c \div b$

    6

28. $\frac{ab}{c}$

    6

29. $\frac{bc}{-6}$

    −9

30. $\frac{3c}{b}$

    2

31. $\frac{12a}{c}$

    −8

32. $\frac{-4b}{a}$

    9

33. $\frac{ac}{6}$

    −4

NAME ______________________ DATE __________ PERIOD ______

Practice

Student Edition
Pages 94–99

Rational Numbers

Write <, >, or = in each blank to make a true sentence.

1. 2.5 ______ -2
2. -1 ______ 0.5
3. 0 ______ -1.9
4. -3.6 ______ -3.7
5. $-7(4)$ ______ $-15 + (-13)$
6. $-18 + 3$ ______ $5(0)(-3)$
7. $-5 + 19$ ______ $-2(7)(1)$
8. $6 - 24$ ______ $-3(2)(-4)$
9. $\frac{1}{4}$ ______ $\frac{1}{8}$
10. $-\frac{1}{2}$ ______ $\frac{3}{5}$
11. $\frac{3}{9}$ ______ $\frac{1}{3}$
12. $\frac{2}{5}$ ______ $-\frac{5}{10}$
13. $\frac{3}{8}$ ______ $\frac{2}{6}$
14. $\frac{4}{5}$ ______ $\frac{3}{4}$
15. $-\frac{2}{3}$ ______ $-\frac{4}{6}$
16. $-\frac{1}{5}$ ______ $\frac{2}{10}$

Write the numbers in each set from least to greatest.

17. $\frac{5}{6}, \frac{3}{8}, \frac{1}{3}$
18. $\frac{2}{5}, 0.\overline{3}, \frac{6}{8}$
19. $-\frac{5}{8}, -\frac{3}{4}, -\frac{4}{5}$
20. $-\frac{2}{3}, -\frac{5}{7}, -\frac{3}{5}$
21. $\frac{6}{10}, \frac{3}{4}, \frac{4}{6}$
22. $\frac{4}{10}, \frac{2}{8}, \frac{3}{9}$
23. $-\frac{2}{4}, -\frac{6}{9}, -\frac{7}{8}$
24. $\frac{8}{10}, -\frac{5}{6}, -\frac{6}{8}$

NAME ______________________ DATE __________ PERIOD ______

3–1 Practice

Student Edition
Pages 94–99

Rational Numbers

Write <, >, or = in each blank to make a true sentence.

1. 2.5 __>__ -2
2. -1 __<__ 0.5
3. 0 __>__ -1.9
4. -3.6 __>__ -3.7
5. $-7(4)$ __=__ $-15 + (-13)$
6. $-18 + 3$ __<__ $5(0)(-3)$
7. $-5 + 19$ __>__ $-2(7)(1)$
8. $6 - 24$ __<__ $-3(2)(-4)$
9. $\frac{1}{4}$ __>__ $\frac{1}{8}$
10. $-\frac{1}{2}$ __<__ $\frac{3}{5}$
11. $\frac{3}{9}$ __=__ $\frac{1}{3}$
12. $\frac{2}{5}$ __>__ $-\frac{5}{10}$
13. $\frac{3}{8}$ __>__ $\frac{2}{6}$
14. $\frac{4}{5}$ __>__ $\frac{3}{4}$
15. $-\frac{2}{3}$ __=__ $-\frac{4}{6}$
16. $-\frac{1}{5}$ __<__ $\frac{2}{10}$

Write the numbers in each set from least to greatest.

17. $\frac{5}{6}, \frac{3}{8}, \frac{1}{3}$ **$\frac{1}{3}, \frac{3}{8}, \frac{5}{6}$**
18. $\frac{2}{5}, 0.\overline{3}, \frac{6}{8}$ **$0.\overline{3}, \frac{2}{5}, \frac{6}{8}$**
19. $-\frac{5}{8}, -\frac{3}{4}, -\frac{4}{5}$ **$-\frac{4}{5}, -\frac{3}{4}, -\frac{5}{8}$**
20. $-\frac{2}{3}, -\frac{5}{7}, -\frac{3}{5}$ **$-\frac{5}{7}, -\frac{2}{3}, -\frac{3}{5}$**
21. $\frac{6}{10}, \frac{3}{4}, \frac{4}{6}$ **$\frac{6}{10}, \frac{4}{6}, \frac{3}{4}$**
22. $\frac{4}{10}, \frac{2}{8}, \frac{3}{9}$ **$\frac{2}{8}, \frac{3}{9}, \frac{4}{10}$**
23. $-\frac{2}{4}, -\frac{6}{9}, -\frac{7}{8}$ **$-\frac{7}{8}, -\frac{6}{9}, -\frac{2}{4}$**
24. $\frac{8}{10}, -\frac{5}{6}, -\frac{6}{8}$ **$-\frac{5}{6}, -\frac{6}{8}, \frac{8}{10}$**

NAME ______________________ DATE ____________ PERIOD ________

Practice

Student Edition
Pages 100–103

Adding and Subtracting Rational Numbers

Find each sum or difference.

1. $6.2 + (-9.4)$

2. $-7.9 + 8.5$

3. $-2.7 - 3.4$

4. $5.6 - 7.1$

5. $-8.3 + (-4.6)$

6. $4.2 - 1.9$

7. $3.7 + (-5.8)$

8. $-1.5 - 2.93$

9. $6.8 + (-4.6) + 5.3$

10. $-4.7 - 8.2 + (-2.5)$

11. $-\frac{1}{4} - \frac{3}{8}$

12. $\frac{1}{3} + \left(-\frac{5}{9}\right)$

13. $-3\frac{3}{8} + \left(-4\frac{1}{2}\right)$

14. $-2\frac{2}{3} + 2\frac{1}{2}$

15. $-7\frac{3}{10} - 2\frac{2}{5}$

16. $5\frac{1}{3} + \left(-3\frac{1}{6}\right)$

17. $2\frac{5}{6} - 6\frac{1}{2}$

18. $-6\frac{1}{5} + 4\frac{7}{10} + \left(-\frac{3}{5}\right)$

19. $3\frac{1}{2} + \left(-5\frac{5}{8}\right) + 3\frac{3}{4}$

20. $2\frac{2}{3} - 9\frac{1}{2} - 8\frac{5}{6}$

21. Evaluate $m + 4\frac{1}{8}$ if $m = -1\frac{3}{4}$.

22. Find the value of k if $k = -7\frac{1}{3} - 1\frac{5}{6} + 4\frac{2}{3}$.

NAME ______________________ DATE __________ PERIOD ______

Practice

Adding and Subtracting Rational Numbers

Find each sum or difference.

1. $6.2 + (-9.4)$ **−3.2**

2. $-7.9 + 8.5$ **0.6**

3. $-2.7 - 3.4$ **−6.1**

4. $5.6 - 7.1$ **−1.5**

5. $-8.3 + (-4.6)$ **−12.9**

6. $4.2 - 1.9$ **2.3**

7. $3.7 + (-5.8)$ **−2.1**

8. $-1.5 - 2.93$ **−4.43**

9. $6.8 + (-4.6) + 5.3$ **7.5**

10. $-4.7 - 8.2 + (-2.5)$ **−15.4**

11. $-\frac{1}{4} - \frac{3}{8}$ $\mathbf{-\frac{5}{8}}$

12. $\frac{1}{3} + \left(-\frac{5}{9}\right)$ $\mathbf{-\frac{2}{9}}$

13. $-3\frac{3}{8} + \left(-4\frac{1}{2}\right)$ $\mathbf{-7\frac{7}{8}}$

14. $-2\frac{2}{3} + 2\frac{1}{2}$ $\mathbf{-\frac{1}{6}}$

15. $-7\frac{3}{10} - 2\frac{2}{5}$ $\mathbf{-9\frac{7}{10}}$

16. $5\frac{1}{3} + \left(-3\frac{1}{6}\right)$ $\mathbf{2\frac{1}{6}}$

17. $2\frac{5}{6} - 6\frac{1}{2}$ $\mathbf{-3\frac{2}{3}}$

18. $-6\frac{1}{5} + 4\frac{7}{10} + \left(-\frac{3}{5}\right)$ $\mathbf{-2\frac{1}{10}}$

19. $3\frac{1}{2} + \left(-5\frac{5}{8}\right) + 3\frac{3}{4}$ $\mathbf{1\frac{5}{8}}$

20. $2\frac{2}{3} - 9\frac{1}{2} - 8\frac{5}{6}$ $\mathbf{-15\frac{2}{3}}$

21. Evaluate $m + 4\frac{1}{8}$ if $m = -1\frac{3}{4}$. $\mathbf{2\frac{3}{8}}$

22. Find the value of k if $k = -7\frac{1}{3} - 1\frac{5}{6} + 4\frac{2}{3}$. $\mathbf{-4\frac{1}{2}}$

Mean, Median, Mode, and Range

Find the mean, median, mode, and range of each set of data.

1. 33, 41, 17, 25, 62

2. 18, 15, 18, 7, 11, 12

3. 12, 27, 19, 38, 14, 15, 19, 27, 19, 14

4. 7.8, 6.2, 5.4, 5.5, 7.8, 6.1, 5.3

5. 13.5, 11.3, 10.7, 15.5, 11.4, 12.6

6. 0.7, 0.4, 0.4, 0.7, 0.4, 0.7

7. 5, 4.1, 4, 3.3, 2.7, 5.2, 3

8. 6.1, 4, 5.3, 6.7, 4, 5.1, 6.7, 4, 9.8, 6.1

9.

Stem	Leaf
6	2 3 5 7
7	2 7
8	0 1 1

6 | 3 = 63

10.

Stem	Leaf
3	1 1
4	2 5 6
5	3 3 7
6	2 5

5 | 3 = 53

11.

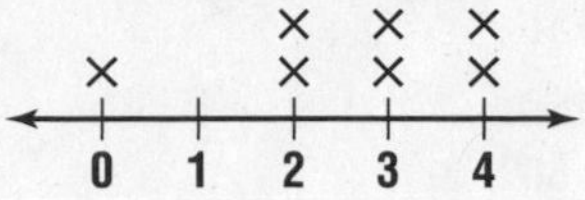

12.

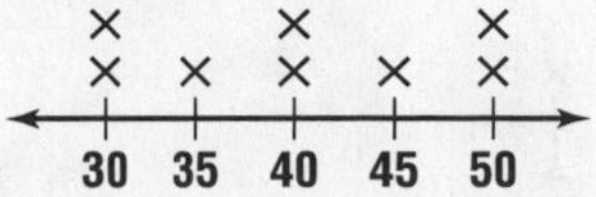

3–3

NAME ______________________ DATE __________ PERIOD ______

Practice

Student Edition
Pages 104–109

Mean, Median, Mode, and Range

Find the mean, median, mode, and range of each set of data.

1. 33, 41, 17, 25, 62

35.6; 33; none; 45

2. 18, 15, 18, 7, 11, 12

13.5; 13.5; 18; 11

3. 12, 27, 19, 38, 14, 15, 19, 27, 19, 14

20.4; 19; 19; 26

4. 7.8, 6.2, 5.4, 5.5, 7.8, 6.1, 5.3

6.3; 6.1; 7.8; 2.5

5. 13.5, 11.3, 10.7, 15.5, 11.4, 12.6

12.5; 12; none; 4.8

6. 0.7, 0.4, 0.4, 0.7, 0.4, 0.7

0.55; 0.55; 0.4 and 0.7; 0.3

7. 5, 4.1, 4, 3.3, 2.7, 5.2, 3

3.9; 4; none; 2.5

8. 6.1, 4, 5.3, 6.7, 4, 5.1, 6.7, 4, 9.8, 6.1

5.78; 5.7; 4; 5.8

9.

Stem	Leaf
6	2 3 5 7
7	2 7
8	0 1 1

6 | 3 = 63

72; 72; 81; 19

10.

Stem	Leaf
3	1 1
4	2 5 6
5	3 3 7
6	2 5

5 | 3 = 53

48.5; 49.5; 31 and 53; 34

11.

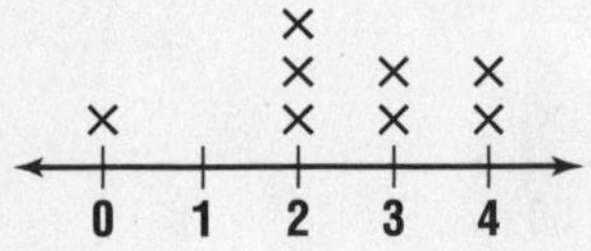

2.5; 2.5; 2; 4

12.

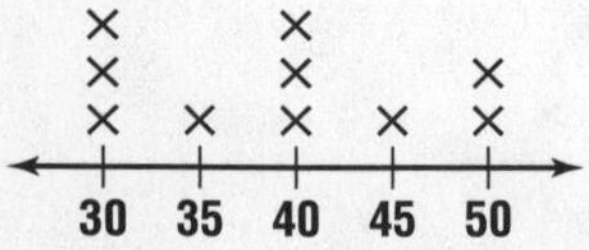

39; 40; 30 and 40; 20

NAME ______________________ DATE __________ PERIOD ______

Practice

Student Edition
Pages 112–116

Equations

Find the solution of each equation if the replacement sets are a = {4, 5, 6}, b = {−2, −1, 0}, and c = {−1, 0, 1, 2}.

1. $8 = a + 3$
2. $b - 3 = -5$
3. $3c = -3$
4. $9 = -a + 13$
5. $5a + 5 = 35$
6. $2c - 4 = 0$
7. $-4b + (-3) = 1$
8. $-9c - 9 = 0$
9. $\frac{8 + 17}{5} = -5c$
10. $\frac{-9 - 23}{4} = 4b$
11. $\frac{11 + 9}{a} + 2 = 7$
12. $\frac{9c}{3} - 5 = -2$

Solve each equation.

13. $q = -9.7 - 0.6$
14. $14 - 1.4 = d$
15. $f = 7 + 6 \cdot 7$
16. $b = -5(3) + 4 - 1$
17. $10 - 8 \cdot 3 \div 3 = w$
18. $z = 6(3 - 6 \div 2)$
19. $-2(-5 + 4 \cdot 3) = h$
20. $g = 3(7) - 9 \div 3$
21. $\frac{6 \cdot 8 - 8}{5} = c$
22. $p = \frac{-18 \div 3 + 2}{16 \div 4}$
23. $\frac{2 \cdot 5 - 8}{9 - 4} = t$
24. $\frac{12 - 3 \cdot 2}{32 \div 4} = m$

NAME ______________________ DATE __________ PERIOD ______

Practice

Student Edition
Pages 112–116

Equations

Find the solution of each equation if the replacement sets are a = {4, 5, 6}, b = {−2, −1, 0}, and c = {−1, 0, 1, 2}.

1. $8 = a + 3$ **5**

2. $b - 3 = -5$ **−2**

3. $3c = -3$ **−1**

4. $9 = -a + 13$ **4**

5. $5a + 5 = 35$ **6**

6. $2c - 4 = 0$ **2**

7. $-4b + (-3) = 1$ **−1**

8. $-9c - 9 = 0$ **−1**

9. $\frac{8 + 17}{5} = -5c$ **−1**

10. $\frac{-9 - 23}{4} = 4b$ **−2**

11. $\frac{11 + 9}{a} + 2 = 7$ **4**

12. $\frac{9c}{3} - 5 = -2$ **1**

Solve each equation.

13. $q = -9.7 - 0.6$ **−10.3**

14. $14 - 1.4 = d$ **12.6**

15. $f = 7 + 6 \cdot 7$ **49**

16. $b = -5(3) + 4 - 1$ **−12**

17. $10 - 8 \cdot 3 \div 3 = w$ **2**

18. $z = 6(3 - 6 \div 2)$ **0**

19. $-2(-5 + 4 \cdot 3) = h$ **−14**

20. $g = 3(7) - 9 \div 3$ **18**

21. $\frac{6 \cdot 8 - 8}{5} = c$ **8**

22. $p = \frac{-18 \div 3 + 2}{16 \div 4}$ **−1**

23. $\frac{2 \cdot 5 - 8}{9 - 4} = t$ $\mathbf{\frac{2}{5}}$

24. $\frac{12 - 3 \cdot 2}{32 \div 4} = m$ $\mathbf{\frac{3}{4}}$

NAME ______________________ DATE __________ PERIOD ______

3–5 Practice

Student Edition
Pages 117–121

Solving Equations by Using Models

Solve each equation. Use algebra tiles if necessary.

1. $-5 = h + (-2)$

2. $p + 3 = -1$

3. $m - 6 = -8$

4. $7 + c = 4$

5. $6 = n - 3$

6. $-5 + x = -1$

7. $2 = -8 + w$

8. $b + (-5) = -3$

9. $z + 4 = 9$

10. $3 + y = -3$

11. $a - 4 = 7$

12. $-10 + s = -6$

13. $6 + d = -4$

14. $f + (-1) = 0$

15. $-10 = j - 10$

16. $q + 4 = -5$

17. $6 = 12 + t$

18. $e - 3 = -2$

19. $u + (-7) = 2$

20. $15 + g = 10$

21. $-9 + r = -5$

22. $-8 = l - 4$

23. $v + (-1) = -2$

24. $-3 - i = 2$

25. What is the value of q if $-7 = q + 2$?

26. What is the value of n if $n - 4 = -2$?

27. If $b + (-3) = -5$, what is the value of b?

NAME ______________________ DATE __________ PERIOD ______

Practice

Solving Equations by Using Models

Solve each equation. Use algebra tiles if necessary.

1. $-5 = h + (-2)$ **−3**
2. $p + 3 = -1$ **−4**
3. $m - 6 = -8$ **−2**
4. $7 + c = 4$ **−3**
5. $6 = n - 3$ **9**
6. $-5 + x = -1$ **4**
7. $2 = -8 + w$ **10**
8. $b + (-5) = -3$ **2**
9. $z + 4 = 9$ **5**
10. $3 + y = -3$ **−6**
11. $a - 4 = 7$ **11**
12. $-10 + s = -6$ **4**
13. $6 + d = -4$ **−10**
14. $f + (-1) = 0$ **1**
15. $-10 = j - 10$ **0**
16. $q + 4 = -5$ **−9**
17. $6 = 12 + t$ **−6**
18. $e - 3 = -2$ **1**
19. $u + (-7) = 2$ **9**
20. $15 + g = 10$ **−5**
21. $-9 + r = -5$ **4**
22. $-8 = l - 4$ **−4**
23. $v + (-1) = -2$ **−1**
24. $-3 - i = 2$ **−5**
25. What is the value of q if $-7 = q + 2$? **−9**
26. What is the value of n if $n - 4 = -2$? **2**
27. If $b + (-3) = -5$, what is the value of b? **−2**

3–6

NAME ______________________ DATE __________ PERIOD ______

Practice

Student Edition
Pages 122–127

Solving Addition and Subtraction Equations

Solve each equation. Check your solution.

1. $b + 8 = -9$

2. $s + (-3) = -5$

3. $-4 + q = -11$

4. $23 = m - 11$

5. $k + (-6) = 2$

6. $x - (-9) = 4$

7. $-16 + z = -8$

8. $-5 + c = -5$

9. $14 = f + (-7)$

10. $x + 12 = -1$

11. $15 - w = -4$

12. $6 = 9 + d$

13. $-31 = 11 + y$

14. $n - (-7) = -1$

15. $a + (-27) = -19$

16. $0 = e - 38$

17. $4.65 + w = 5.95$

18. $g + (-1.54) = 1.07$

19. $u - 9.8 = 0.3$

20. $7.2 = p - (-6.1)$

21. $\frac{7}{8} + t = \frac{1}{4}$

22. $h - \frac{1}{3} = -\frac{5}{6}$

23. $q + \left(-\frac{2}{9}\right) = \frac{1}{3}$

24. $\frac{1}{2} + f = -\frac{1}{4}$

NAME ______________________ DATE ________ PERIOD ________

Practice

Student Edition
Pages 122–127

Solving Addition and Subtraction Equations

Solve each equation. Check your solution.

1. $b + 8 = -9$ **−17**
2. $s + (-3) = -5$ **−2**
3. $-4 + q = -11$ **−7**
4. $23 = m - 11$ **34**
5. $k + (-6) = 2$ **8**
6. $x - (-9) = 4$ **−5**
7. $-16 + z = -8$ **8**
8. $-5 + c = -5$ **0**
9. $14 = f + (-7)$ **21**
10. $x + 12 = -1$ **−13**
11. $15 - w = -4$ **19**
12. $6 = 9 + d$ **−3**
13. $-31 = 11 + y$ **−42**
14. $n - (-7) = -1$ **−8**
15. $a + (-27) = -19$ **8**
16. $0 = e - 38$ **38**
17. $4.65 + w = 5.95$ **1.3**
18. $g + (-1.54) = 1.07$ **2.61**
19. $u - 9.8 = 0.3$ **10.1**
20. $7.2 = p - (-6.1)$ **1.1**
21. $\frac{7}{8} + t = \frac{1}{4}$ $\mathbf{-\frac{5}{8}}$
22. $h - \frac{1}{3} = -\frac{5}{6}$ $\mathbf{-\frac{1}{2}}$
23. $q + \left(-\frac{2}{9}\right) = \frac{1}{3}$ $\mathbf{\frac{5}{9}}$
24. $\frac{1}{2} + f = -\frac{1}{4}$ $\mathbf{-\frac{3}{4}}$

NAME ______________________ DATE __________ PERIOD ______

Practice

Solving Equations Involving Absolute Value

Solve each equation. Check your solution.

1. $|x| = 7$

2. $|c| = -11$

3. $3 + |a| = 6$

4. $|s| - 4 = 2$

5. $|q| + 5 = 1$

6. $|h - 5| = 8$

7. $|y + 7| = 9$

8. $-2 = |10 + b|$

9. $|p + (-3)| = 12$

10. $|w - 1| = 6$

11. $|4 + r| = -3$

12. $8 = |l - 3|$

13. $|n - 5| = 7$

14. $|-2 + f| = 1$

15. $9 = |e + 8|$

16. $|m - (-3)| = 12$

17. $|k + 2| + 3 = 7$

18. $|g - 5| + 8 = 14$

19. $10 = |4 + v| + 1$

20. $|-6 + p| + 5 = 19$

NAME ______________________ DATE __________ PERIOD ______

Practice

Student Edition
Pages 128–131

Solving Equations Involving Absolute Value

Solve each equation. Check your solution.

1. $|x| = 7$ **{−7, 7}**

2. $|c| = -11$ **∅**

3. $3 + |a| = 6$ **{−3, 3}**

4. $|s| - 4 = 2$ **{−6, 6}**

5. $|q| + 5 = 1$ **∅**

6. $|h - 5| = 8$ **{−3, 13}**

7. $|y + 7| = 9$ **{−16, 2}**

8. $-2 = |10 + b|$ **∅**

9. $|p + (-3)| = 12$ **{−9, 15}**

10. $|w - 1| = 6$ **{−5, 7}**

11. $|4 + r| = -3$ **∅**

12. $8 = |l - 3|$ **{−5, 11}**

13. $|n - 5| = 7$ **{−2, 12}**

14. $|-2 + f| = 1$ **{1, 3}**

15. $9 = |e + 8|$ **{−17, 1}**

16. $|m - (-3)| = 12$ **{−15, 9}**

17. $|k + 2| + 3 = 7$ **{−6, 2}**

18. $|g - 5| + 8 = 14$ **{−1, 11}**

19. $10 = |4 + v| + 1$ **{−13, 5}**

20. $|-6 + p| + 5 = 19$ **{−8, 20}**

NAME ______________________ DATE __________ PERIOD ________

Practice

Student Edition
Pages 140–145

Multiplying Rational Numbers

Find each product.

1. $3.9 \cdot (-3)$

2. $-6(-5.4)$

3. $4 \cdot (-7.3)$

4. $-2.6(1.5)$

5. $(-4.4)(-0.5)$

6. $-3.7 \cdot 2$

7. $(-8.3)(-1)$

8. $-2.5(2.8)$

9. $-3 \cdot (-6.3)$

10. $-\frac{1}{4}\left(-\frac{3}{5}\right)$

11. $-5 \cdot \frac{2}{3}$

12. $\frac{5}{6}\left(\frac{7}{9}\right)$

13. $-\frac{6}{7} \cdot \frac{1}{3}$

14. $-\frac{3}{8}(-3)$

15. $\frac{2}{5}\left(-\frac{8}{9}\right)$

16. $6\frac{3}{4}\left(\frac{1}{6}\right)$

17. $-\frac{2}{3} \cdot \left(-4\frac{1}{2}\right)$

18. $1\frac{4}{5}\left(-\frac{3}{7}\right)$

Simplify each expression.

19. $4(-2.3z)$

20. $-5.5x(-0.8)$

21. $-4.2r(1.5s)$

22. $6\left(\frac{1}{7}t\right)$

23. $-\frac{1}{3} \cdot \frac{4}{5}g$

24. $\frac{2}{9}k\left(-\frac{1}{2}\right)$

25. $\left(\frac{1}{4}a\right)\left(\frac{5}{8}b\right)$

26. $\frac{5}{6}m\left(-\frac{1}{3}n\right)$

27. $3x\left(\frac{4}{9}y\right)$

Practice

Multiplying Rational Numbers

Find each product.

1. $3.9 \cdot (-3)$ **−11.7**
2. $-6(-5.4)$ **32.4**
3. $4 \cdot (-7.3)$ **−29.2**
4. $-2.6(1.5)$ **−3.9**
5. $(-4.4)(-0.5)$ **2.2**
6. $-3.7 \cdot 2$ **−7.4**
7. $(-8.3)(-1)$ **8.3**
8. $-2.5(2.8)$ **−7**
9. $-3 \cdot (-6.3)$ **18.9**
10. $-\frac{1}{4}\left(-\frac{3}{5}\right)$ $\mathbf{\frac{3}{20}}$
11. $-5 \cdot \frac{2}{3}$ $\mathbf{-\frac{10}{3}}$ **or** $\mathbf{-3\frac{1}{3}}$
12. $\frac{5}{6}\left(\frac{7}{9}\right)$ $\mathbf{\frac{35}{54}}$
13. $-\frac{6}{7} \cdot \frac{1}{3}$ $\mathbf{-\frac{6}{21}}$ **or** $\mathbf{-\frac{2}{7}}$
14. $-\frac{3}{8}(-3)$ $\mathbf{\frac{9}{8}}$ **or** $\mathbf{1\frac{1}{8}}$
15. $\frac{2}{5}\left(-\frac{8}{9}\right)$ $\mathbf{-\frac{16}{45}}$
16. $6\frac{3}{4}\left(\frac{1}{6}\right)$ $\mathbf{\frac{27}{24}}$ **or** $\mathbf{1\frac{1}{8}}$
17. $-\frac{2}{3} \cdot \left(-4\frac{1}{2}\right)$ **3**
18. $1\frac{4}{5}\left(-\frac{3}{7}\right)$ $\mathbf{-\frac{27}{35}}$

Simplify each expression.

19. $4(-2.3z)$ **−9.2*z***
20. $-5.5x(-0.8)$ **4.4*x***
21. $-4.2r(1.5s)$ **−6.3*rs***
22. $6\left(\frac{1}{7}t\right)$ $\mathbf{\frac{6}{7}t}$
23. $-\frac{1}{3} \cdot \frac{4}{5}g$ $\mathbf{-\frac{4}{15}g}$
24. $\frac{2}{9}k\left(-\frac{1}{2}\right)$ $\mathbf{-\frac{1}{9}k}$
25. $\left(\frac{1}{4}a\right)\left(\frac{5}{8}b\right)$ $\mathbf{\frac{5}{32}ab}$
26. $\frac{5}{6}m\left(-\frac{1}{3}n\right)$ $\mathbf{-\frac{5}{18}mn}$
27. $3x\left(\frac{4}{9}y\right)$ $\mathbf{\frac{12}{9}xy}$ **or** $\mathbf{1\frac{1}{3}xy}$

NAME ______________________ DATE __________ PERIOD ______

Practice

Counting Outcomes

Determine whether each is an outcome or a sample space for the given experiment.

1. (H, T, H); tossing a coin three times
2. (green, black); choosing one marble from a box of green and black marbles
3. (green, green), (green, black), (black, green), (black, black); choosing two marbles, one at a time, from a box of several green and several black marbles
4. (3, 1, 4, 5); rolling a number cube four times
5. (1, 2, 3, 4, 5, 6); rolling a number cube once
6. (red, black); choosing two cards from a standard deck
7. (dime, penny); choosing two coins from a bag of dimes, nickels, and pennies
8. (dime, nickel, penny); choosing one coin from a bag of dimes, nickels, and pennies

Find the number of possible outcomes by drawing a tree diagram.

9. Suppose you can have granola or wheat flakes for cereal with a choice of strawberries, bananas, peaches, or blackberries.

10. Suppose you can travel by car, train, or bus to meet a friend. You can leave either in the morning or the afternoon.

Find the number of possible outcomes by using the Fundamental Counting Principle.

11. Suppose you toss a coin five times.
12. Suppose you can make an outfit from six sweaters, four pairs of jeans, and two pairs of shoes.

NAME ______________________ DATE __________ PERIOD ______

Practice

Student Edition
Pages 146–151

Counting Outcomes

Determine whether each is an outcome or a sample space for the given experiment.

1. (H, T, H); tossing a coin three times **outcome**
2. (green, black); choosing one marble from a box of green and black marbles **sample space**
3. (green, green), (green, black), (black, green), (black, black); choosing two marbles, one at a time, from a box of several green and several black marbles **sample space**
4. (3, 1, 4, 5); rolling a number cube four times **outcome**
5. (1, 2, 3, 4, 5, 6); rolling a number cube once **sample space**
6. (red, black); choosing two cards from a standard deck **outcome**
7. (dime, penny); choosing two coins from a bag of dimes, nickels, and pennies **outcome**
8. (dime, nickel, penny); choosing one coin from a bag of dimes, nickels, and pennies **sample space**

Find the number of possible outcomes by drawing a tree diagram.

9. Suppose you can have granola or wheat flakes for cereal with a choice of strawberries, bananas, peaches, or blackberries. **8**

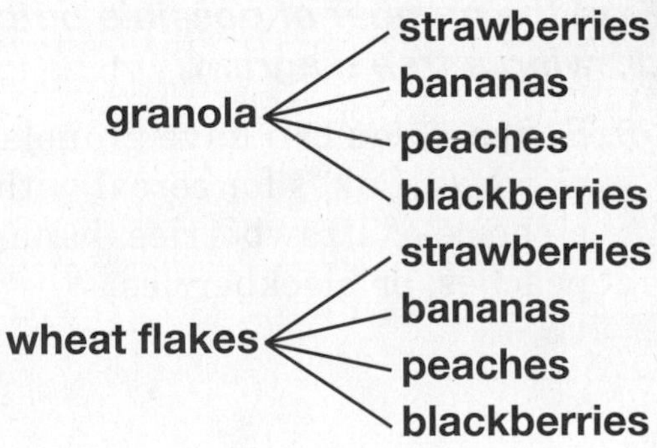

10. Suppose you can travel by car, train, or bus to meet a friend. You can leave either in the morning or the afternoon. **6**

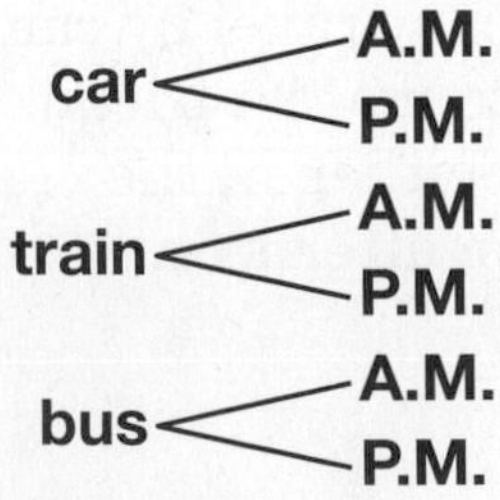

Find the number of possible outcomes by using the Fundamental Counting Principle.

11. Suppose you toss a coin five times. **32**
12. Suppose you can make an outfit from six sweaters, four pairs of jeans, and two pairs of shoes. **48**

NAME ______________________ DATE __________ PERIOD ______

Practice

Dividing Rational Numbers

Find each quotient.

1. $-8.5 \div 5$
2. $4.2 \div 14$
3. $2.8 \div (-0.5)$
4. $3.6 \div (-6)$
5. $-5.1 \div (-1.7)$
6. $7.8 \div (-0.3)$
7. $-4.8 \div 1.2$
8. $7.5 \div (-1.5)$
9. $-3.7 \div (-0.1)$
10. $-\frac{3}{4} \div \frac{5}{2}$
11. $\frac{1}{5} \div \frac{1}{3}$
12. $4 \div \frac{9}{10}$
13. $\frac{5}{6} \div \left(-\frac{2}{3}\right)$
14. $-\frac{3}{8} \div 6$
15. $-\frac{2}{7} \div (-3)$
16. $-\frac{4}{5} \div 4\frac{1}{2}$
17. $-2\frac{2}{3} \div \frac{3}{4}$
18. $-1\frac{1}{8} \div \left(-\frac{5}{7}\right)$

Evaluate each expression if $m = \frac{1}{5}$ and $n = -\frac{3}{4}$.

19. $\frac{m}{4}$
20. $\frac{5}{n}$
21. $-\frac{m}{7}$
22. $\frac{6}{m}$
23. $\frac{n}{3}$
24. $\frac{n}{m}$
25. $\frac{m}{n}$
26. $-\frac{2m}{3}$
27. $-\frac{1}{3n}$

NAME ______________________ DATE __________ PERIOD _____

Practice

Student Edition
Pages 154–159

Dividing Rational Numbers

Find each quotient.

1. $-8.5 \div 5$ **−1.7**
2. $4.2 \div 14$ **0.3**
3. $2.8 \div (-0.5)$ **−5.6**
4. $3.6 \div (-6)$ **−0.6**
5. $-5.1 \div (-1.7)$ **3**
6. $7.8 \div (-0.3)$ **26**
7. $-4.8 \div 1.2$ **−4**
8. $7.5 \div (-1.5)$ **−5**
9. $-3.7 \div (-0.1)$ **37**
10. $-\frac{3}{4} \div \frac{5}{2}$ $\mathbf{-\frac{3}{10}}$
11. $\frac{1}{5} \div \frac{1}{3}$ $\mathbf{\frac{3}{5}}$
12. $4 \div \frac{9}{10}$ $\mathbf{\frac{40}{9}}$ **or** $\mathbf{4\frac{4}{9}}$
13. $\frac{5}{6} \div \left(-\frac{2}{3}\right)$ $\mathbf{-\frac{5}{4}}$ **or** $\mathbf{-1\frac{1}{4}}$
14. $-\frac{3}{8} \div 6$ $\mathbf{-\frac{1}{16}}$
15. $-\frac{2}{7} \div (-3)$ $\mathbf{\frac{2}{21}}$
16. $-\frac{4}{5} \div 4\frac{1}{2}$ $\mathbf{-\frac{8}{45}}$
17. $-2\frac{2}{3} \div \frac{3}{4}$ $\mathbf{-\frac{32}{9}}$ **or** $\mathbf{-3\frac{5}{9}}$
18. $-1\frac{1}{8} \div \left(-\frac{5}{7}\right)$ $\mathbf{\frac{63}{40}}$ **or** $\mathbf{1\frac{23}{40}}$

Evaluate each expression if $m = \frac{1}{5}$ and $n = -\frac{3}{4}$.

19. $\frac{m}{4}$ $\mathbf{\frac{1}{20}}$
20. $\frac{5}{n}$ $\mathbf{-\frac{20}{3}}$ **or** $\mathbf{-6\frac{2}{3}}$
21. $-\frac{m}{7}$ $\mathbf{-\frac{1}{35}}$
22. $\frac{6}{m}$ **30**
23. $\frac{n}{3}$ $\mathbf{-\frac{1}{4}}$
24. $\frac{n}{m}$ $\mathbf{-\frac{15}{4}}$ **or** $\mathbf{-3\frac{3}{4}}$
25. $\frac{m}{n}$ $\mathbf{-\frac{4}{15}}$
26. $-\frac{2m}{3}$ $\mathbf{-\frac{2}{15}}$
27. $-\frac{1}{3n}$ $\mathbf{\frac{4}{9}}$

Practice

Solving Multiplication and Division Equations

Solve each equation.

1. $7p = -42$

2. $-3z = 27$

3. $-8q = -56$

4. $-28 = 2a$

5. $5f = 40$

6. $-9g = 18$

7. $-48 = -12r$

8. $4 = 0.8w$

9. $-2.4t = 6$

10. $0 = 5.3k$

11. $-1.6s = -8$

12. $2.5d = -11$

13. $\frac{m}{9} = 2$

14. $-8 = \frac{y}{4}$

15. $\frac{2}{5}s = 18$

16. $-2 = -\frac{8}{3}b$

17. $-\frac{c}{6} = 6$

18. $-\frac{v}{12} = -5$

19. $\frac{1}{8}d = -1$

20. $4 = \frac{4}{5}x$

21. $-\frac{7}{6}r = 28$

22. $\frac{9}{10}z = -9$

23. $-\frac{b}{18} = 2$

24. $-\frac{3}{7}n = -21$

Practice

Solving Multiplication and Division Equations

Solve each equation.

1. $7p = -42$ **−6**
2. $-3z = 27$ **−9**
3. $-8q = -56$ **7**
4. $-28 = 2a$ **−14**
5. $5f = 40$ **8**
6. $-9g = 18$ **−2**
7. $-48 = -12r$ **4**
8. $4 = 0.8w$ **5**
9. $-2.4t = 6$ **−2.5**
10. $0 = 5.3k$ **0**
11. $-1.6s = -8$ **5**
12. $2.5d = -11$ **−4.4**
13. $\frac{m}{9} = 2$ **18**
14. $-8 = \frac{y}{4}$ **−32**
15. $\frac{2}{5}s = 18$ **45**
16. $-2 = -\frac{8}{3}b$ $\mathbf{\frac{3}{4}}$
17. $-\frac{c}{6} = 6$ **−36**
18. $-\frac{v}{12} = -5$ **60**
19. $\frac{1}{8}d = -1$ **−8**
20. $4 = \frac{4}{5}x$ **5**
21. $-\frac{7}{6}r = 28$ **−24**
22. $\frac{9}{10}z = -9$ **−10**
23. $-\frac{b}{18} = 2$ **−36**
24. $-\frac{3}{7}n = -21$ **49**

NAME ______________________ DATE __________ PERIOD ______

Practice

Solving Multi-Step Equations

Solve each equation. Check your solution.

1. $8z - 6 = 18$

2. $-4s + 1 = 9$

3. $12 = -3k + 3$

4. $5 - 2f = 19$

5. $-31 = -6w - 7$

6. $6 + 7r = 13$

7. $-8 = 8 - 2c$

8. $0.4u + 1 = 6.6$

9. $3b - 2.5 = 5$

10. $4.7 + 2g = 7.3$

11. $-2.1q - 1 = -1$

12. $-2 = \frac{t}{4} - 3$

13. $\frac{p}{9} + 4 = 7$

14. $7 - \frac{m}{2} = 0$

15. $8 = 5 - \frac{c}{6}$

16. $\frac{y - 5}{3} = 2$

17. $1 = \frac{c + 1}{-8}$

18. $\frac{-4a + 4}{5} = -4$

19. $-4 = \frac{x}{7} + 3$

20. $\frac{8h - 2}{9} = 6$

21. $9 - \frac{1}{4}j = 5$

NAME ____________ DATE ________ PERIOD ______

Practice

Student Edition
Pages 165–170

Solving Multi-Step Equations

Solve each equation. Check your solution.

1. $8z - 6 = 18$ **3**

2. $-4s + 1 = 9$ **−2**

3. $12 = -3k + 3$ **−3**

4. $5 - 2f = 19$ **−7**

5. $-31 = -6w - 7$ **4**

6. $6 + 7r = 13$ **1**

7. $-8 = 8 - 2c$ **8**

8. $0.4u + 1 = 6.6$ **14**

9. $3b - 2.5 = 5$ **2.5**

10. $4.7 + 2g = 7.3$ **1.3**

11. $-2.1q - 1 = -1$ **0**

12. $-2 = \frac{t}{4} - 3$ **4**

13. $\frac{p}{9} + 4 = 7$ **27**

14. $7 - \frac{m}{2} = 0$ **14**

15. $8 = 5 - \frac{c}{6}$ **−18**

16. $\frac{y - 5}{3} = 2$ **11**

17. $1 = \frac{c + 1}{-8}$ **−9**

18. $\frac{-4a + 4}{5} = -4$ **6**

19. $-4 = \frac{x}{7} + 3$ **−49**

20. $\frac{8h - 2}{9} = 6$ **7**

21. $9 - \frac{1}{4}j = 5$ **16**

NAME ______________________ DATE __________ PERIOD ______

Practice

Variables on Both Sides

Solve each equation. Check your solution.

1. $9r = 3r + 6$

2. $5s - 6 = 2s$

3. $7p - 12 = 3p$

4. $11w = -16 + 7w$

5. $-3b + 9 = 9 - 3b$

6. $8 + 2m = -2m - 16$

7. $12x + 5 = 11 + 12x$

8. $-6g + 14 = -12 - 8g$

9. $-15 + 7t = 30 - 2t$

10. $5a + 4 = -2a - 10$

11. $1.4h - 3 = 2 + h$

12. $5.3 + d = -2d + 4.7$

13. $3.6z + 6 = -2 + 2z$

14. $4f - 3.7 = 3f - 1.8$

15. $\frac{3}{5}n - 10 = \frac{2}{5}n$

16. $\frac{5}{8}j = 8 + \frac{3}{8}j$

17. $\frac{2}{3}q - 2 = \frac{1}{3}q + 7$

18. $-\frac{1}{4}p + 4 = \frac{3}{4}p + 8$

NAME ______________________ DATE __________ PERIOD ______

Practice

Student Edition
Pages 171–175

Variables on Both Sides

Solve each equation. Check your solution.

1. $9r = 3r + 6$ **1**

2. $5s - 6 = 2s$ **2**

3. $7p - 12 = 3p$ **3**

4. $11w = -16 + 7w$ **−4**

5. $-3b + 9 = 9 - 3b$ **identity**

6. $8 + 2m = -2m - 16$ **−6**

7. $12x + 5 = 11 + 12x$ **no solution**

8. $-6g + 14 = -12 - 8g$ **−13**

9. $-15 + 7t = 30 - 2t$ **5**

10. $5a + 4 = -2a - 10$ **−2**

11. $1.4h - 3 = 2 + h$ **12.5**

12. $5.3 + d = -2d + 4.7$ **−0.2**

13. $3.6z + 6 = -2 + 2z$ **−5**

14. $4f - 3.7 = 3f - 1.8$ **1.9**

15. $\frac{3}{5}n - 10 = \frac{2}{5}n$ **50**

16. $\frac{5}{8}j = 8 + \frac{3}{8}j$ **32**

17. $\frac{2}{3}q - 2 = \frac{1}{3}q + 7$ **27**

18. $-\frac{1}{4}p + 4 = \frac{3}{4}p + 8$ **−4**

NAME ______________________ DATE __________ PERIOD ______

Practice

Grouping Symbols

Solve each equation. Check your solution.

1. $15 = 3(h - 1)$

2. $3(2z + 8) = -6$

3. $7 = 4(5 - 2x) + 3$

4. $2(p + 6) - 10 = 12$

5. $4a - 7 = 4(a - 2) + 1$

6. $13 = 3g - 2(-5 + g)$

7. $6(k + 2) + 2(2k - 5) = 22$

8. $-2 = 7(q + 2) + 3(2q - 1)$

9. $5(d - 4) + 2 = 2(d + 2) - 4$

10. $2b + 6(2 - b) = -b$

11. $6(n - 1) = 4.4n - 2$

12. $2(s + 1.6) - 5(2 - s) = -1.9$

13. $4(y + 2) + 1.3 = 3(y + 2.1)$

14. $8(e + 2.5) = 2(4e - 2)$

15. $7 - \frac{1}{4}(j - 8) = 6$

16. $\frac{1}{3}(x + 9) + 5 = \frac{x}{3} + 8$

17. $\frac{3(a + 4)}{9} = 2a - 12$

18. $1 + \frac{1}{6}p = 2(p - 5)$

4–7

NAME ______________________ DATE __________ PERIOD ______

Practice

Student Edition
Pages 176–179

Grouping Symbols

Solve each equation. Check your solution.

1. $15 = 3(h - 1)$ **6**

2. $3(2z + 8) = -6$ **−5**

3. $7 = 4(5 - 2x) + 3$ **2**

4. $2(p + 6) - 10 = 12$ **5**

5. $4a - 7 = 4(a - 2) + 1$ **identity**

6. $13 = 3g - 2(-5 + g)$ **3**

7. $6(k + 2) + 2(2k - 5) = 22$ **2**

8. $-2 = 7(q + 2) + 3(2q - 1)$ **−1**

9. $5(d - 4) + 2 = 2(d + 2) - 4$ **6**

10. $2b + 6(2 - b) = -b$ **4**

11. $6(n - 1) = 4.4n - 2$ **2.5**

12. $2(s + 1.6) - 5(2 - s) = -1.9$ **0.7**

13. $4(y + 2) + 1.3 = 3(y + 2.1)$ **−3**

14. $8(e + 2.5) = 2(4e - 2)$ **no solution**

15. $7 - \frac{1}{4}(j - 8) = 6$ **12**

16. $\frac{1}{3}(x + 9) + 5 = \frac{x}{3} + 8$ **identity**

17. $\frac{3(a + 4)}{9} = 2a - 12$ **8**

18. $1 + \frac{1}{6}p = 2(p - 5)$ **6**

NAME ______________________ DATE __________ PERIOD ______

Practice

Solving Proportions

Solve each proportion.

1. $\frac{1}{7} = \frac{a}{14}$

2. $\frac{8}{2} = \frac{12}{h}$

3. $\frac{5}{b} = \frac{3}{9}$

4. $\frac{9}{6} = \frac{15}{b}$

5. $\frac{3}{y} = \frac{9}{21}$

6. $\frac{21}{24} = \frac{c}{8}$

7. $\frac{8}{3} = \frac{32}{x}$

8. $\frac{4}{5} = \frac{p}{25}$

9. $\frac{24}{g} = \frac{3}{8}$

10. $\frac{5}{2} = \frac{13}{a}$

11. $\frac{1.5}{c} = \frac{15}{5}$

12. $\frac{6}{2.4} = \frac{x}{4}$

13. $\frac{4}{2} = \frac{x + 2}{3}$

14. $\frac{c + 5}{15} = \frac{8}{6}$

15. $\frac{7}{7} = \frac{10}{b + 3}$

16. $\frac{y}{y + 3} = \frac{2}{5}$

17. $\frac{z + 6}{12} = \frac{z}{4}$

18. $\frac{5}{4} = \frac{a + 4}{2a}$

Convert each measurement as indicated.

19. 5 pounds to ounces

20. 3000 grams to kilograms

21. 7 feet to inches

22. 4 meters to centimeters

23. 6 quarts to gallons

24. 250 centimeters to meters

NAME ______________________ DATE __________ PERIOD ______

5–1 Practice

Student Edition Pages 188–193

Solving Proportions

Solve each proportion.

1. $\frac{1}{7} = \frac{a}{14}$

2

2. $\frac{8}{2} = \frac{12}{h}$

3

3. $\frac{5}{b} = \frac{3}{9}$

15

4. $\frac{9}{6} = \frac{15}{b}$

10

5. $\frac{3}{y} = \frac{9}{21}$

7

6. $\frac{21}{24} = \frac{c}{8}$

7

7. $\frac{8}{3} = \frac{32}{x}$

12

8. $\frac{4}{5} = \frac{p}{25}$

20

9. $\frac{24}{g} = \frac{3}{8}$

64

10. $\frac{5}{2} = \frac{13}{a}$

5.2

11. $\frac{1.5}{c} = \frac{15}{5}$

0.5

12. $\frac{6}{2.4} = \frac{x}{4}$

10

13. $\frac{4}{2} = \frac{x + 2}{3}$

4

14. $\frac{c + 5}{15} = \frac{8}{6}$

15

15. $\frac{7}{7} = \frac{10}{b + 3}$

7

16. $\frac{y}{y + 3} = \frac{2}{5}$

2

17. $\frac{z + 6}{12} = \frac{z}{4}$

3

18. $\frac{5}{4} = \frac{a + 4}{2a}$

$\mathbf{2\frac{2}{3}}$

Convert each measurement as indicated.

19. 5 pounds to ounces

80 oz

20. 3000 grams to kilograms

3 kg

21. 7 feet to inches

84 in.

22. 4 meters to centimeters

400 cm

23. 6 quarts to gallons

1.5 gal

24. 250 centimeters to meters

2.5 m

NAME ______________________ DATE __________ PERIOD ______

Practice

Scale Drawings and Models

On a map, the scale is 1 inch = 30 miles. Find the actual distance for each map distance.

1. Los Angeles, CA, to San Bernardino, CA; 2 inches

2. Kalamazoo, MI, to Chicago, IL; 4.5 inches

3. Nashville, TN, to Union City, TN; 6 inches

4. Springfield, MO, to Joplin, MO; 2.5 inches

5. Albuquerque, NM, to Santa Fe, NM; $1\frac{3}{4}$ inches

6. Montgomery, AL, to Birmingham, AL; 3 inches

7. Columbus, OH, to Cincinnati, OH; 3.5 inches

8. Des Moines, IA, to Sioux City, IA; $6\frac{3}{4}$ inches

9. Concord, NH, to Boston, MA; $2\frac{1}{4}$ inches

10. Providence, RI, to Newport, RI; 1 inch

11. Raleigh, NC, to Wilmington, NC; 4 inches

12. St. Paul, MN, to Minneapolis, MN; $\frac{1}{4}$ inch

13. Portland, OR, to Seattle, WA; $5\frac{3}{4}$ inches

5–2

NAME ______________________ DATE __________ PERIOD ______

Practice

Student Edition
Pages 194–197

Scale Drawings and Models

On a map, the scale is 1 inch = 30 miles. Find the actual distance for each map distance.

1. Los Angeles, CA, to San Bernardino, CA; 2 inches **60 mi**

2. Kalamazoo, MI, to Chicago, IL; 4.5 inches **135 mi**

3. Nashville, TN, to Union City, TN; 6 inches **180 mi**

4. Springfield, MO, to Joplin, MO; 2.5 inches **75 mi**

5. Albuquerque, NM, to Santa Fe, NM; $1\frac{3}{4}$ inches **52.5 mi**

6. Montgomery, AL, to Birmingham, AL; 3 inches **90 mi**

7. Columbus, OH, to Cincinnati, OH; 3.5 inches **105 mi**

8. Des Moines, IA, to Sioux City, IA; $6\frac{3}{4}$ inches **202.5 mi**

9. Concord, NH, to Boston, MA; $2\frac{1}{4}$ inches **67.5 mi**

10. Providence, RI, to Newport, RI; 1 inch **30 mi**

11. Raleigh, NC, to Wilmington, NC; 4 inches **120 mi**

12. St. Paul, MN, to Minneapolis, MN; $\frac{1}{4}$ inch **7.5 mi**

13. Portland, OR, to Seattle, WA; $5\frac{3}{4}$ inches **172.5 mi**

5–3

NAME ______________________ DATE __________ PERIOD _____

Practice

Student Edition
Pages 198–203

The Percent Proportion

Express each fraction or ratio as a percent.

1. $\frac{3}{4}$

2. 4 out of 5

3. 4 to 10

4. 7 to 4

5. $\frac{13}{20}$

6. 1 out of 8

7. $\frac{1}{5}$

8. 2 out of 4

9. 6 to 5

10. Two out of 50 students scored above 98 on a geometry test.

11. At a computer convention, 19 out of 20 people accepted a free mouse pad.

12. In a recent inspection, three-eighths of the apartments at Kendall Heights had fire extinguishers.

Use the percent proportion to find each number.

13. 20 is what percent of 125?

14. Find 30% of 75.

15. 18 is 45% of what number?

16. 85% of what number is 85?

17. 15 is what percent of 50?

18. What number is 3% of 40?

19. 40% of what number is 28?

20. Find 130% of 20.

21. 78 is 65% of what number?

22. What is 10% of 73?

23. 30 is what percent of 150?

24. Find 6% of 15.

5–3

NAME ______________________________ DATE ____________ PERIOD _______

Practice

Student Edition
Pages 198–203

The Percent Proportion

Express each fraction or ratio as a percent.

1. $\frac{3}{4}$ **75%**
2. 4 out of 5 **80%**
3. 4 to 10 **40%**
4. 7 to 4 **175%**
5. $\frac{13}{20}$ **65%**
6. 1 out of 8 **12.5%**
7. $\frac{1}{5}$ **20%**
8. 2 out of 4 **50%**
9. 6 to 5 **120%**
10. Two out of 50 students scored above 98 on a geometry test. **4%**
11. At a computer convention, 19 out of 20 people accepted a free mouse pad. **95%**
12. In a recent inspection, three-eighths of the apartments at Kendall Heights had fire extinguishers. **37.5%**

Use the percent proportion to find each number.

13. 20 is what percent of 125? **16%**
14. Find 30% of 75. **22.5**
15. 18 is 45% of what number? **40**
16. 85% of what number is 85? **100**
17. 15 is what percent of 50? **30%**
18. What number is 3% of 40? **1.2**
19. 40% of what number is 28? **70**
20. Find 130% of 20. **26**
21. 78 is 65% of what number? **120**
22. What is 10% of 73? **7.3**
23. 30 is what percent of 150? **20%**
24. Find 6% of 15. **0.9**

NAME ______________________ DATE ________ PERIOD ______

Practice

The Percent Equation

Use the percent equation to find each number.

1. Find 60% of 150.

2. What number is 40% of 95?

3. 21 is 70% of what number?

4. Find 20% of 120.

5. Find 7% of 80.

6. 63 is 60% of what number?

7. 12 is 30% of what number?

8. 90 is 45% of what number?

9. What number is 27% of 50?

10. What number is 70% of 122?

11. What number is 12% of 85?

12. Find 14% of 150.

13. 26 is 65% of what number?

14. What number is 67% of 140?

15. 108 is 90% of what number?

16. Find 34% of 85.

17. 50 is 25% of what number?

18. What number is 95% of 90?

19. 21 is 35% of what number?

20. Find 22% of 55.

21. Find 14.5% of 500.

22. 4 is 0.8% of what number?

NAME ______________________ DATE ________ PERIOD ______

Practice

The Percent Equation

Use the percent equation to find each number.

1. Find 60% of 150. **90**

2. What number is 40% of 95? **38**

3. 21 is 70% of what number? **30**

4. Find 20% of 120. **24**

5. Find 7% of 80. **5.6**

6. 63 is 60% of what number? **105**

7. 12 is 30% of what number? **40**

8. 90 is 45% of what number? **200**

9. What number is 27% of 50? **13.5**

10. What number is 70% of 122? **85.4**

11. What number is 12% of 85? **10.2**

12. Find 14% of 150. **21**

13. 26 is 65% of what number? **40**

14. What number is 67% of 140? **93.8**

15. 108 is 90% of what number? **120**

16. Find 34% of 85. **28.9**

17. 50 is 25% of what number? **200**

18. What number is 95% of 90? **85.5**

19. 21 is 35% of what number? **60**

20. Find 22% of 55. **12.1**

21. Find 14.5% of 500. **72.5**

22. 4 is 0.8% of what number? **500**

NAME ______________________ DATE __________ PERIOD ______

Practice

Student Edition
Pages 212–218

Percent of Change

Find the percent of increase or decrease. Round to the nearest percent.

1. original: 60
new: 54

2. original: 20
new: 25

3. original: 18
new: 36

4. original: 50
new: 32

5. original: 32
new: 20

6. original: 35
new: 98

The cost of an item and a sales tax rate are given. Find the total price of each item to the nearest cent.

7. guitar: $120; 5%

8. shirt: $22.95; 6%

9. shoes: $49.99; 7%

10. jacket: $89.95; 6%

11. ruler: $1.49; 5%

12. weight bench: $79; 6%

The original cost of an item and a discount rate are given. Find the sale price of each item to the nearest cent.

13. stereo: $900; 10%

14. jeans: $54; 25%

15. VCR: $129.95; 20%

16. golf club: $69.95; 15%

17. barrette: $6.99; 15%

18. sweat pants: $12; 25%

5-5 NAME ______________________ DATE __________ PERIOD ______

Practice

Student Edition
Pages 212–218

Percent of Change

Find the percent of increase or decrease. Round to the nearest percent.

1. original: 60 **10% decrease**
new: 54

2. original: 20 **25% increase**
new: 25

3. original: 18 **100% increase**
new: 36

4. original: 50 **36% decrease**
new: 32

5. original: 32 **38% decrease**
new: 20

6. original: 35 **180% increase**
new: 98

The cost of an item and a sales tax rate are given. Find the total price of each item to the nearest cent.

7. guitar: $120; 5% **$126**

8. shirt: $22.95; 6% **$24.33**

9. shoes: $49.99; 7% **$53.49**

10. jacket: $89.95; 6% **$95.35**

11. ruler: $1.49; 5% **$1.56**

12. weight bench: $79; 6% **$83.74**

The original cost of an item and a discount rate are given. Find the sale price of each item to the nearest cent.

13. stereo: $900; 10% **$810**

14. jeans: $54; 25% **$40.50**

15. VCR: $129.95; 20% **$103.96**

16. golf club: $69.95; 15% **$59.46**

17. barrette: $6.99; 15% **$5.94**

18. sweat pants: $12; 25% **$9**

NAME ______________________ DATE __________ PERIOD ______

Practice

Probability and Odds

Find the probability of each outcome if a pair of dice are rolled. Refer to the table below, which shows all of the possible outcomes when you roll a pair of dice.

	1	2	3	4	5	6
1	(1, 1)	(1, 2)	(1, 3)	(1, 4)	(1, 5)	(1, 6)
2	(2, 1)	(2, 2)	(2, 3)	(2, 4)	(2, 5)	(2, 6)
3	(3, 1)	(3, 2)	(3, 3)	(3, 4)	(3, 5)	(3, 6)
4	(4, 1)	(4, 2)	(4, 3)	(4, 4)	(4, 5)	(4, 6)
5	(5, 1)	(5, 2)	(5, 3)	(5, 4)	(5, 5)	(5, 6)
6	(6, 1)	(6, 2)	(6, 3)	(6, 4)	(6, 5)	(6, 6)

1. an even number on the second die

2. a sum of 8

3. a sum of 7

4. an odd sum

5. a sum less than 6

6. a sum greater than 7

7. both die are the same number

8. a sum less than 2

Find the odds of each outcome if a bag contains 7 blue marbles, 3 yellow marbles, and 2 red marbles.

9. choosing a blue marble

10. choosing a red marble

11. choosing a yellow marble

12. choosing a yellow or red marble

13. choosing a yellow or blue marble

14. choosing a blue or red marble

15. not choosing a blue or red marble

16. not choosing a blue marble

5–6

NAME ______________ DATE __________ PERIOD ______

Practice

Student Edition
Pages 219–223

Probability and Odds

Find the probability of each outcome if a pair of dice are rolled. Refer to the table below, which shows all of the possible outcomes when you roll a pair of dice.

	1	2	3	4	5	6
1	(1, 1)	(1, 2)	(1, 3)	(1, 4)	(1, 5)	(1, 6)
2	(2, 1)	(2, 2)	(2, 3)	(2, 4)	(2, 5)	(2, 6)
3	(3, 1)	(3, 2)	(3, 3)	(3, 4)	(3, 5)	(3, 6)
4	(4, 1)	(4, 2)	(4, 3)	(4, 4)	(4, 5)	(4, 6)
5	(5, 1)	(5, 2)	(5, 3)	(5, 4)	(5, 5)	(5, 6)
6	(6, 1)	(6, 2)	(6, 3)	(6, 4)	(6, 5)	(6, 6)

1. an even number on the second die $\frac{1}{2}$

2. a sum of 8 $\frac{5}{36}$

3. a sum of 7 $\frac{1}{6}$

4. an odd sum $\frac{1}{2}$

5. a sum less than 6 $\frac{5}{18}$

6. a sum greater than 7 $\frac{5}{12}$

7. both die are the same number $\frac{1}{6}$

8. a sum less than 2 **0**

Find the odds of each outcome if a bag contains 7 blue marbles, 3 yellow marbles, and 2 red marbles.

9. choosing a blue marble **7:5**

10. choosing a red marble **1:5**

11. choosing a yellow marble **1:3**

12. choosing a yellow or red marble **5:7**

13. choosing a yellow or blue marble **5:1**

14. choosing a blue or red marble **3:1**

15. not choosing a blue or red marble **1:3**

16. not choosing a blue marble **5:7**

NAME ______________________ DATE __________ PERIOD ______

Practice

Compound Events

Two dice are rolled. Find the probability of each outcome.

1. P(even number and 2)

2. P(5 and 5)

3. P(odd number and a number less than 6)

4. P(3 and a number less than 3)

5. P(even number and a number greater than 2)

6. P(6 and a number greater than 2)

A card is drawn from a standard deck of cards. Determine whether the evens are* mutually exclusive *or* inclusive. *Then find each probability.

7. P(jack or five)

8. P(ace or club)

9. P(red card or four)

10. P(face card or black card)

11. P(spade or diamond)

12. P(black card or odd-numbered card)

13. P(heart or black card)

14. P(heart or even-numbered card)

15. P(face card or diamond)

16. P(red card or black card)

17. P(even-numbered card or ace)

18. P(red card or heart)

NAME ______________________ DATE __________ PERIOD ______

Practice

Student Edition
Pages 224–229

Compound Events

Two dice are rolled. Find the probability of each outcome.

1. P(even number and 2) $\frac{1}{12}$
2. P(5 and 5) $\frac{1}{36}$
3. P(odd number and a number less than 6) $\frac{5}{12}$
4. P(3 and a number less than 3) $\frac{1}{18}$
5. P(even number and a number greater than 2) $\frac{1}{3}$
6. P(6 and a number greater than 2) $\frac{1}{9}$

A card is drawn from a standard deck of cards. Determine whether the evens are* mutually exclusive *or* inclusive*. Then find each probability.

7. P(jack or five)

   mutually exclusive; $\frac{2}{13}$

8. P(ace or club)

   inclusive; $\frac{4}{13}$

9. P(red card or four)

   inclusive; $\frac{7}{13}$

10. P(face card or black card)

    inclusive; $\frac{8}{13}$

11. P(spade or diamond)

    mutually exclusive; $\frac{1}{2}$

12. P(black card or odd-numbered card)

    inclusive; $\frac{17}{26}$

13. P(heart or black card)

    mutually exclusive; $\frac{3}{4}$

14. P(heart or even-numbered card)

    inclusive; $\frac{7}{13}$

15. P(face card or diamond)

    inclusive; $\frac{11}{26}$

16. P(red card or black card)

    mutually exclusive; 1

17. P(even-numbered card or ace)

    mutually exclusive; $\frac{6}{13}$

18. P(red card or heart)

    inclusive; $\frac{1}{2}$

NAME ______________________ DATE __________ PERIOD ______

Practice

Student Edition
Pages 238–243

Relations

Express each relation as a table and as a graph. Then determine the domain and the range.

1. $\{(-3, 1), (-2, 0), (1, 2), (3, -4), (5, 3)\}$

x	*y*

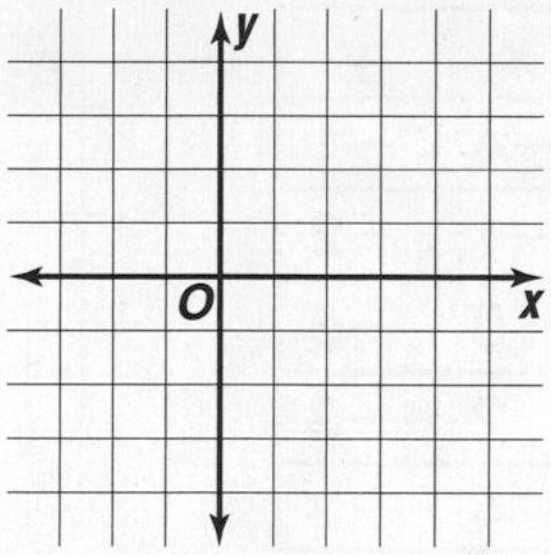

2. $\{(-4, -1), (-1, 2), (0, -5), (2, -3), (4, 3)\}$

x	*y*

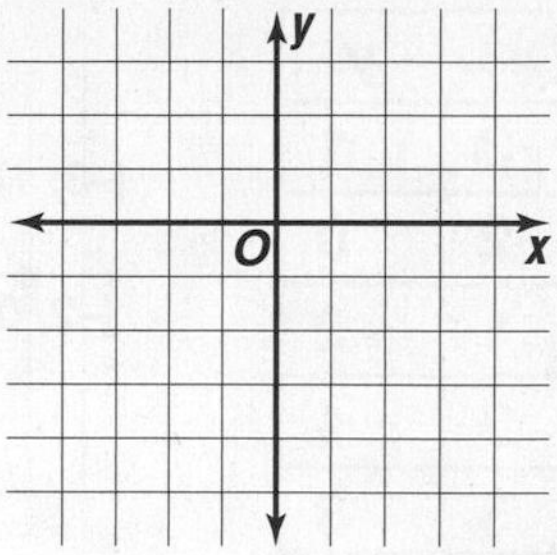

3. $\{(-5, 3.5), (-3, -4), (1.5, -5), (3, 3), (4.5, -1)\}$

x	*y*

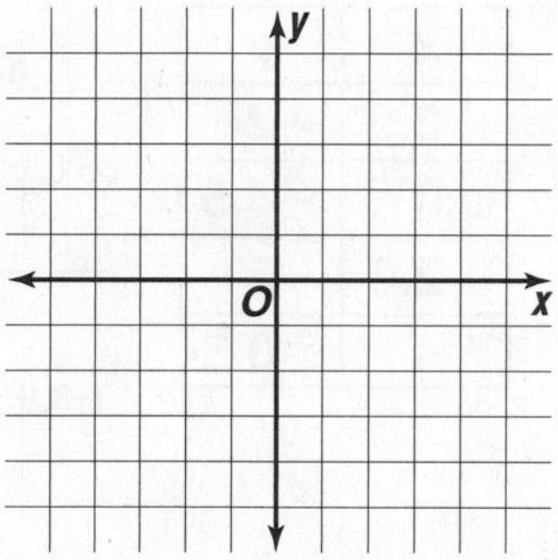

4. $\{(-3.9, -2), (0, 4.5), (2.5, -5), (4, 0.5)\}$

x	*y*

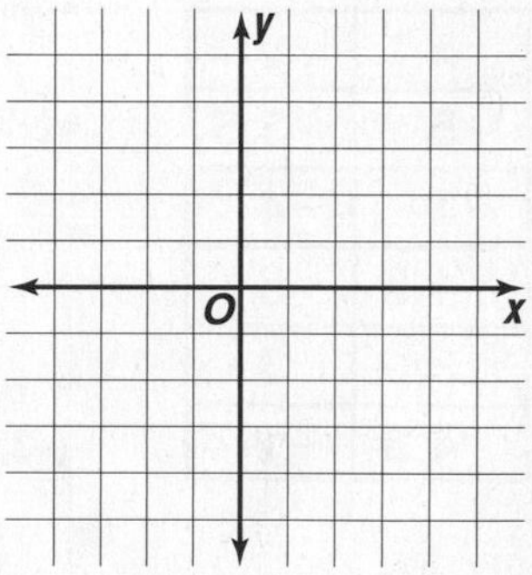

Express each relation as a set of ordered pairs and in a table. Then determine the domain and the range.

5.

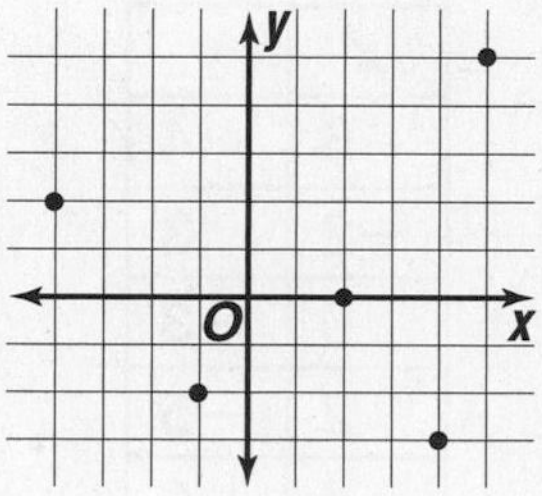

x	*y*

6.

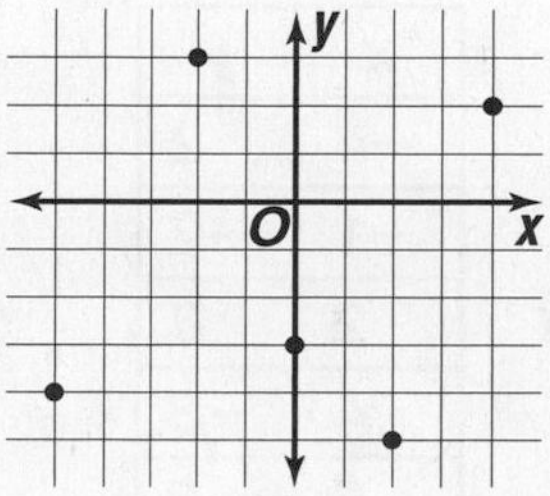

x	*y*

6–1

NAME ______________________ DATE __________ PERIOD ______

Practice

Student Edition
Pages 238–243

Relations

Express each relation as a table and as a graph. Then determine the domain and the range.

1. {(−3, 1), (−2, 0), (1, 2), (3, −4), (5, 3)}

x	y
−3	1
−2	0
1	2
3	−4
5	3

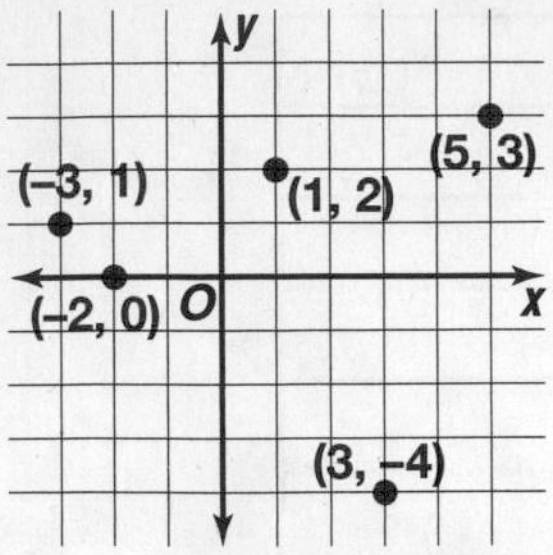

domain: {−3, −2, 1, 3, 5}
range: {1, 0, 2, −4, 3}

2. {(−4, −1), (−1, 2), (0, −5), (2, −3), (4, 3)}

x	y
−4	−1
−1	2
0	−5
2	−3
4	3

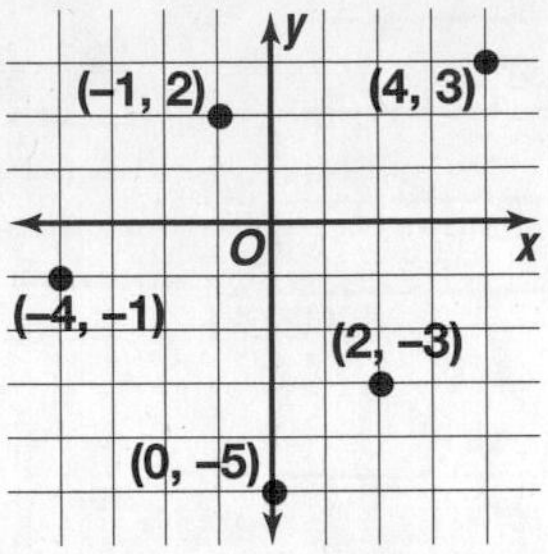

domain: {−4, −1, 0, 2, 4}
range: {−1, 2, −5, −3, 3}

3. {(−5, 3.5), (−3, −4), (1.5, −5), (3, 3), (4.5, −1)}

x	y
−5	3.5
−3	−4
1.5	−5
3	3
4.5	−1

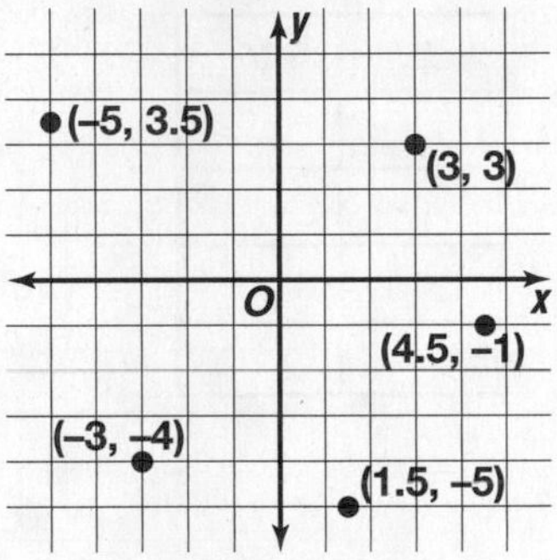

domain: {−5, −3, 1.5, 3, 4.5}
range: {3.5, −4, −5, 3, −1}

4. {(−3.9, −2), (0, 4.5), (2.5, −5), (4, 0.5)}

x	y
−3.9	−2
0	−4.5
2.5	−5
4	0.5

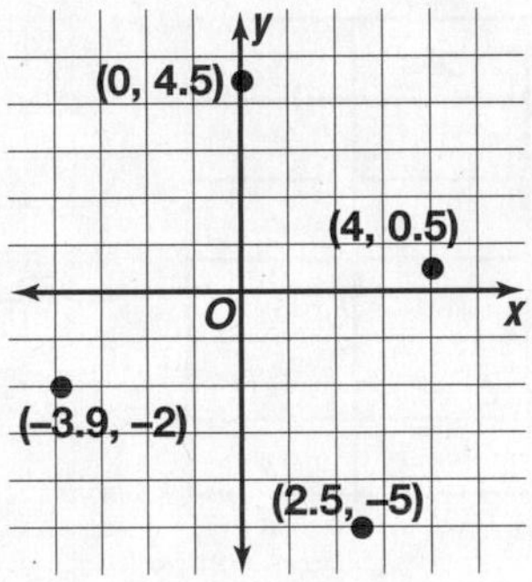

domain: {−3.9, 0, 2.5, 4}
range: {−2, 4.5, −5, 0.5}

Express each relation as a set of ordered pairs and in a table. Then determine the domain and the range.

5.

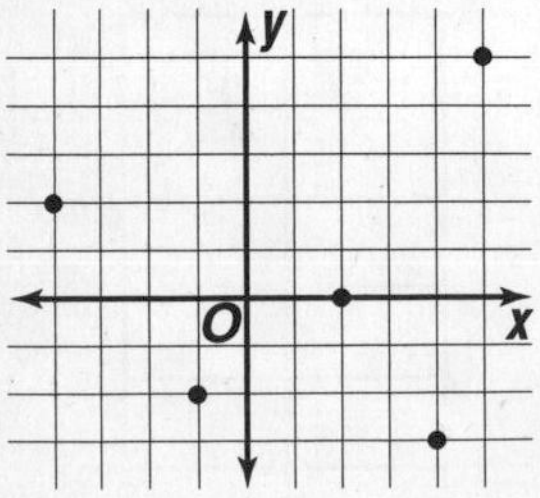

x	y
−4	2
−1	−2
2	0
4	−3
5	5

{(−4, 2), (−1, −2), (2, 0), (4, −3), (5, 5)}

domain: {−4, −1, 2, 4, 5}
range: {2, −2, 0, −3, 5}

6.

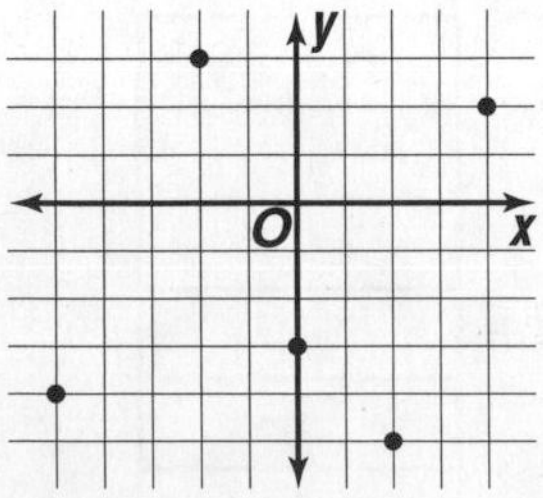

x	y
−5	−4
−2	3
0	−3
2	−5
4	2

{(−5, −4), (−2, 3), (0, −3), (2, −5), (4, 2)}

domain: {−5, −2, 0, 2, 4}
range: {−4, 3, −3, −5, 2}

NAME ______________________ DATE __________ PERIOD ______

6–2 Practice

Student Edition
Pages 244–249

Equations as Relations

Which ordered pairs are solutions of each equation?

1. $a + 3b = 5$	**a.** (2, 1)	**b.** (1, −2)	**c.** (−3, 3)	**d.** (8, −1)
2. $2g + 4h = 4$	**a.** (2, −2)	**b.** (4, −1)	**c.** (−2, 2)	**d.** (−4, 3)
3. $-3x + y = 1$	**a.** (4, 11)	**b.** (1, 4)	**c.** (−2, −5)	**d.** (−1, −2)
4. $9 = 5c - d$	**a.** (2, 1)	**b.** (1, −4)	**c.** (−2, −1)	**d.** (4, 11)
5. $2m = n + 6$	**a.** (4, −2)	**b.** (3, −2)	**c.** (3, 0)	**d.** (4, 2)

Solve each equation if the domain is {−2, −1, 0, 1, 2}. Graph the solution set.

6. $-3x = y$

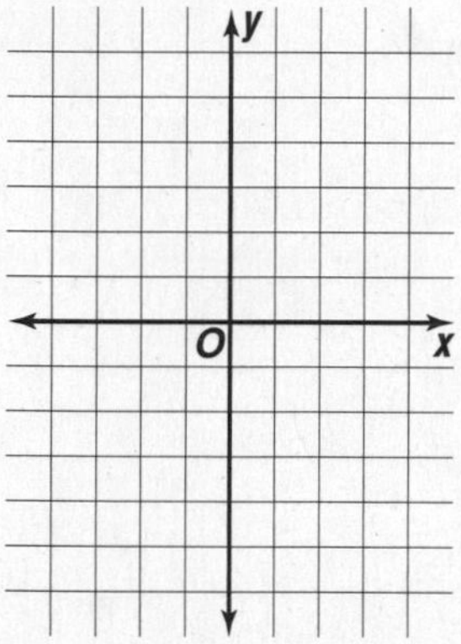

7. $y = 2x + 1$

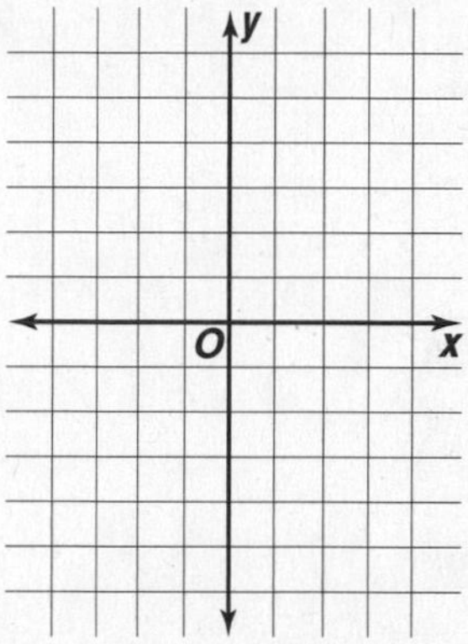

8. $-2x - 2 = y$

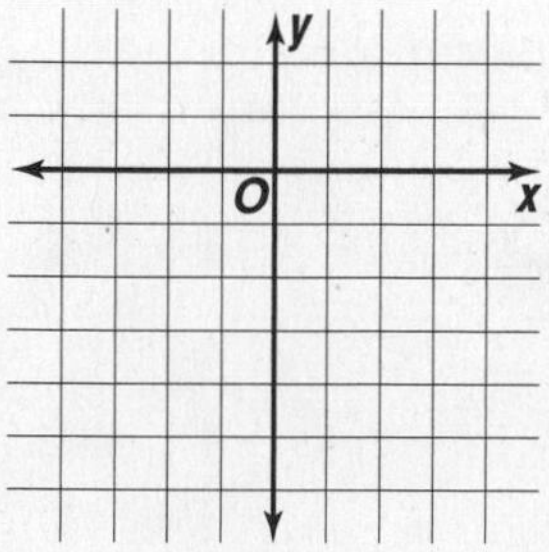

9. $2 + 2b = 4a$

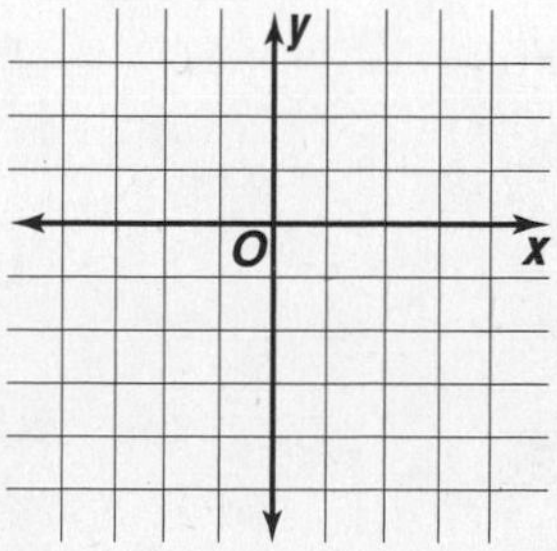

Find the domain of each equation if the range is {−4, −2, 0, 1, 2}.

10. $y = x + 5$

11. $3y = 2x$

NAME ______________________ DATE __________ PERIOD ________

Practice

Student Edition
Pages 244–249

Equations as Relations

Which ordered pairs are solutions of each equation?

1. $a + 3b = 5$	**a, d**	a. (2, 1)	b. (1, −2)	c. (−3, 3)	d. (8, −1)
2. $2g + 4h = 4$	**b, c, d**	a. (2, −2)	b. (4, −1)	c. (−2, 2)	d. (−4, 3)
3. $-3x + y = 1$	**b, c, d**	a. (4, 11)	b. (1, 4)	c. (−2, −5)	d. (−1, −2)
4. $9 = 5c - d$	**a, b, d**	a. (2, 1)	b. (1, −4)	c. (−2, −1)	d. (4, 11)
5. $2m = n + 6$	**c, d**	a. (4, −2)	b. (3, −2)	c. (3, 0)	d. (4, 2)

Solve each equation if the domain is {−2, −1, 0, 1, 2}. Graph the solution set.

6. $-3x = y$

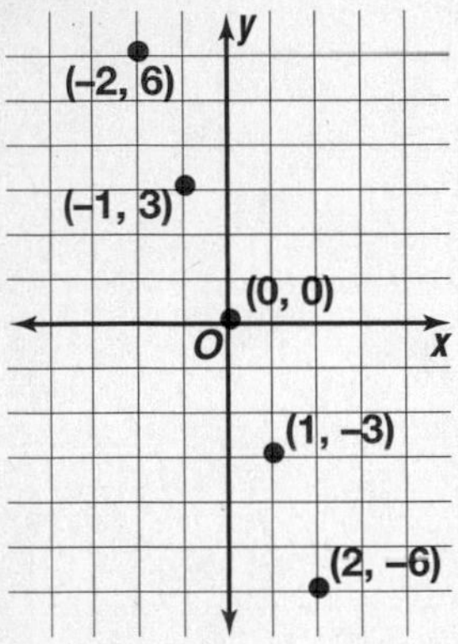

{(−2, 6), (−1, 3), (0, 0), (1, −3), (2, −6)}

7. $y = 2x + 1$

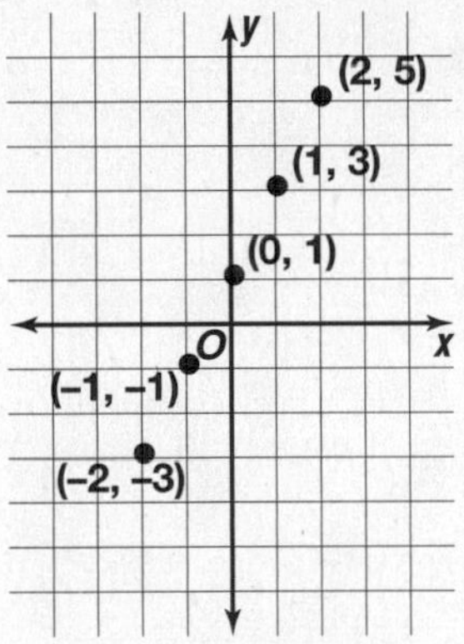

{(−2, −3), (−1, −1), (0, 1), (1, 3), (2, 5)}

8. $-2x - 2 = y$

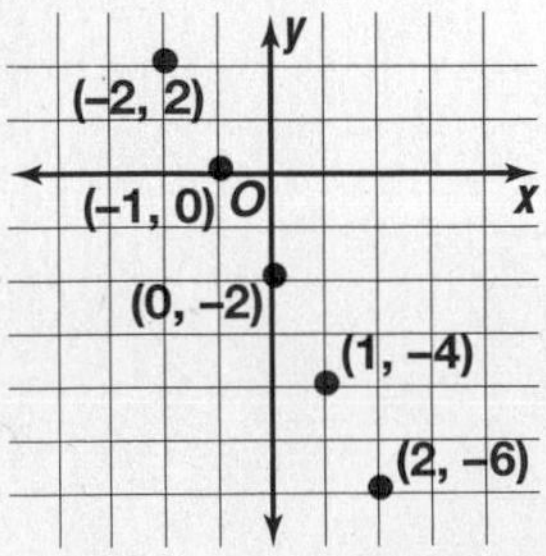

{(−2, 2), (−1, 0), (0, −2), (1, −4), (2, −6)}

9. $2 + 2b = 4a$

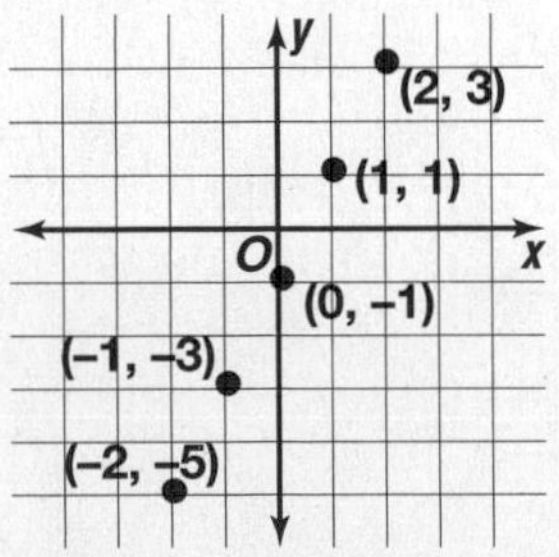

{(−2, −5), (−1, −3), (0, −1), (1, 1), (2, 3)}

Find the domain of each equation if the range is {−4, −2, 0, 1, 2}.

10. $y = x + 5$

{−9, −7, −5, −4, −3}

11. $3y = 2x$

{−6, −3, 0, 1.5, 3}

NAME ______________________ DATE ________ PERIOD ______

Practice

Graphing Linear Relations

Determine whether each equation is a linear equation. Explain. If an equation is linear, identify A, B, and C.

1. $2xy = 6$

2. $3x = y$

3. $4y - 2x = 2$

4. $x = -3$

5. $4x + 5xy = 18$

6. $x + 3y = 7$

7. $\frac{2}{x} = 8$

8. $5y = x$

9. $3x^2 + 4y = 2$

Graph each equation.

10. $y = 4x - 2$

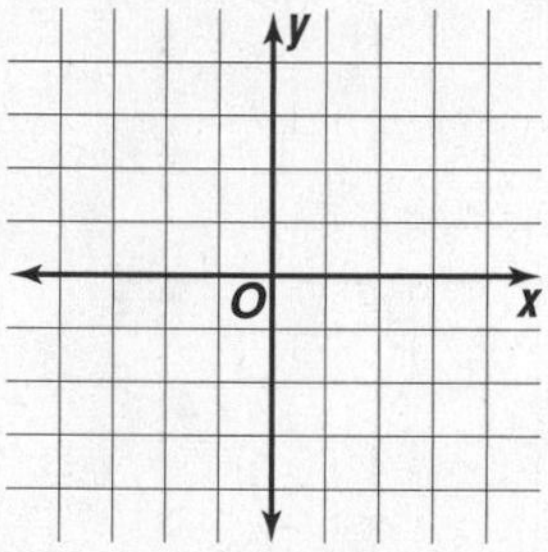

11. $y = 2x$

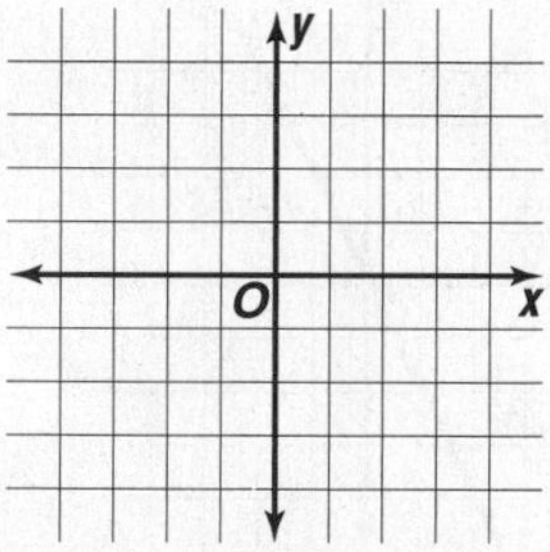

12. $x = 4$

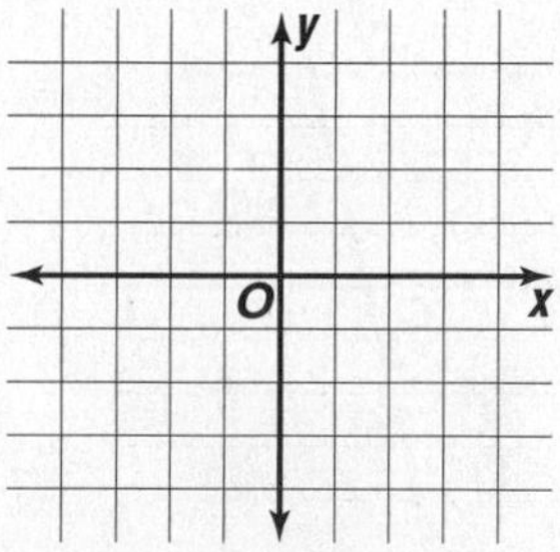

13. $y = -3x + 4$

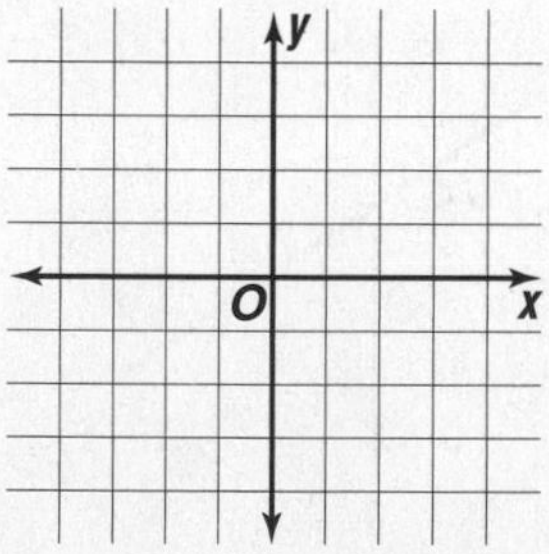

14. $y = -5$

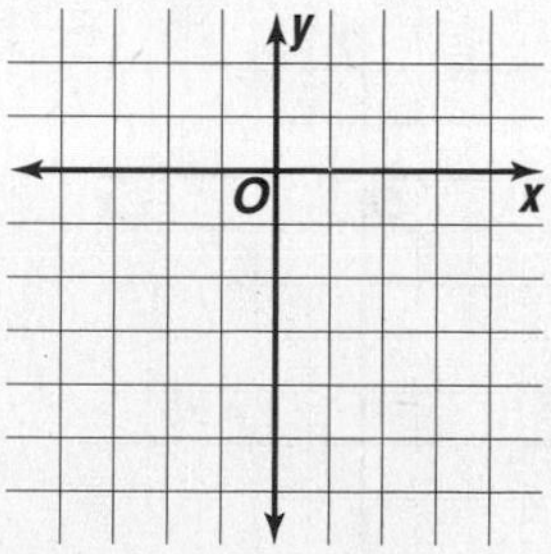

15. $2x + 3y = 4$

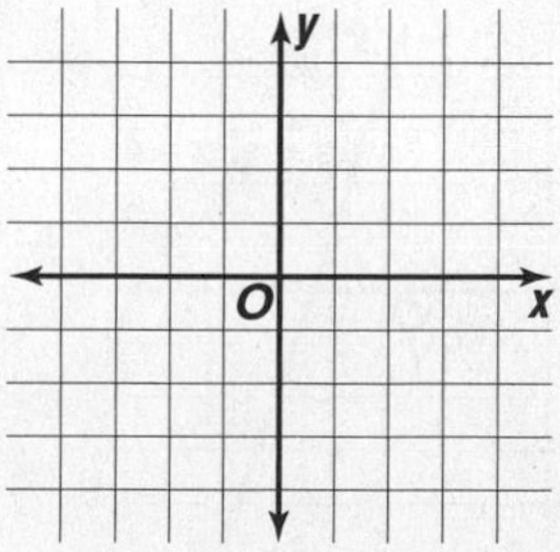

16. $-3 = x + y$

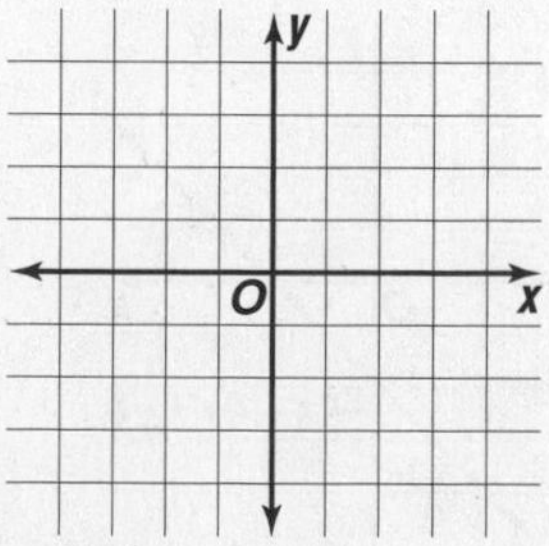

17. $6y = 2x + 4$

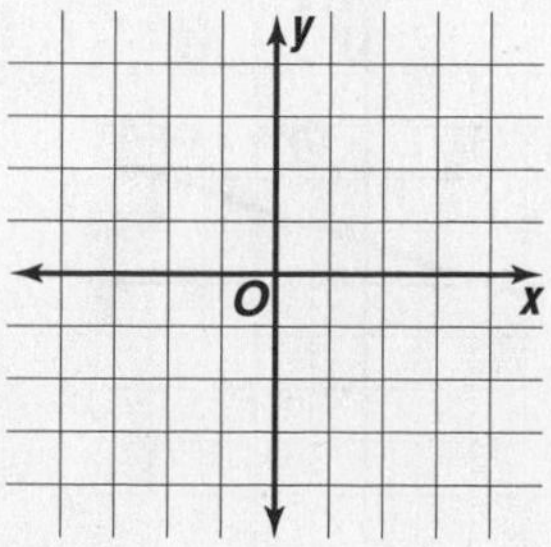

18. $-4x + 4y = -8$

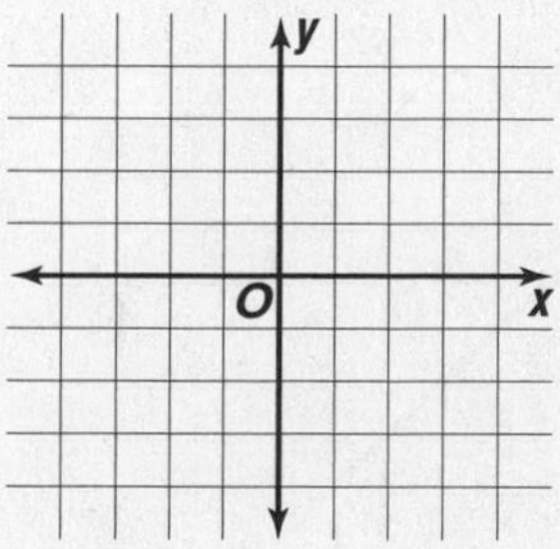

6–3

NAME ______________________ DATE __________ PERIOD ______

Practice

Student Edition
Pages 250–255

Graphing Linear Relations

Determine whether each equation is a linear equation. Explain. If an equation is linear, identify A, B, and C.

1. $2xy = 6$
   no

2. $3x = y$
   yes; $A = 3$, $B = -1$, $C = 0$

3. $4y - 2x = 2$
   yes; $A = -2$, $B = 4$, $C = 2$

4. $x = -3$
   yes; $A = 1$, $B = 0$, $C = -3$

5. $4x + 5xy = 18$
   no

6. $x + 3y = 7$
   yes; $A = 1$, $B = 3$, $C = 7$

7. $\frac{2}{x} = 8$
   no

8. $5y = x$
   yes; $A = -1$, $B = 5$, $C = 0$

9. $3x^2 + 4y = 2$
   no

Graph each equation.

10. $y = 4x - 2$

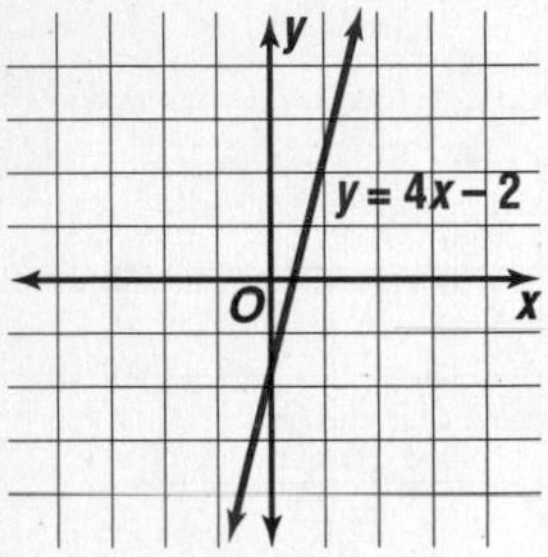

11. $y = 2x$

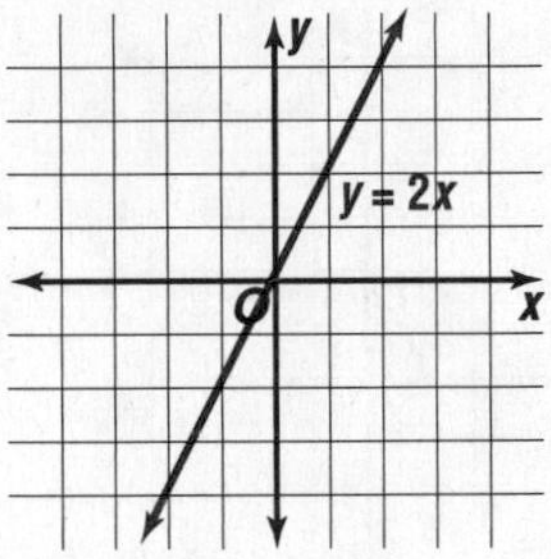

12. $x = 4$

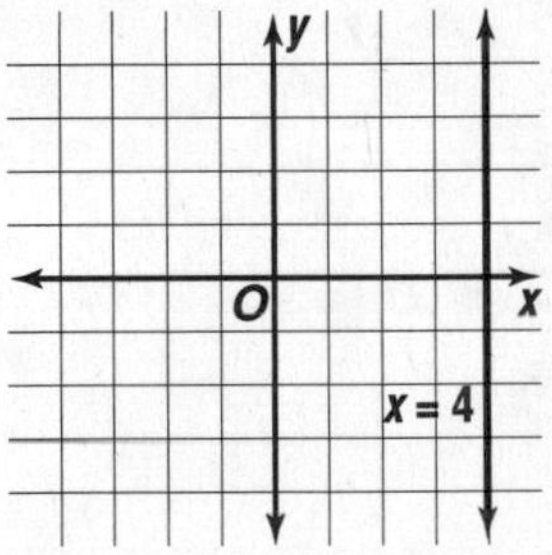

13. $y = -3x + 4$

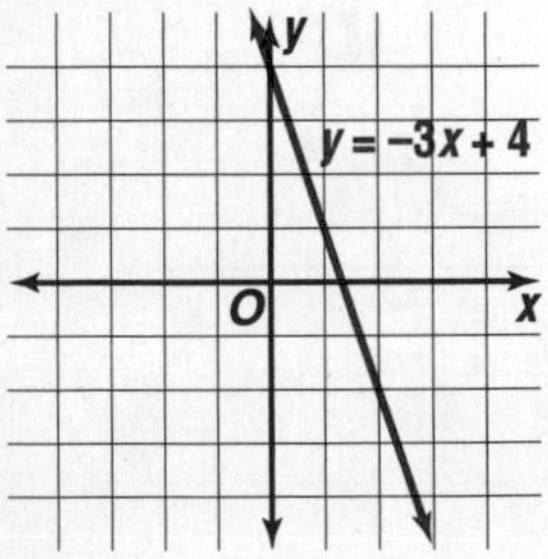

14. $y = -5$

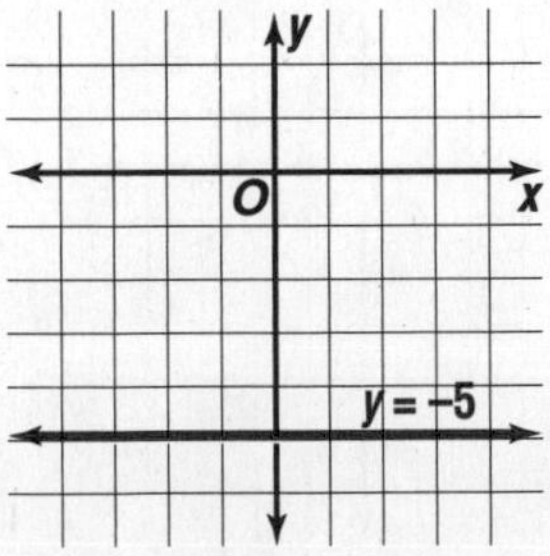

15. $2x + 3y = 4$

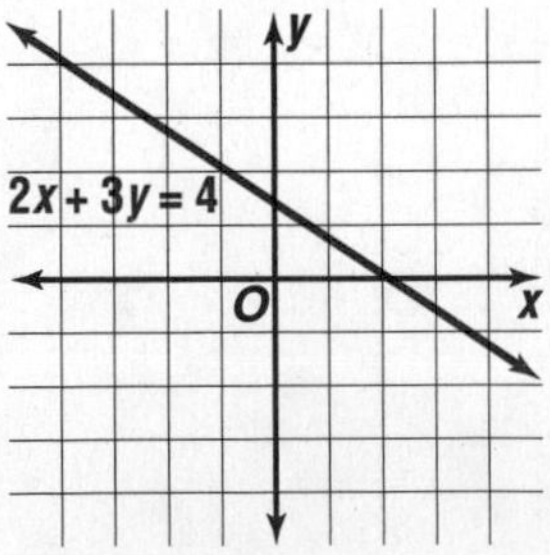

16. $-3 = x + y$

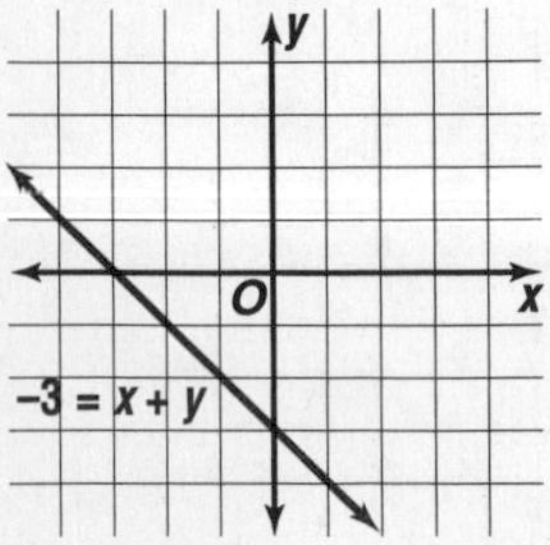

17. $6y = 2x + 4$

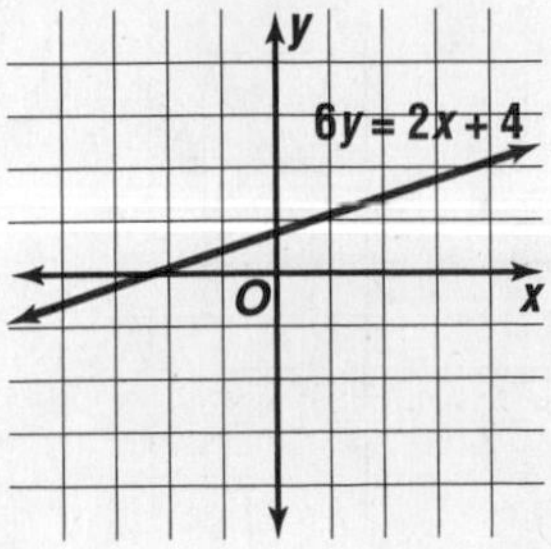

18. $-4x + 4y = -8$

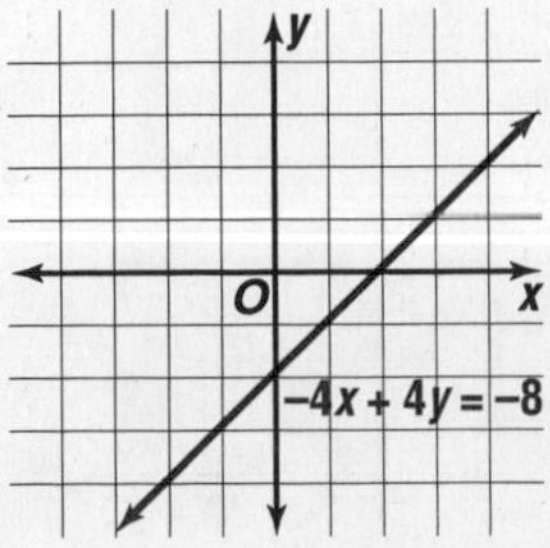

NAME ______________________ DATE __________ PERIOD ______

Practice

Student Edition
Pages 256–261

Functions

Determine whether each relation is a function.

1. $\{(-2, 1), (2, 0), (3, 6), (3, -4), (5, 3)\}$

2. $\{(-3, 2), (-2, 2), (1, 2), (-3, 1), (0, 3)\}$

3. $\{(-4, 1), (-2, 1), (1, 2), (3, 2), (0, 3)\}$

4. $\{(3, 3), (-2, -2), (5, 3), (1, -4), (2, 3)\}$

5. $\{(4, -1), (-1, 4), (1, 4), (3, -4), (-4, 3)\}$

6. $\{(-1, 0), (-2, 2), (1, -2), (3, 5), (1, 3)\}$

7.

x	y
−2	3
1	3
−4	2
0	1
2	3

8.

x	y
2	−3
−1	0
5	5
3	2
2	1

9.

x	y
−4	3
2	0
1	4
−3	5
3	5

10.

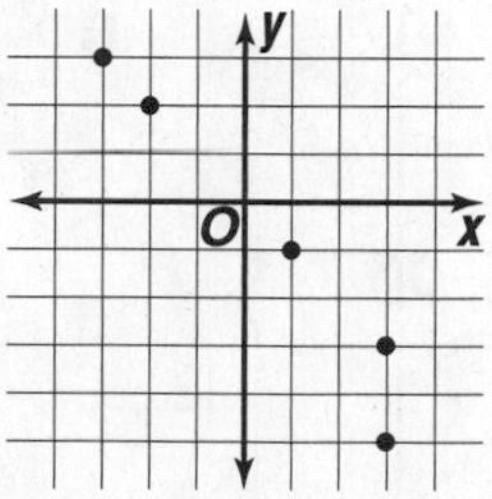

11.

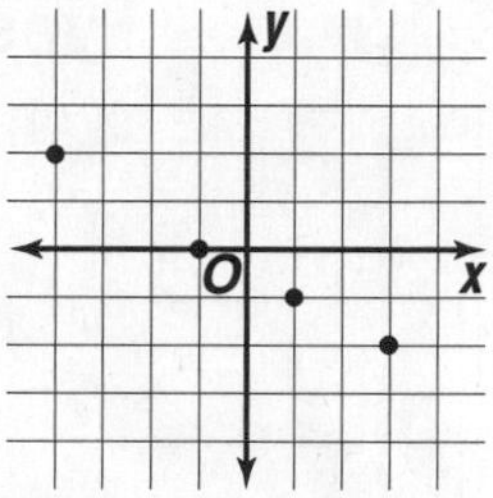

12.

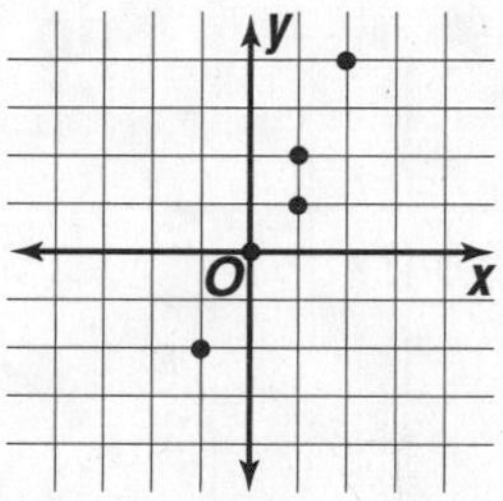

Use the vertical line test to determine whether each relation is a function.

13.

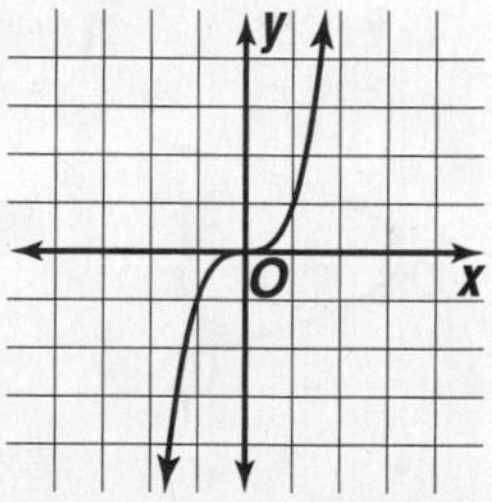

14.

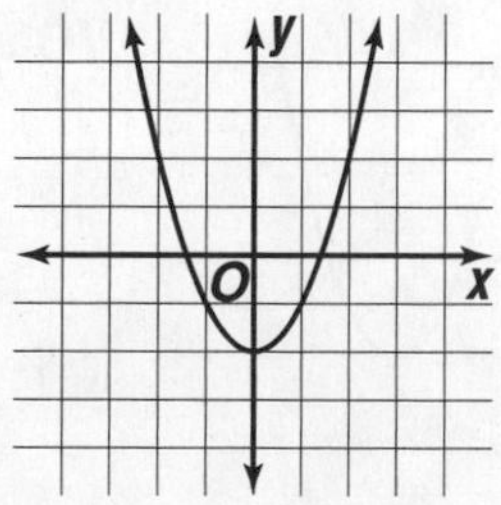

15.

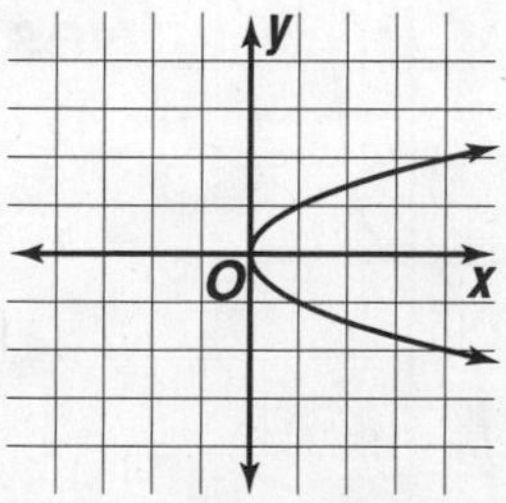

If f(x) = 3x − 2, find each value.

16. $f(4)$

17. $f(-2)$

18. $f(8)$

19. $f(-5)$

20. $f(1.5)$

21. $f(2.4)$

22. $f\left(\frac{1}{3}\right)$

23. $f\left(-\frac{2}{3}\right)$

24. $f(b)$

25. $f(2g)$

26. $f(-3c)$

27. $f(2.5a)$

NAME ______________________ DATE __________ PERIOD ______

Practice

Student Edition
Pages 256–261

Functions

Determine whether each relation is a function.

1. {(−2, 1), (2, 0), (3, 6), (3, −4), (5, 3)}
no

2. {(−3, 2), (−2, 2), (1, 2), (−3, 1), (0, 3)}
no

3. {(−4, 1), (−2, 1), (1, 2), (3, 2), (0, 3)}
yes

4. {(3, 3), (−2, −2), (5, 3), (1, −4), (2, 3)}
yes

5. {(4, −1), (−1, 4), (1, 4), (3, −4), (−4, 3)}
yes

6. {(−1, 0), (−2, 2), (1, −2), (3, 5), (1, 3)}
no

7. **yes**

x	y
−2	3
1	3
−4	2
0	1
2	3

8. **no**

x	y
2	−3
−1	0
5	5
3	2
2	1

9. **yes**

x	y
−4	3
2	0
1	4
−3	5
3	5

10. 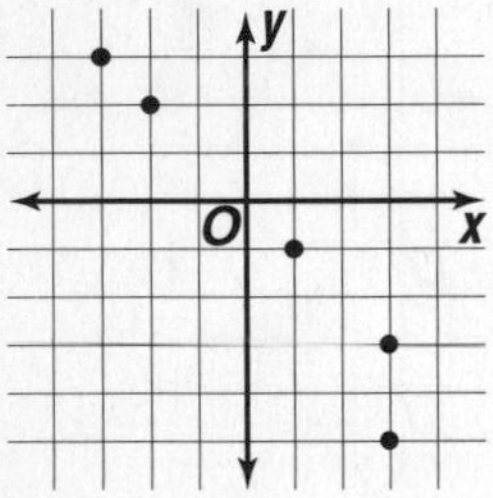

no

11. 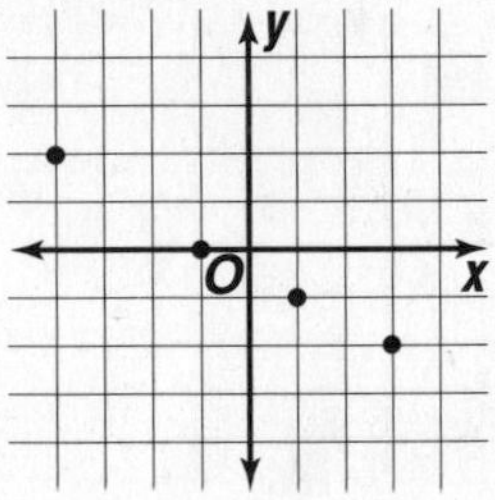

yes

12. 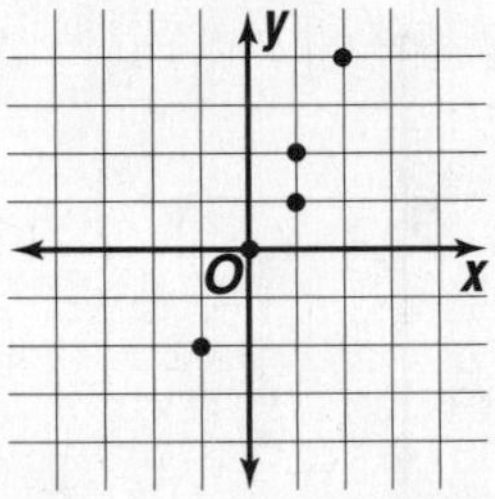

no

Use the vertical line test to determine whether each relation is a function.

13. 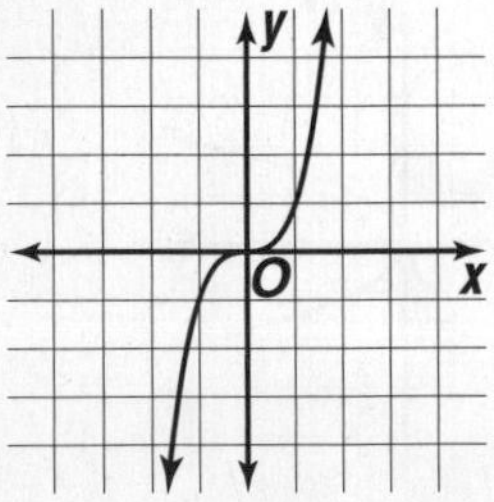

yes

14. 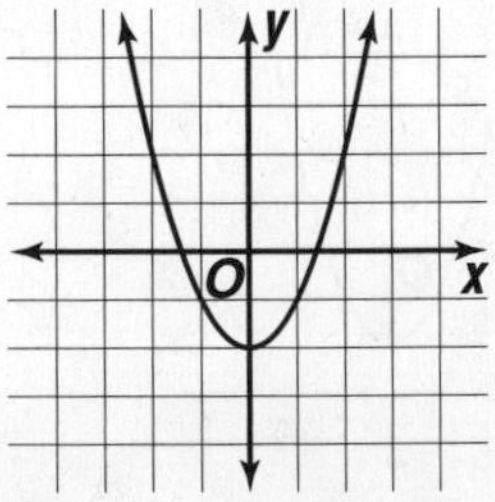

yes

15. 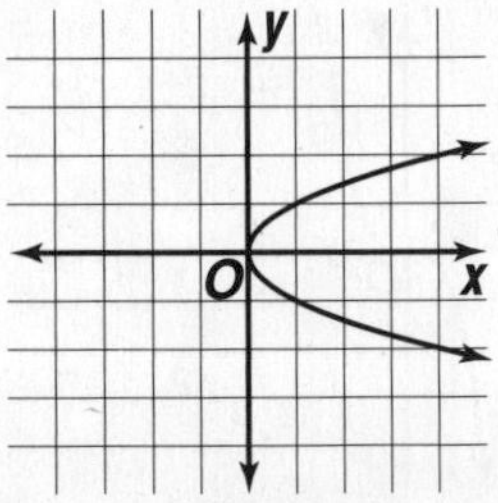

no

If f(x) = 3x − 2, find each value.

16. $f(4)$ **10**

17. $f(-2)$ **−8**

18. $f(8)$ **22**

19. $f(-5)$ **−17**

20. $f(1.5)$ **2.5**

21. $f(2.4)$ **5.2**

22. $f\left(\frac{1}{3}\right)$ **−1**

23. $f\left(-\frac{2}{3}\right)$ **−4**

24. $f(b)$
3*b* − 2

25. $f(2g)$
6*g* − 2

26. $f(-3c)$
−9*c* − 2

27. $f(2.5a)$
7.5*a* − 2

NAME ______ DATE ______ PERIOD ______

6–5 Practice

Student Edition
Pages 264–269

Direct Variation

Determine whether each equation is a direct variation. Verify the answer with a graph.

1. $y = 3x$

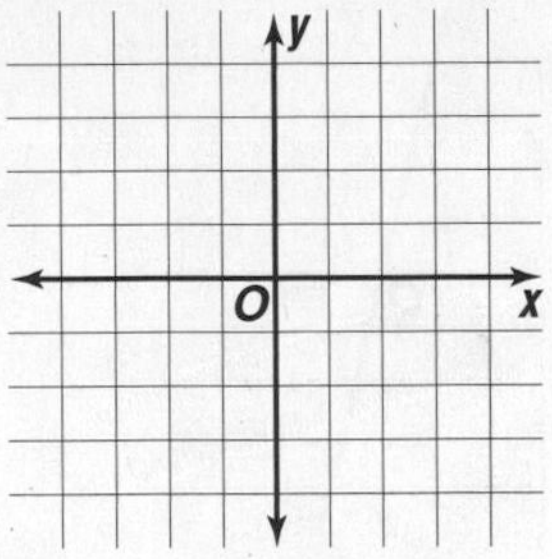

2. $y = x + 2$

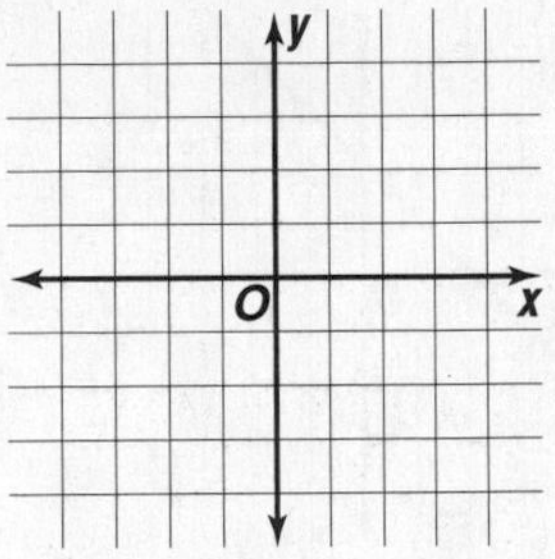

3. $y = -4x$

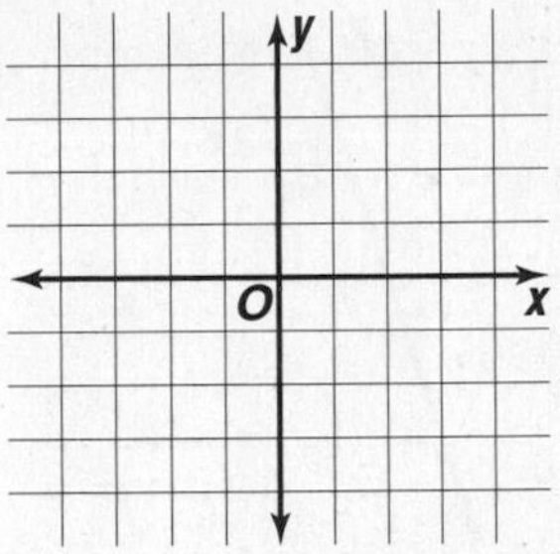

4. $y = -x - 1$

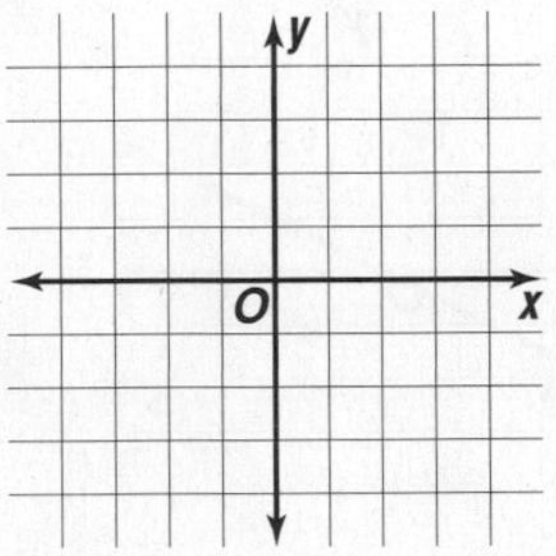

5. $y = 2$

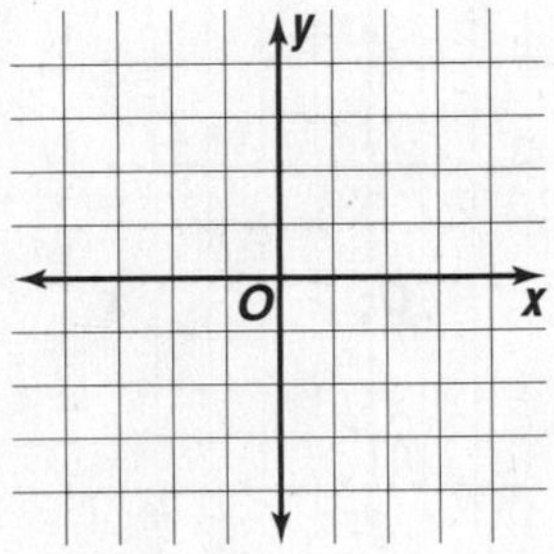

6. $y = \frac{1}{2}x$

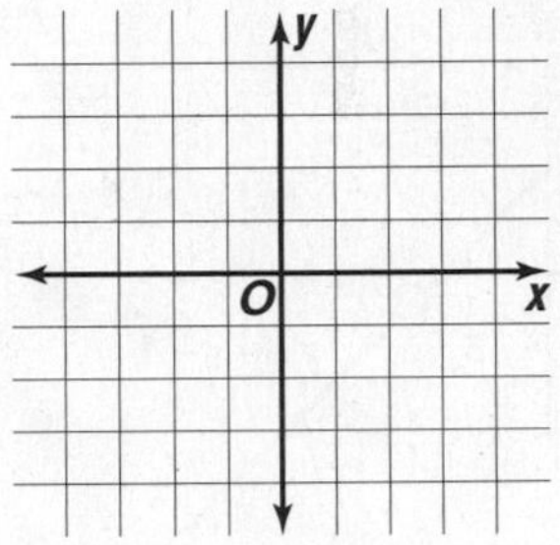

Solve. Assume that y varies directly as x.

7. If $y = 14$ when $x = 5$, find x when $y = 28$.

8. Find y when $x = 5$ if $y = -6$ when $x = 2$.

9. If $x = 9$ when $y = 18$, find x when $y = 24$.

10. If $y = 36$ when $x = -6$, find x when $y = 54$.

11. Find y when $x = 3$ if $y = -3$ when $x = 6$.

12. Find y when $x = 8$ if $y = 4$ when $x = 5$.

Solve by using direct variation.

13. If there are 4 quarts in a gallon, how many quarts are in 4.5 gallons?

14. How many feet are in 62.4 inches if there are 12 inches in a foot?

15. If there are 2 cups in a pint, how many cups are in 7.2 pints?

NAME ____________________ DATE __________ PERIOD ______

Practice

Student Edition
Pages 264–269

Direct Variation

Determine whether each equation is a direct variation. Verify the answer with a graph.

1. $y = 3x$ **yes**

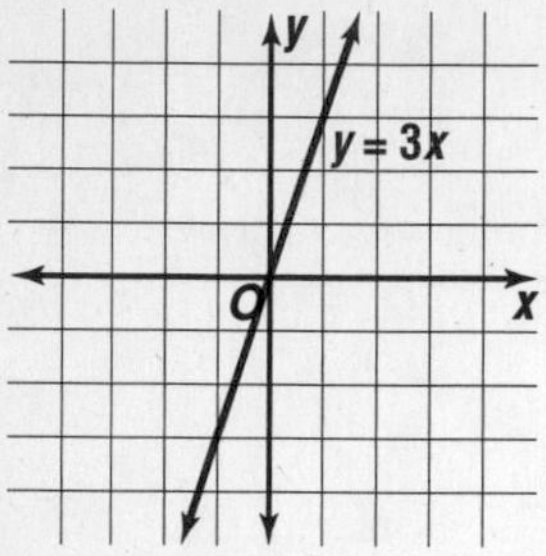

2. $y = x + 2$ **no**

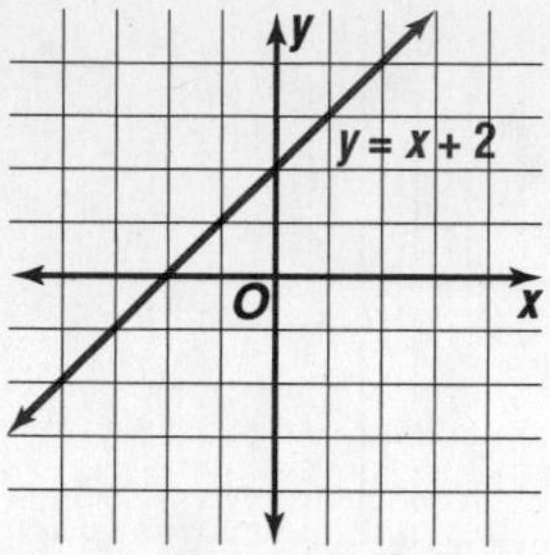

3. $y = -4x$ **yes**

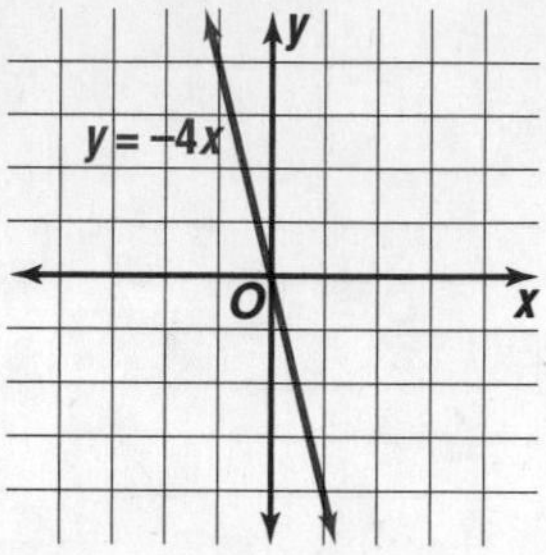

4. $y = -x - 1$ **no**

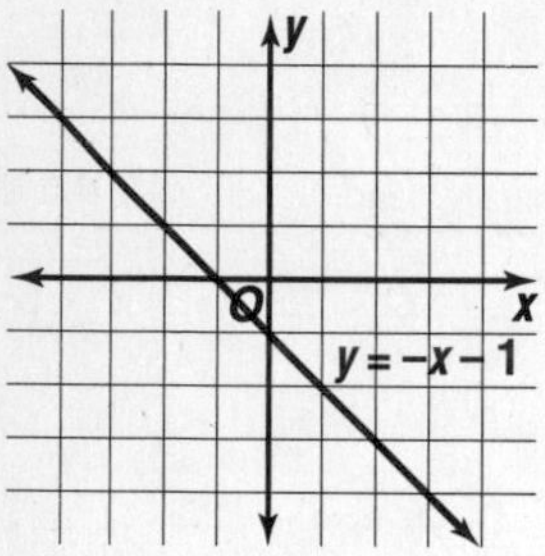

5. $y = 2$ **no**

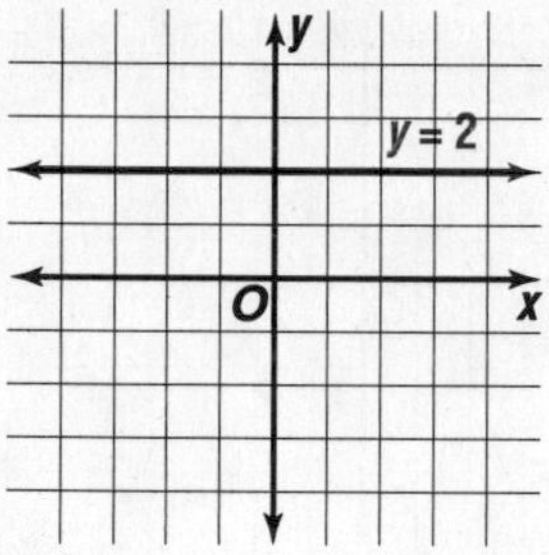

6. $y = \frac{1}{2}x$ **yes**

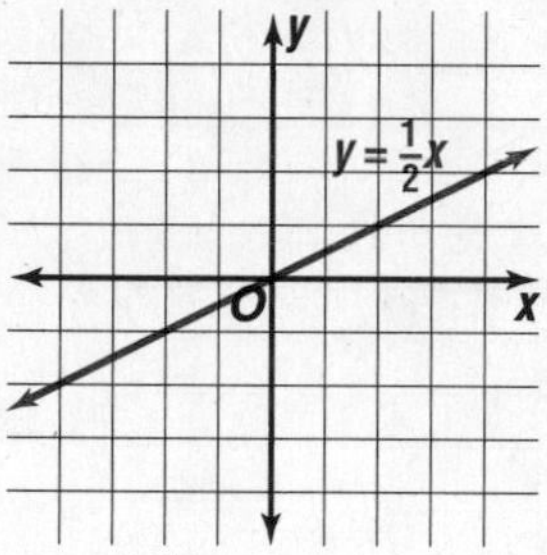

Solve. Assume that y varies directly as x.

7. If $y = 14$ when $x = 5$, find x when $y = 28$.
10

8. Find y when $x = 5$ if $y = -6$ when $x = 2$.
−15

9. If $x = 9$ when $y = 18$, find x when $y = 24$.
12

10. If $y = 36$ when $x = -6$, find x when $y = 54$.
−9

11. Find y when $x = 3$ if $y = -3$ when $x = 6$.
−1.5

12. Find y when $x = 8$ if $y = 4$ when $x = 5$.
6.4

Solve by using direct variation.

13. If there are 4 quarts in a gallon, how many quarts are in 4.5 gallons? **18 qt**

14. How many feet are in 62.4 inches if there are 12 inches in a foot? **5.2 ft**

15. If there are 2 cups in a pint, how many cups are in 7.2 pints?
14.4 c

NAME ______________________ DATE __________ PERIOD ______

Practice

Student Edition
Pages 270–275

Inverse Variation

Solve. Assume that y varies inversely as x.

1. Suppose $y = 9$ when $x = 4$. Find y when $x = 12$.

2. Find x when $y = 4$ if $y = -4$ when $x = 6$.

3. Find x when $y = 7$ if $y = -2$ when $x = -14$.

4. Suppose $y = -2$ when $x = 8$. Find y when $x = 4$.

5. Suppose $y = -9$ when $x = 2$. Find y when $x = -3$.

6. Suppose $y = 22$ when $x = 3$. Find y when $x = -6$.

7. Find x when $y = 9$ if $y = -3$ when $x = -18$.

8. Suppose $y = 5$ when $x = 8$. Find y when $x = 4$.

9. Find x when $y = 15$ if $y = -6$ when $x = 2.5$.

10. If $y = 3.5$ when $x = 2$, find y when $x = 5$.

11. If $y = 2.4$ when $x = 5$, find y when $x = 6$.

12. Find x when $y = -10$ if $y = -8$ when $x = 12$.

13. Suppose $y = -3$ when $x = -0.4$. Find y when $x = -6$.

14. If $y = -3.8$ when $x = -4$, find y when $x = 2$.

NAME ______________________ DATE __________ PERIOD ______

Practice

Student Edition
Pages 270–275

Inverse Variation

Solve. Assume that y varies inversely as x.

1. Suppose $y = 9$ when $x = 4$. Find y when $x = 12$. **3**

2. Find x when $y = 4$ if $y = -4$ when $x = 6$. **−6**

3. Find x when $y = 7$ if $y = -2$ when $x = -14$. **4**

4. Suppose $y = -2$ when $x = 8$. Find y when $x = 4$. **−4**

5. Suppose $y = -9$ when $x = 2$. Find y when $x = -3$. **6**

6. Suppose $y = 22$ when $x = 3$. Find y when $x = -6$. **−11**

7. Find x when $y = 9$ if $y = -3$ when $x = -18$. **6**

8. Suppose $y = 5$ when $x = 8$. Find y when $x = 4$. **10**

9. Find x when $y = 15$ if $y = -6$ when $x = 2.5$. **−1**

10. If $y = 3.5$ when $x = 2$, find y when $x = 5$. **1.4**

11. If $y = 2.4$ when $x = 5$, find y when $x = 6$. **2**

12. Find x when $y = -10$ if $y = -8$ when $x = 12$. **9.6**

13. Suppose $y = -3$ when $x = -0.4$. Find y when $x = -6$. **−0.2**

14. If $y = -3.8$ when $x = -4$, find y when $x = 2$. **7.6**

NAME ________________________ DATE __________ PERIOD ______

Practice

Slope

Determine the slope of each line.

1. 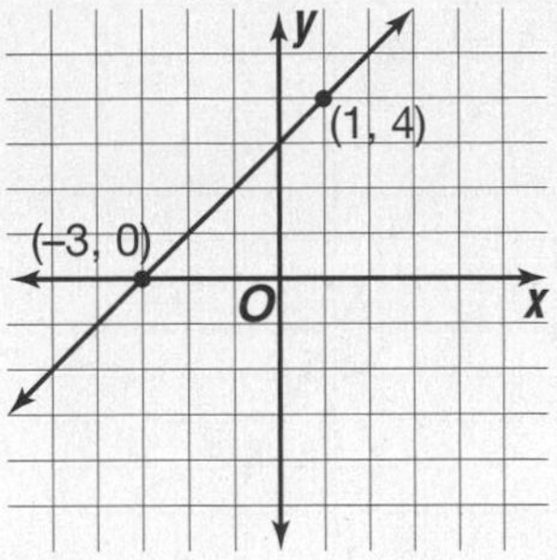

2. 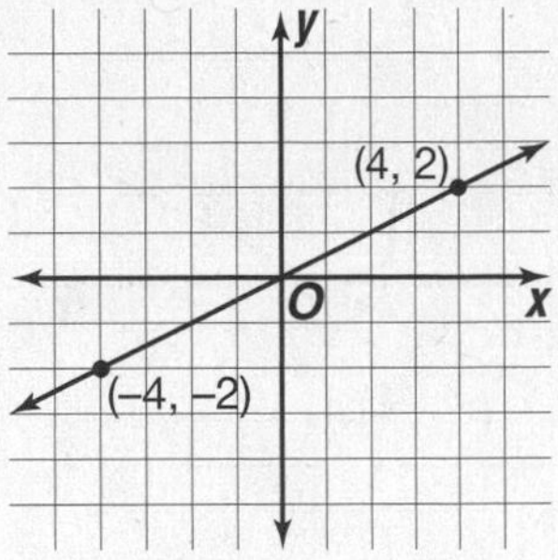

3. 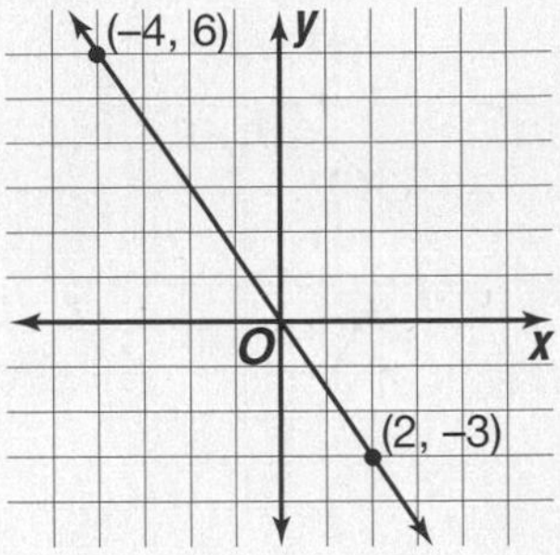

4. 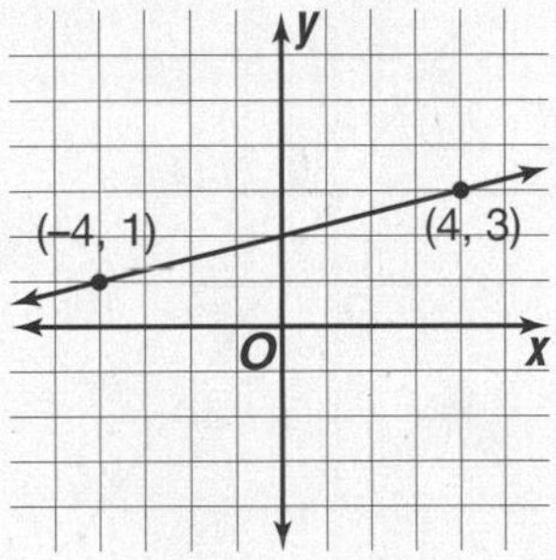

5. 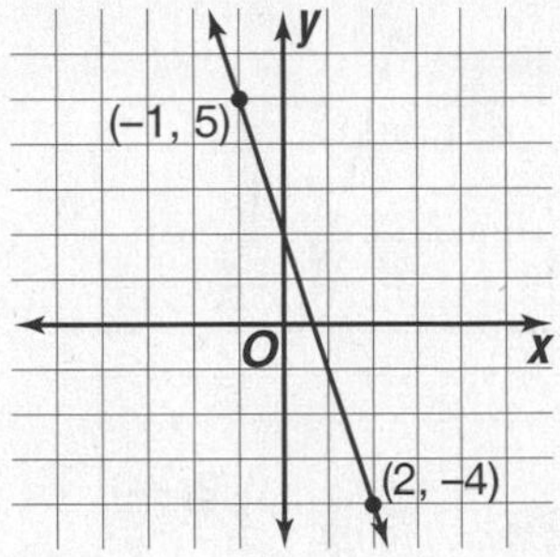

6. 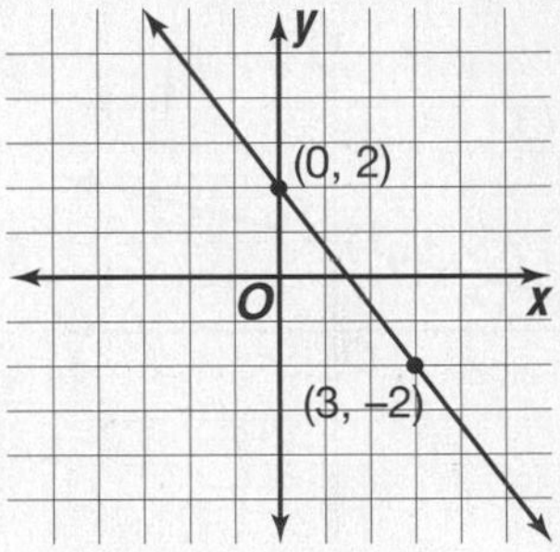

Determine the slope of the line passing through the points whose coordinates are listed in each table.

7.

x	*y*
−1	−3
0	0
1	3
2	6

8.

x	*y*
−2	5
2	4
6	3
10	2

9.

x	*y*
−3	4
−1	5
1	6
3	7

Determine the slope of each line.

10. the line through points at (3, 4) and (4, 6)

11. the line through points at (−3, −2) and (−2, −5)

12. the line through points at (2, 3) and (−5, 1)

13. the line through points at (4, −1) and (9, 6)

14. the line through points at (−4, 4) and (−9, −8)

15. the line through points at (−6, 2) and (7, −3)

NAME ______________________ DATE __________ PERIOD ______

Practice

Student Edition
Pages 284–289

Slope

Determine the slope of each line.

1.

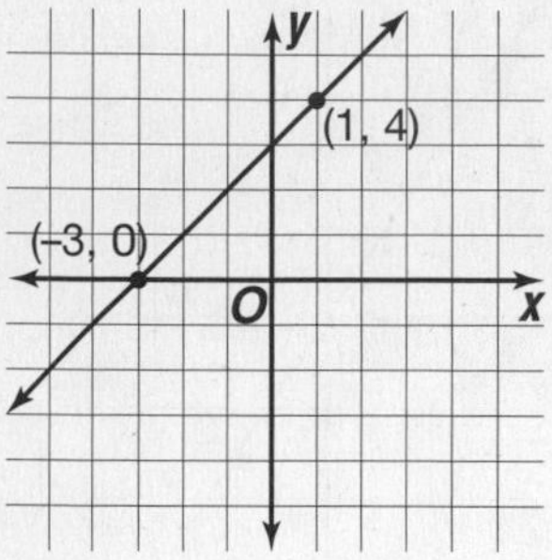

1

2.

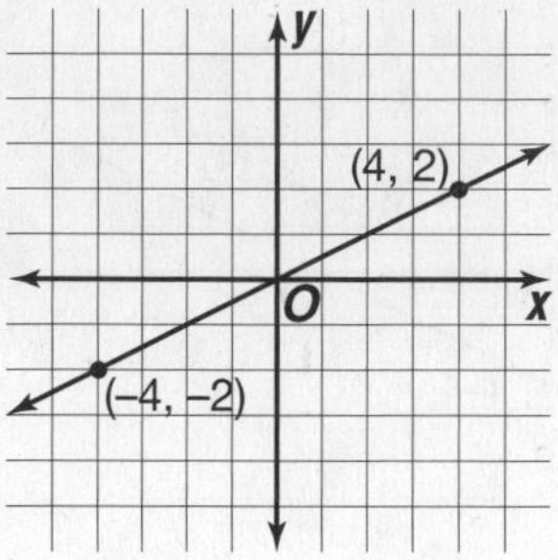

$\mathbf{\frac{1}{2}}$

3.

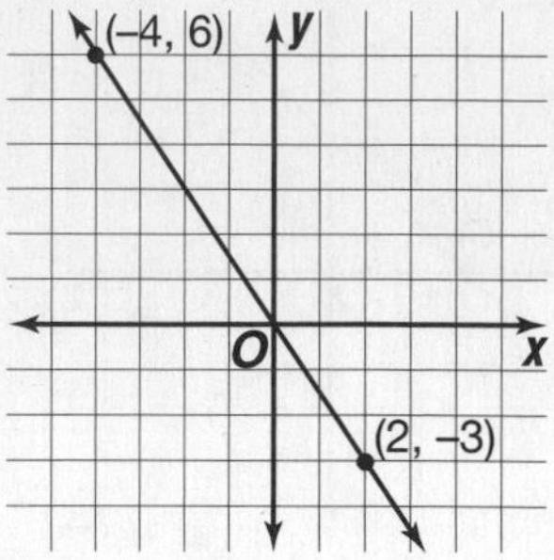

$\mathbf{-\frac{3}{2}}$

4.

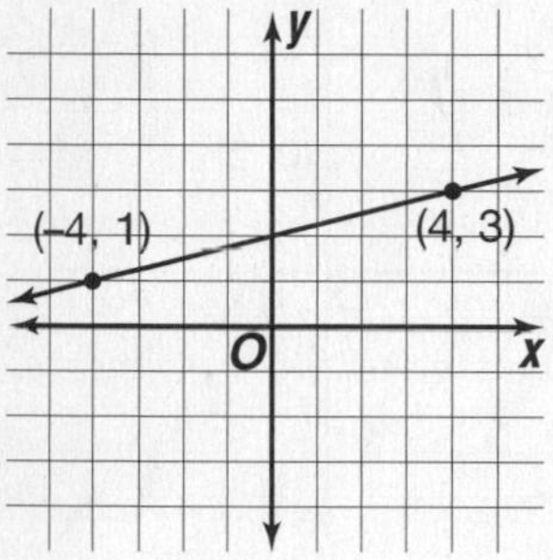

$\mathbf{\frac{1}{4}}$

5.

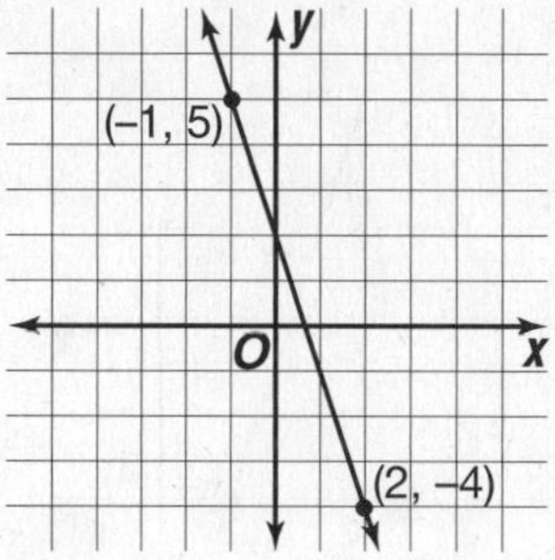

−3

6.

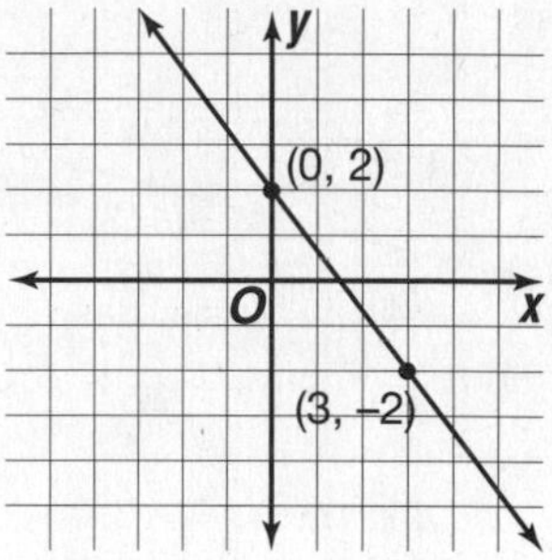

$\mathbf{-\frac{4}{3}}$

Determine the slope of the line passing through the points whose coordinates are listed in each table.

7.

x	*y*
−1	−3
0	0
1	3
2	6

3

8.

x	*y*
−2	5
2	4
6	3
10	2

$\mathbf{-\frac{1}{4}}$

9.

x	*y*
−3	4
−1	5
1	6
3	7

$\mathbf{\frac{1}{2}}$

Determine the slope of each line.

10. the line through points at (3, 4) and (4, 6) **2**

11. the line through points at (−3, −2) and (−2, −5) **−3**

12. the line through points at (2, 3) and (−5, 1) $\mathbf{\frac{2}{7}}$

13. the line through points at (4, −1) and (9, 6) $\mathbf{\frac{7}{5}}$

14. the line through points at (−4, 4) and (−9, −8) $\mathbf{\frac{12}{5}}$

15. the line through points at (−6, 2) and (7, −3) $\mathbf{-\frac{5}{13}}$

NAME ______________________ DATE ________ PERIOD ______

7–2

Practice

Student Edition
Pages 290–295

Writing Equations in Point-Slope Form

Write the point-slope form of an equation for each line passing through the given point and having the given slope.

1. $(4, 7), m = 3$

2. $(-2, 3), m = 5$

3. $(6, -1), m = -2$

4. $(-5, -2), m = 0$

5. $(-4, -6), m = \frac{2}{3}$

6. $(-8, 3), m = -\frac{3}{5}$

7. $(7, -9), m = 4$

8. $(-6, 3), m = -\frac{1}{2}$

9. $(-2, -5), m = 8$

Write the point-slope form of an equation for each line.

10.

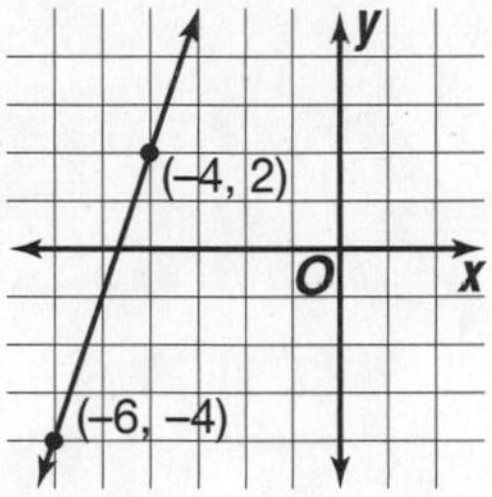

11.

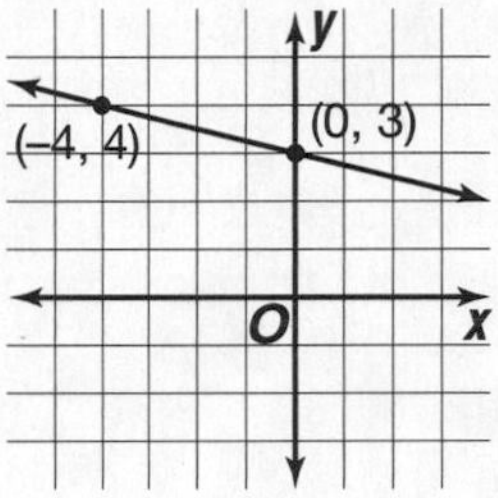

12.

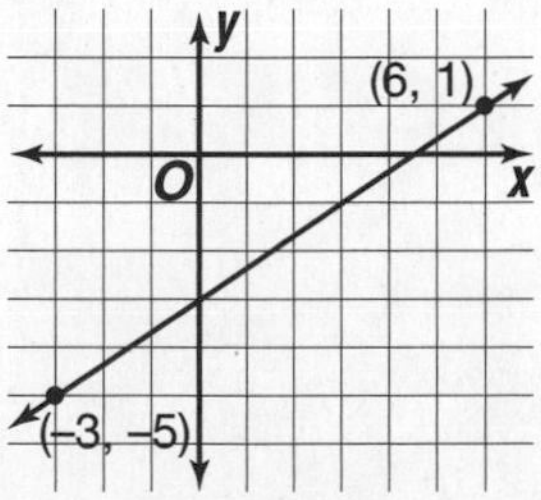

13.

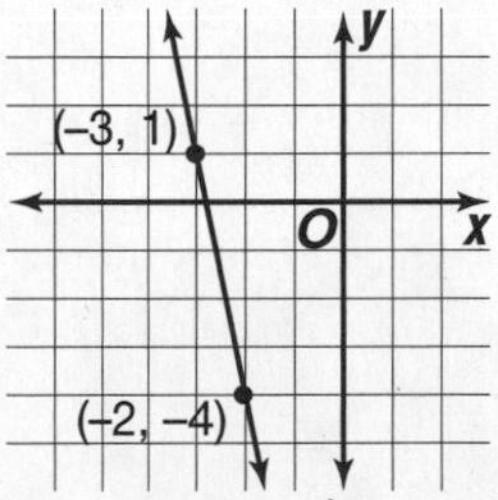

14. the line through points at $(-2, -2)$ and $(-1, -6)$

15. the line through points at $(-7, -3)$ and $(5, -1)$

7–2

NAME ______________________ DATE __________ PERIOD ______

Practice

Student Edition
Pages 290–295

Writing Equations in Point-Slope Form

Write the point-slope form of an equation for each line passing through the given point and having the given slope.

1. $(4, 7)$, $m = 3$

$y - 7 = 3(x - 4)$

2. $(-2, 3)$, $m = 5$

$y - 3 = 5(x + 2)$

3. $(6, -1)$, $m = -2$

$y + 1 = -2(x - 6)$

4. $(-5, -2)$, $m = 0$

$y = -2$

5. $(-4, -6)$, $m = \frac{2}{3}$

$y + 6 = \frac{2}{3}(x + 4)$

6. $(-8, 3)$, $m = -\frac{3}{5}$

$y - 3 = -\frac{3}{5}(x + 8)$

7. $(7, -9)$, $m = 4$

$y + 9 = 4(x - 7)$

8. $(-6, 3)$, $m = -\frac{1}{2}$

$y - 3 = -\frac{1}{2}(x + 6)$

9. $(-2, -5)$, $m = 8$

$y + 5 = 8(x + 2)$

Write the point-slope form of an equation for each line.

10.

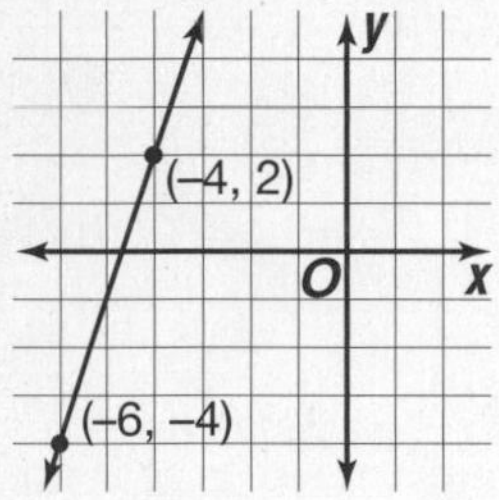

$y - 2 = 3(x + 4)$ or
$y + 4 = 3(x + 6)$

11.

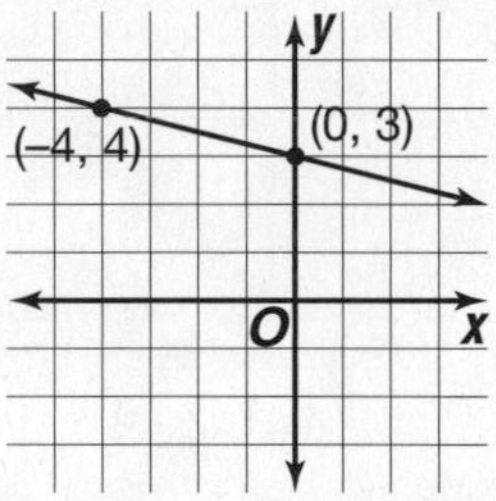

$y - 3 = -\frac{1}{4}x$ or

$y - 4 = -\frac{1}{4}(x + 4)$

12.

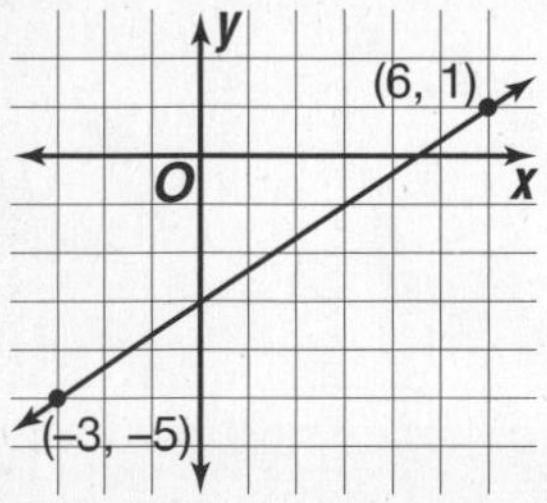

$y - 1 = \frac{2}{3}(x - 6)$ or

$y + 5 = \frac{2}{3}(x + 3)$

13.

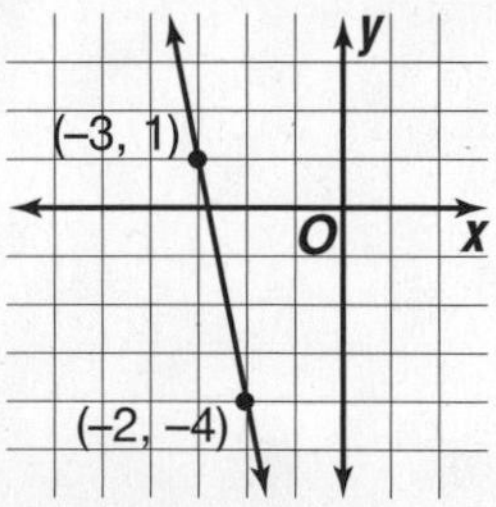

$y - 1 = -5(x + 3)$ or
$y + 4 = -5(x + 2)$

14. the line through points at $(-2, -2)$ and $(-1, -6)$

$y + 6 = -4(x + 1)$ or
$y + 2 = -4(x + 2)$

15. the line through points at $(-7, -3)$ and $(5, -1)$

$y + 3 = \frac{1}{6}(x + 7)$ or

$y + 1 = \frac{1}{6}(x - 5)$

7–3

NAME ______________________ DATE __________ PERIOD ______

Practice

Student Edition
Pages 296–301

Writing Equations in Point-Intercept Form

Write an equation in slope-intercept form of the line with each slope and y-intercept.

1. $m = -3, b = 5$ **2.** $m = 6, b = 2$ **3.** $m = 4, b = -1$

4. $m = 0, b = 4$ **5.** $m = \frac{2}{5}, b = -7$ **6.** $m = -\frac{3}{4}, b = 8$

7. $m = -\frac{4}{3}, b = -2$ **8.** $m = -5, b = 6$ **9.** $m = \frac{1}{2}, b = -9$

Write an equation in slope-intercept form of the line having the given slope and passing through the given point.

10. $m = 3, (4, 2)$ **11.** $m = -2, (-1, 3)$ **12.** $m = 4, (0, -7)$

13. $m = -\frac{3}{5}, (-5, -3)$ **14.** $m = \frac{1}{4}, (-8, 6)$ **15.** $m = -\frac{2}{3}, (9, -4)$

16. $m = \frac{5}{6}, (6, -6)$ **17.** $m = 0, (-8, -7)$ **18.** $m = -\frac{3}{2}, (-8, 9)$

Write an equation in slope-intercept form of the line passing through each pair of points.

19. (1, 3) and (− 3, −5) **20.** (0, 5) and (3, −4) **21.** (2, 1) and (3, 6)

22. (− 3, 0) and (6, −6) **23.** (4, 5) and (− 5, 5) **24.** (0, 6) and (− 4, 3)

25. (−3, 2) and (3, −6) **26.** (−7, −6) and (−5, −3) **27.** (6, −4) and (0, 2)

7–3

NAME ______________________________ DATE __________ PERIOD ______

Practice

Student Edition
Pages 296–301

Writing Equations in Point-Intercept Form

Write an equation in slope-intercept form of the line with each slope and y-intercept.

1. $m = -3, b = 5$

$y = -3x + 5$

2. $m = 6, b = 2$

$y = 6x + 2$

3. $m = 4, b = -1$

$y = 4x - 1$

4. $m = 0, b = 4$

$y = 4$

5. $m = \frac{2}{5}, b = -7$

$y = \frac{2}{5}x - 7$

6. $m = -\frac{3}{4}, b = 8$

$y = -\frac{3}{4}x + 8$

7. $m = -\frac{4}{3}, b = -2$

$y = -\frac{4}{3}x - 2$

8. $m = -5, b = 6$

$y = -5x + 6$

9. $m = \frac{1}{2}, b = -9$

$y = \frac{1}{2}x - 9$

Write an equation in slope-intercept form of the line having the given slope and passing through the given point.

10. $m = 3, (4, 2)$

$y = 3x - 10$

11. $m = -2, (-1, 3)$

$y = -2x + 1$

12. $m = 4, (0, -7)$

$y = 4x - 7$

13. $m = -\frac{3}{5}, (-5, -3)$

$y = -\frac{3}{5}x - 6$

14. $m = \frac{1}{4}, (-8, 6)$

$y = \frac{1}{4}x + 8$

15. $m = -\frac{2}{3}, (9, -4)$

$y = -\frac{2}{3}x + 2$

16. $m = \frac{5}{6}, (6, -6)$

$y = \frac{5}{6}x - 11$

17. $m = 0, (-8, -7)$

$y = -7$

18. $m = -\frac{3}{2}, (-8, 9)$

$y = -\frac{3}{2}x - 3$

Write an equation in slope-intercept form of the line passing through each pair of points.

19. (1, 3) and (– 3, –5)

$y = 2x + 1$

20. (0, 5) and (3, –4)

$y = -3x + 5$

21. (2, 1) and (3, 6)

$y = 5x - 9$

22. (– 3, 0) and (6, –6)

$y = -\frac{2}{3}x - 2$

23. (4, 5) and (– 5, 5)

$y = 5$

24. (0, 6) and (– 4, 3)

$y = \frac{3}{4}x + 6$

25. (–3, 2) and (3, –6)

$y = -\frac{4}{3}x - 2$

26. (–7, –6) and (–5, –3)

$y = \frac{3}{2}x + \frac{9}{2}$

27. (6, –4) and (0, 2)

$y = -x + 2$

NAME ______________________ DATE __________ PERIOD _____

Practice

Student Edition
Pages 302–307

Scatter Plots

Determine whether each scatter plot has a positive relationship, negative relationship, or no relationship. If there is a relationship, describe it.

1.

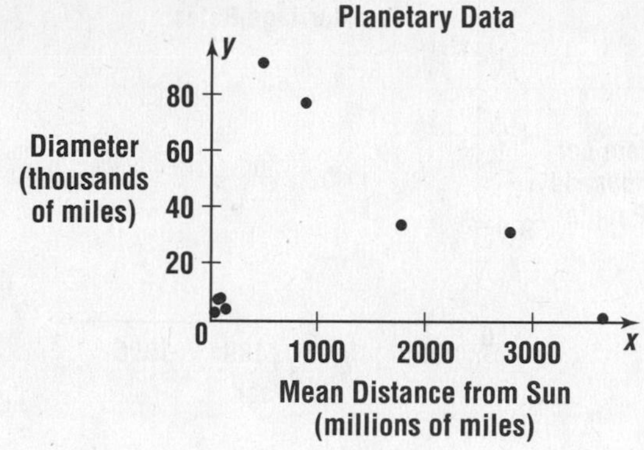

2.

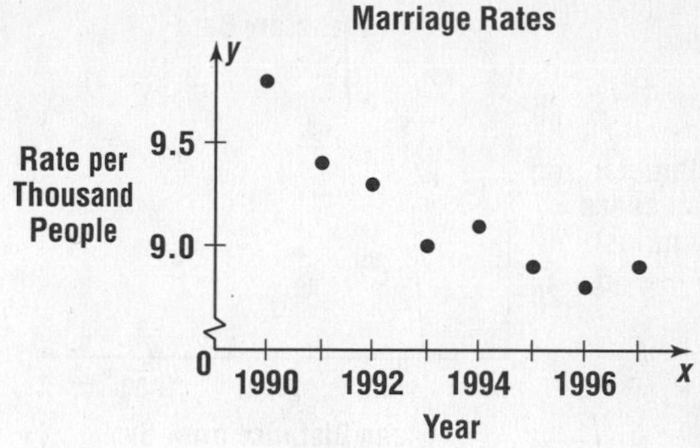

3.

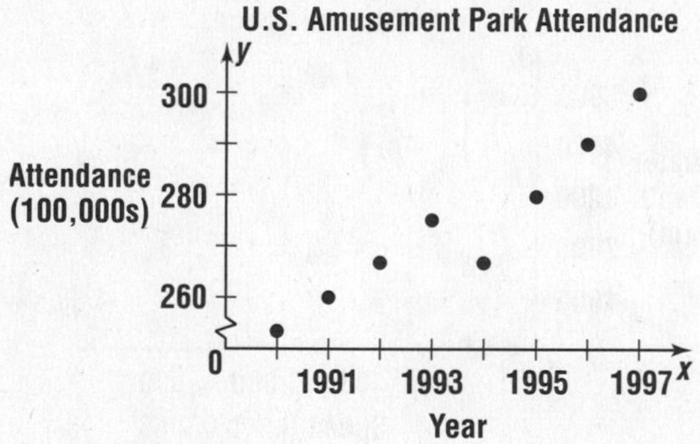

4.

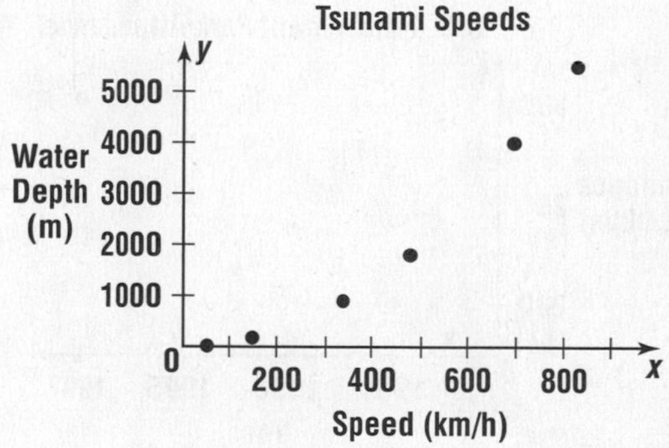

5.

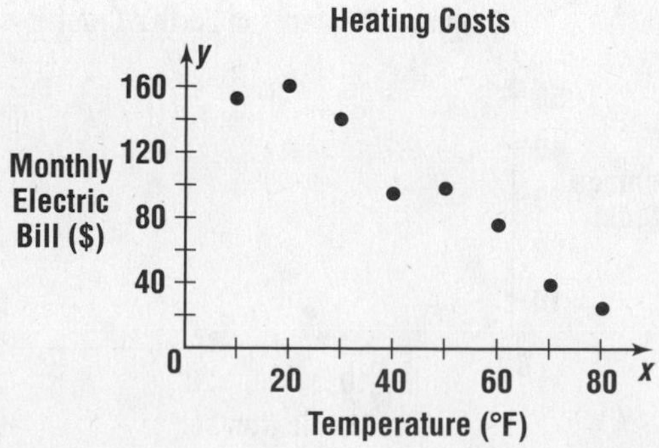

6.

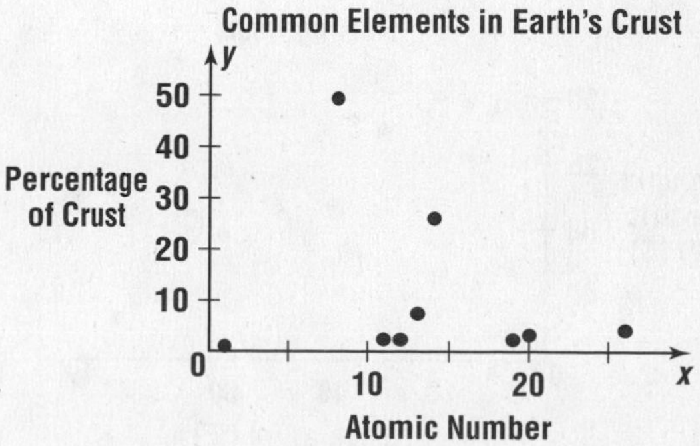

NAME ______________________ DATE __________ PERIOD ______

7–4 Practice

Student Edition
Pages 302–307

Scatter Plots

Determine whether each scatter plot has a* positive *relationship,* negative *relationship, or* no *relationship. If there is a relationship, describe it.

1.

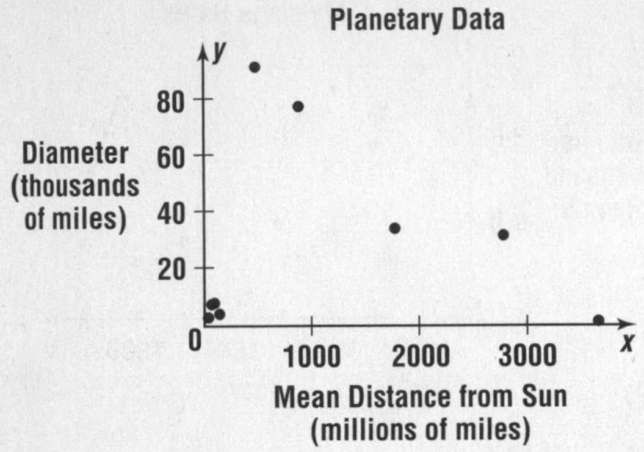

no relationship

2.

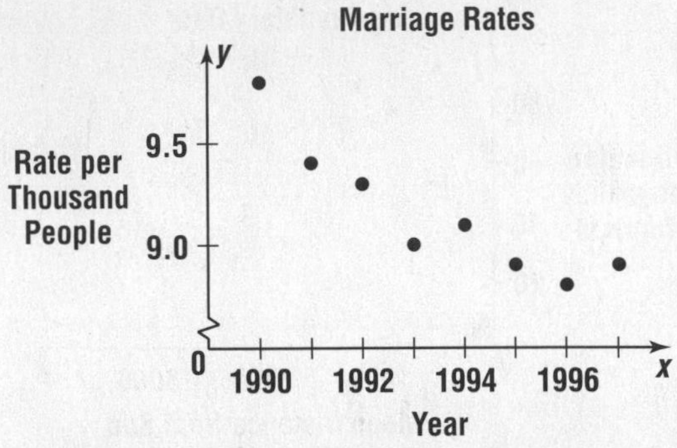

Negative relationship; over time, marriage rate is declining.

3.

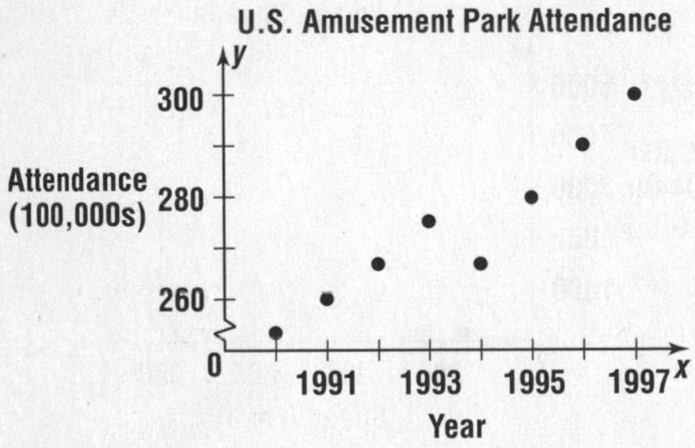

Positive relationship; over time, attendance is increasing.

4.

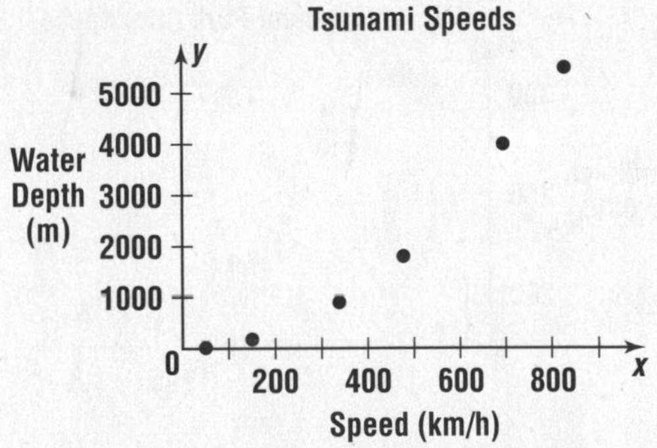

Positive relationship; water depth increases as speed increases.

5.

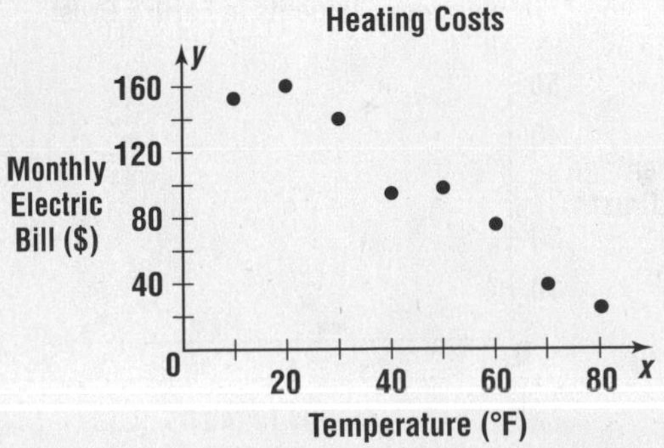

Negative relationship; as temperature increases, heating costs decrease.

6.

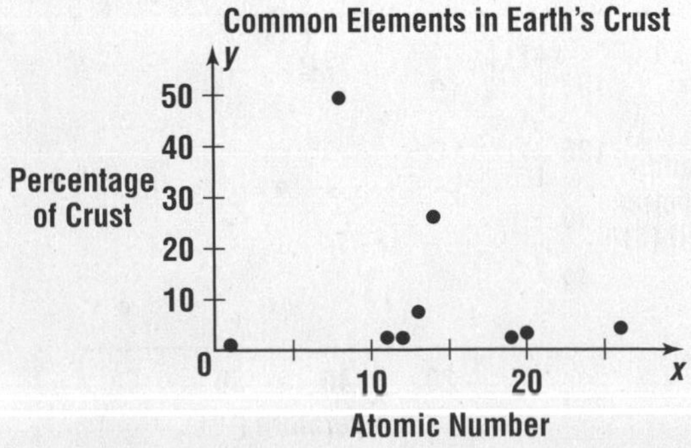

no relationship

7–5

NAME ______________________ DATE __________ PERIOD ______

Practice

Student Edition
Pages 310–315

Graphing Linear Equations

Determine the x-intercept and y-intercept of the graph of each equation. Then graph the equation.

1. $x + y = -2$

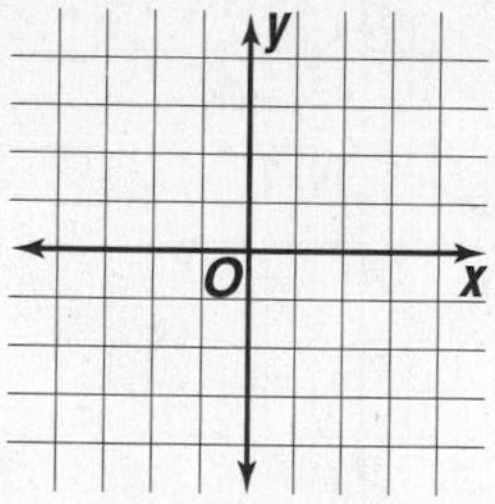

2. $2x + y = 6$

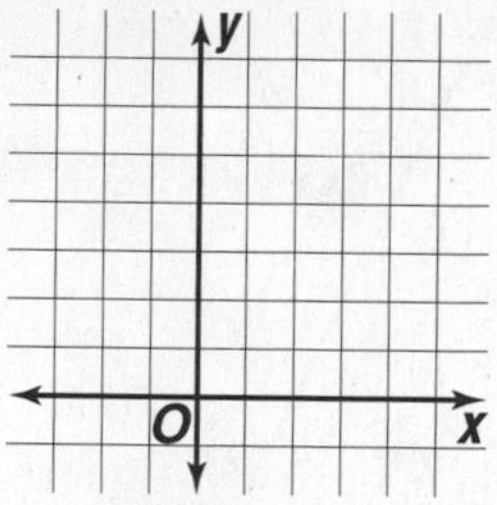

3. $x - 2y = -4$

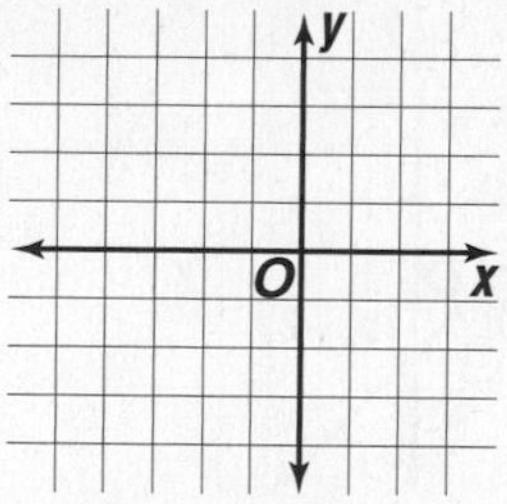

4. $2x + 3y = 12$

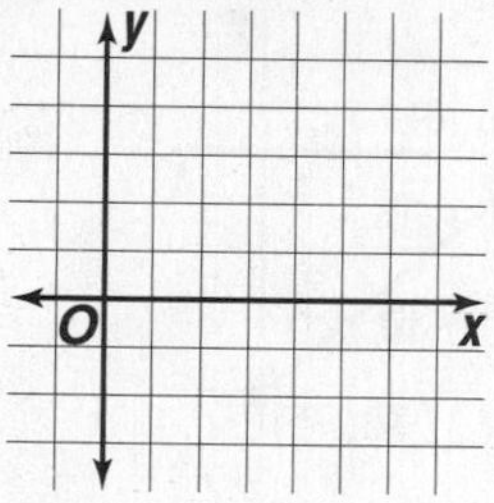

5. $3x - 3y = 9$

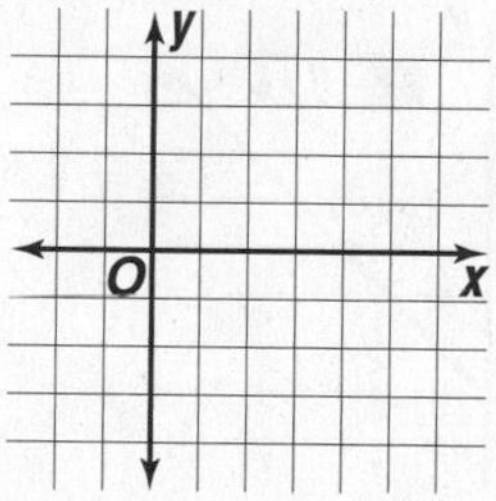

6. $5x + 6y = -30$

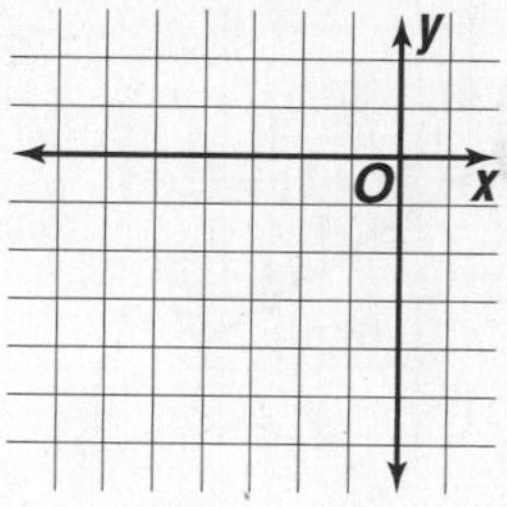

Determine the slope and y-intercept of the graph of each equation. Then graph the equation.

7. $y = -x + 3$

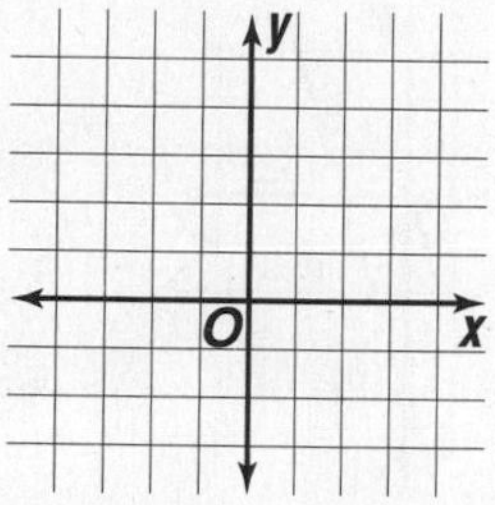

8. $y = 5$

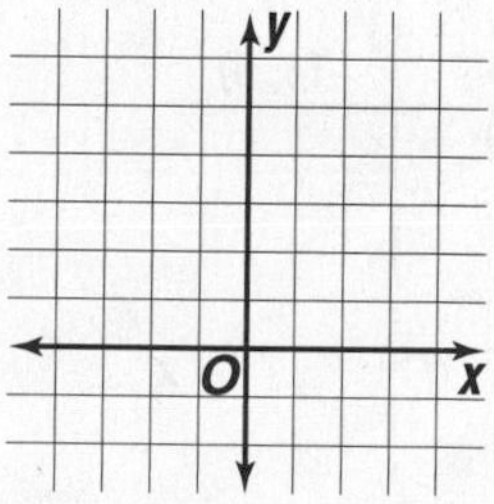

9. $y = 3x - 4$

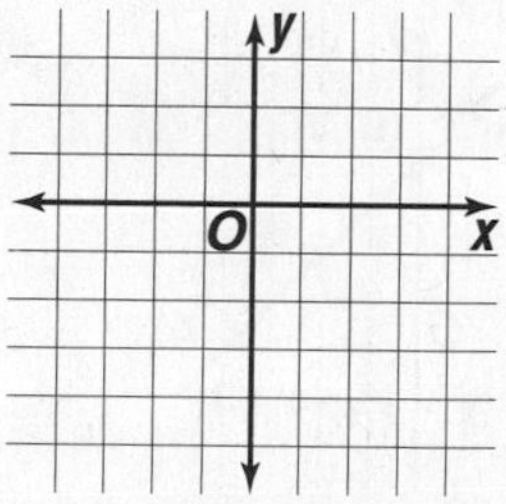

10. $y = \frac{2}{5}x + 2$

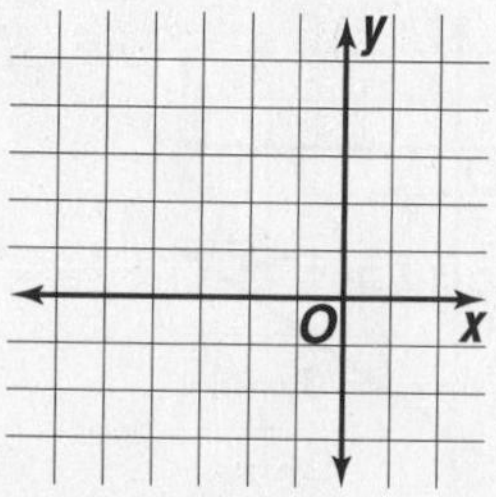

11. $y = -\frac{3}{4}x + 1$

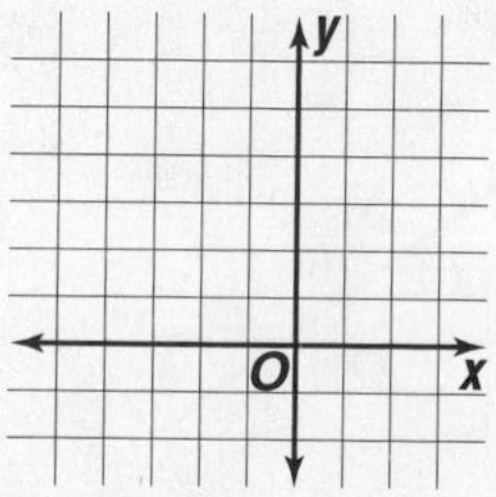

12. $y = \frac{2}{3}x - 6$

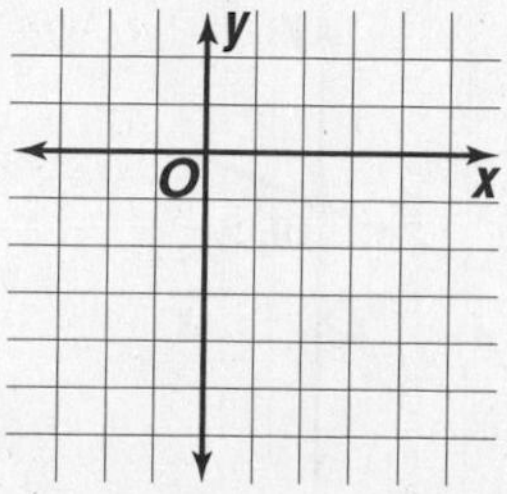

7–5 Practice

NAME ______________________________ DATE __________ PERIOD ______

Student Edition
Pages 310–315

Graphing Linear Equations

Determine the x-intercept and y-intercept of the graph of each equation. Then graph the equation.

1. $x + y = -2$ **−2, −2**

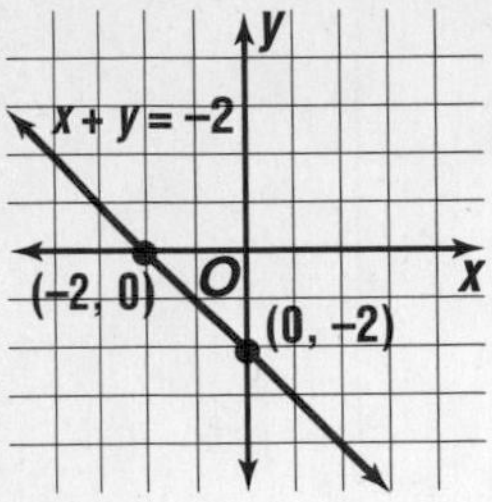

2. $2x + y = 6$ **3, 6**

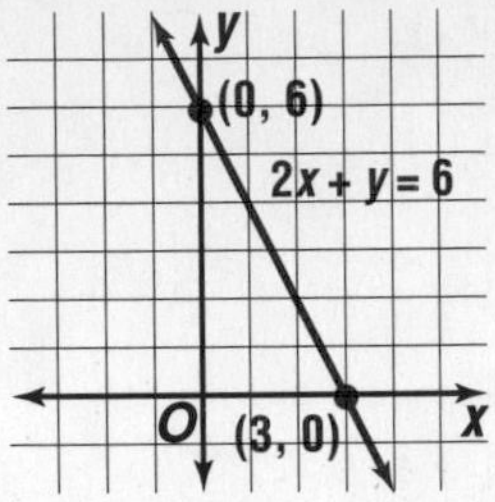

3. $x - 2y = -4$ **−4, 2**

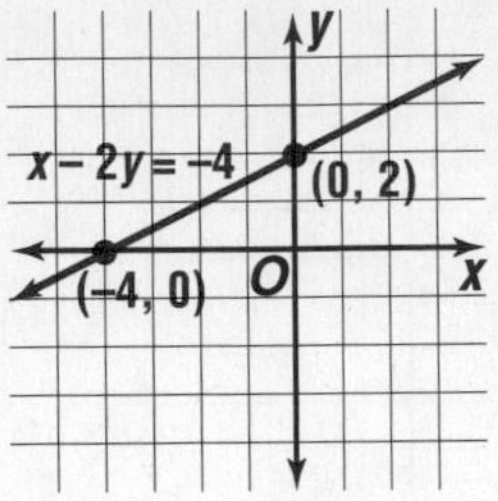

4. $2x + 3y = 12$ **6, 4**

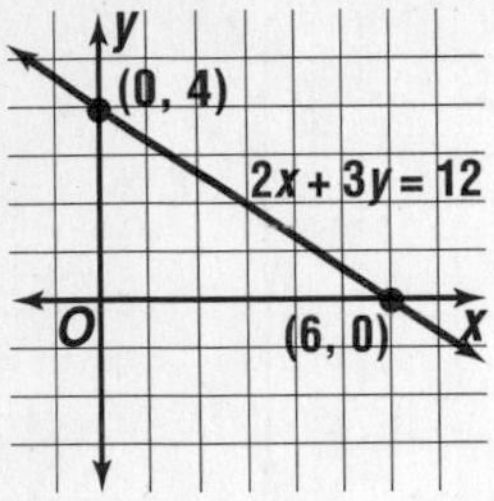

5. $3x - 3y = 9$ **3, −3**

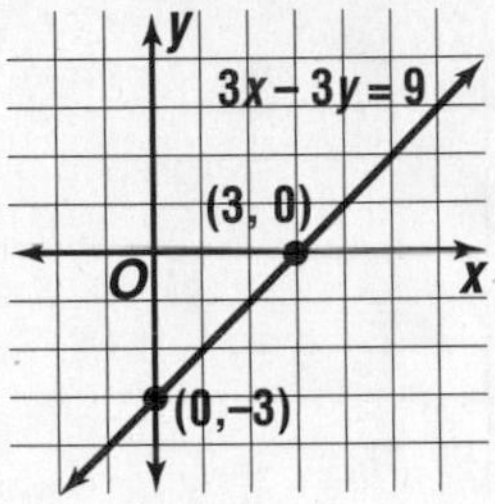

6. $5x + 6y = -30$ **−6, −5**

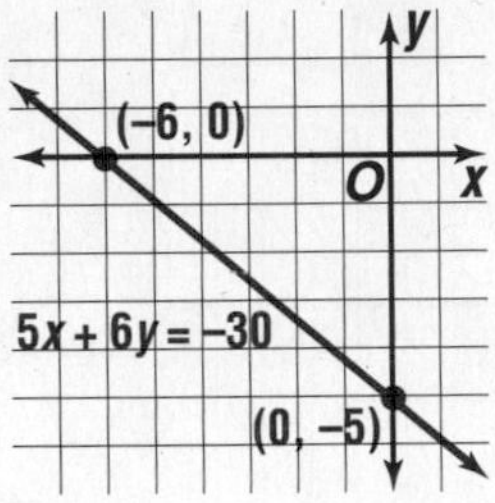

Determine the slope and y-intercept of the graph of each equation. Then graph the equation.

7. $y = -x + 3$

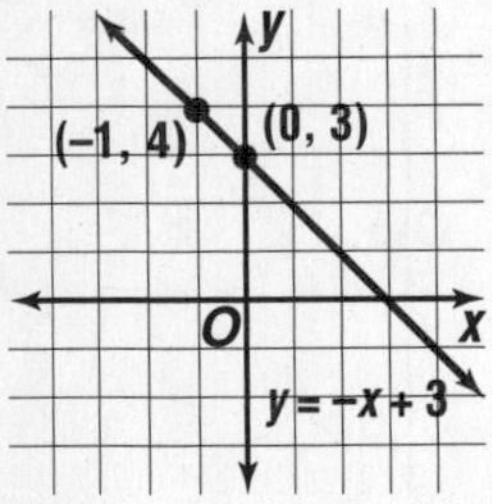

$m = -1, b = 3$

8. $y = 5$

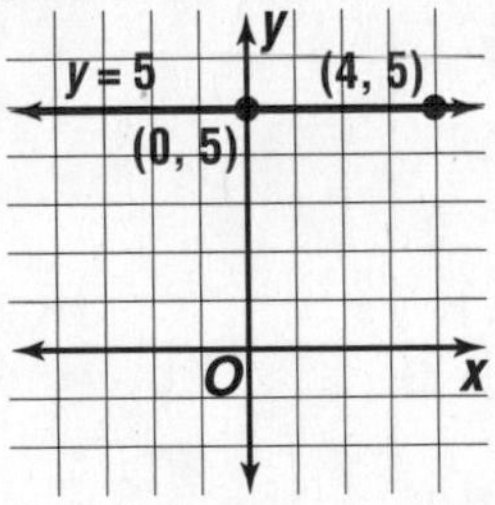

$m = 0, b = 5$

9. $y = 3x - 4$

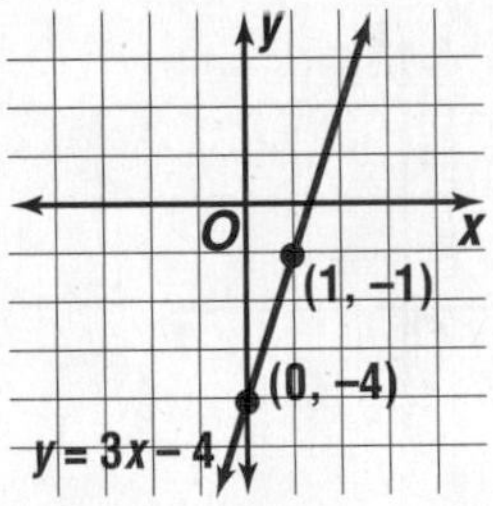

$m = 3, b = -4$

10. $y = \frac{2}{5}x + 2$

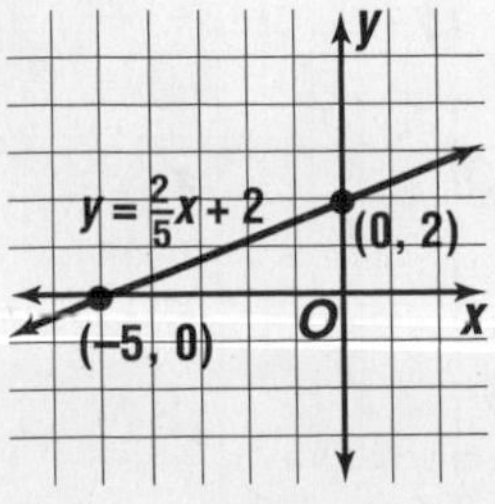

$m = \frac{2}{5}, b = 2$

11. $y = -\frac{3}{4}x + 1$

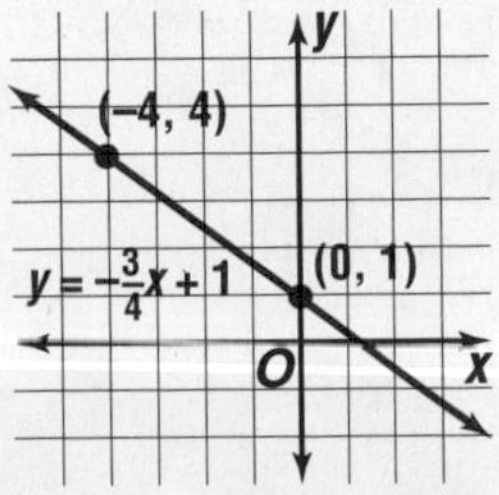

$m = -\frac{3}{4}, b = 1$

12. $y = \frac{2}{3}x - 6$

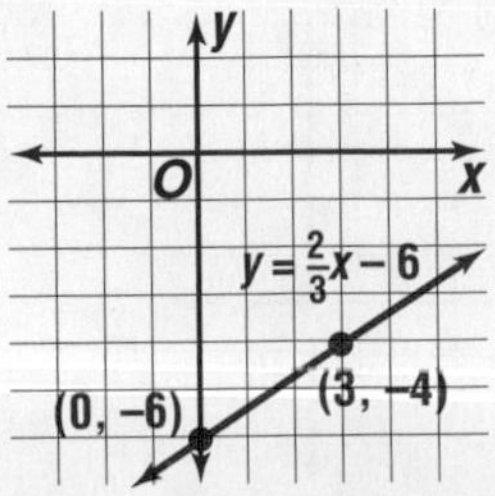

$m = \frac{2}{3}, b = -6$

NAME ________________ DATE ________ PERIOD ______

7–6 Practice

Student Edition
Pages 316–321

Families of Linear Graphs

Graph each pair of equations. Describe any similarities or differences and explain why they are a family of graphs.

1. $y = 2x + 3$
$y = 2x - 3$

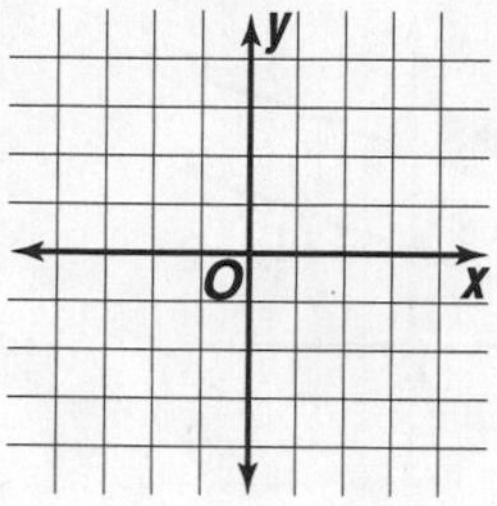

2. $y = 4x + 5$
$y = -3x + 5$

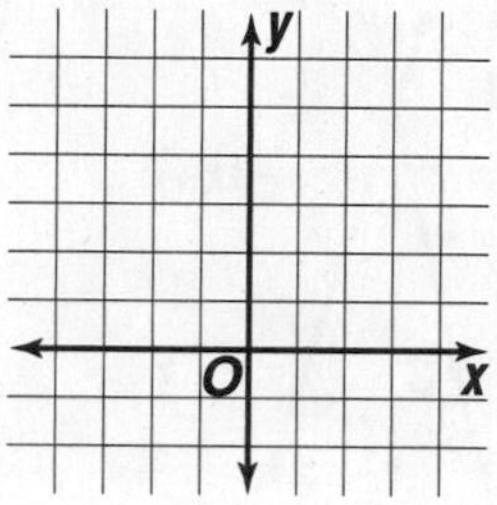

3. $y = \frac{1}{3}x + 2$
$y = \frac{1}{3}x + 4$

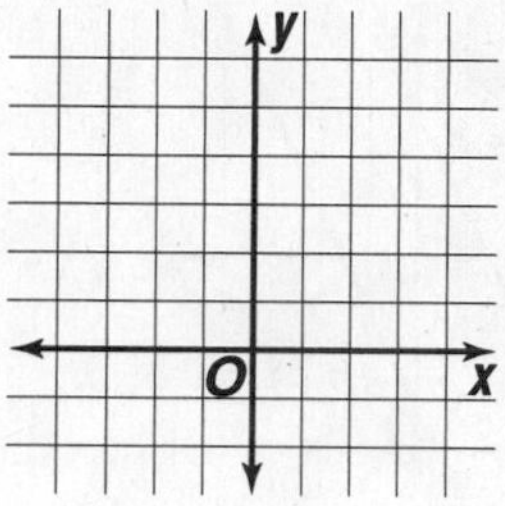

Compare and contrast the graphs of each pair of equations. Verify by graphing the equations.

4. $y = -\frac{1}{2}x - 4$
$y = -2x - 4$

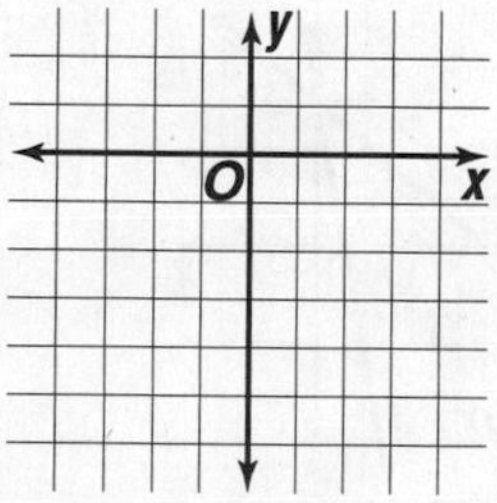

5. $3x + 6 = y$
$3x = y$

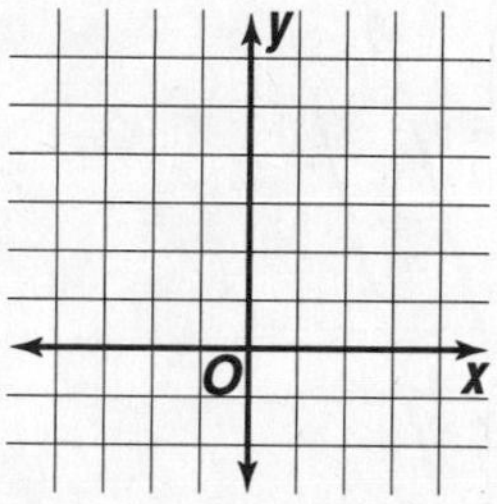

6. $y = \frac{5}{6}x + 3$
$y = 5x + 3$

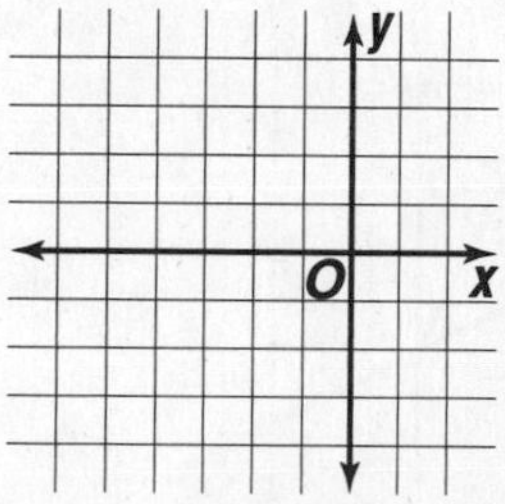

Change $y = -x + 2$ so that the graph of the new equation fits each description.

7. same slope, shifted down 2 units

8. same y-intercept, steeper negative slope

9. positive slope, same y-intercept

10. same y-intercept, less steep negative slope

11. same slope, shifted up 4 units

12. same slope, shifted down 6 units

NAME ____________________ DATE __________ PERIOD ______

Practice

Student Edition
Pages 316–321

Families of Linear Graphs

Graph each pair of equations. Describe any similarities or differences and explain why they are a family of graphs.

1. $y = 2x + 3$
$y = 2x - 3$

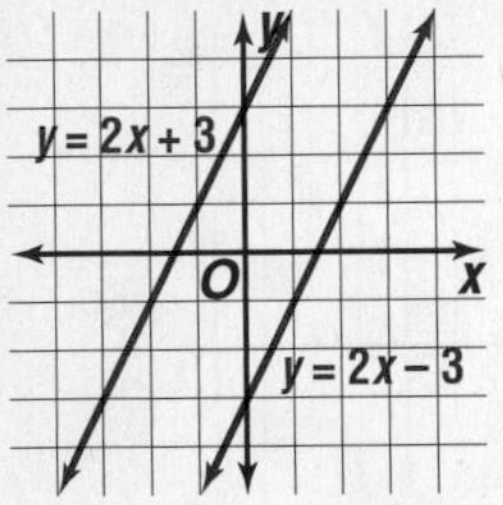

different *y*-intercepts; family because both slopes are 2

2. $y = 4x + 5$
$y = -3x + 5$

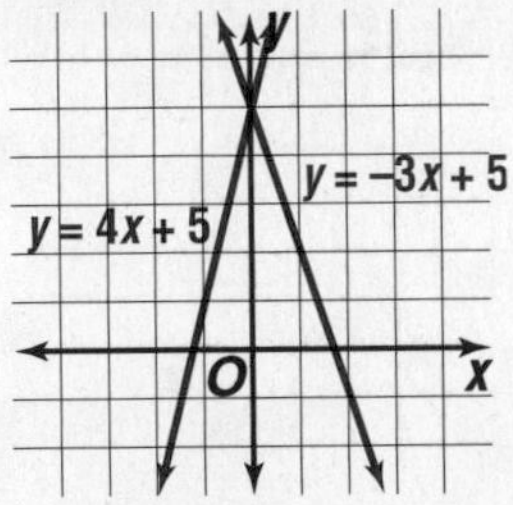

different slopes; family because both *y*-intercepts are 5

3. $y = \frac{1}{3}x + 2$
$y = \frac{1}{3}x + 4$

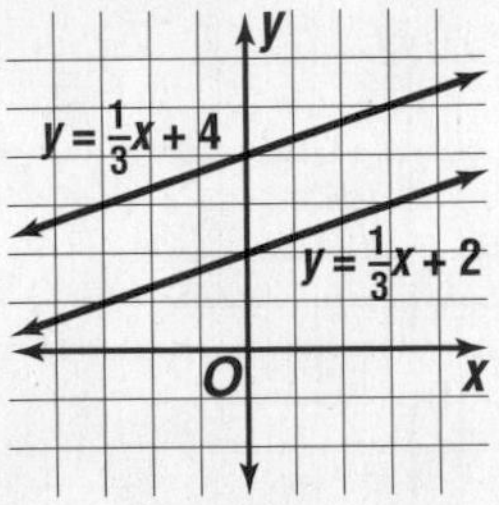

different *y*-intercepts; family because both slopes are $\frac{1}{3}$

Compare and contrast the graphs of each pair of equations. Verify by graphing the equations.

4. $y = -\frac{1}{2}x - 4$
$y = -2x - 4$

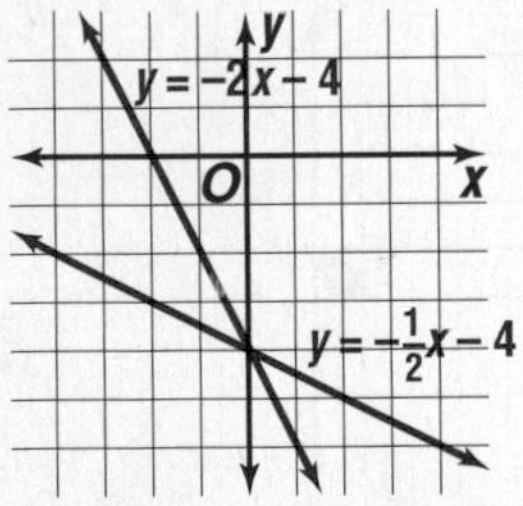

same *y*-intercept, different slopes

5. $3x + 6 = y$
$3x = y$

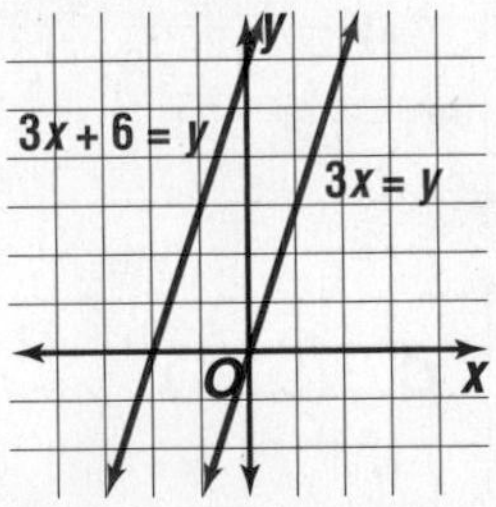

same slope, different *y*-intercepts

6. $y = \frac{5}{6}x + 3$
$y = 5x + 3$

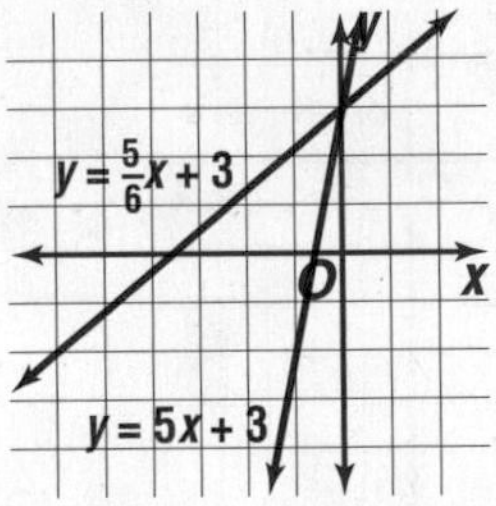

same *y*-intercept, different slopes

Change $y = -x + 2$ so that the graph of the new equation fits each description.

7. same slope, shifted down 2 units
$\mathbf{y = -x}$

8. same *y*-intercept, steeper negative slope
Sample: $\mathbf{y = -3x + 2}$

9. positive slope, same *y*-intercept
Sample: $\mathbf{y = x + 2}$

10. same *y*-intercept, less steep negative slope
Sample: $\mathbf{y = -\frac{1}{3}x + 2}$

11. same slope, shifted up 4 units
$\mathbf{y = -x + 6}$

12. same slope, shifted down 6 units
$\mathbf{y = -x - 4}$

NAME ______________________ DATE __________ PERIOD ______

7–7 Practice

Student Edition
Pages 322–327

Parallel and Perpendicular Lines

Determine whether the graphs of each pair of equations are parallel, perpendicular,** or **neither.

1. $y = 3x + 4$
   $y = 3x + 7$

2. $y = -4x + 1$
   $4y = x + 3$

3. $y = 2x - 5$
   $y = 5x - 5$

4. $y = -\frac{1}{3}x + 2$
   $y = 3x - 5$

5. $y = \frac{3}{5}x - 3$
   $5y = 3x - 10$

6. $y = 4$
   $4y = 6$

7. $y = 7x + 2$
   $x + 7y = 8$

8. $y = \frac{5}{6}x - 6$
   $x + 5y = 4$

9. $y = -\frac{3}{8}x - 9$
   $y = \frac{8}{3}x + 3$

Write an equation in slope-intercept form of the line that is parallel to the graph of each equation and passes through the given point.

10. $y = 3x + 6; (4, 7)$

11. $y = x - 4; (-2, 3)$

12. $y = \frac{1}{2}x + 5; (4, -5)$

13. $y + \frac{2}{3}x = 3; (-6, 1)$

14. $y - \frac{2}{5}x = -5; (5, 3)$

15. $y + 2x = 4; (-1, 2)$

Write an equation in slope-intercept form of the line that is perpendicular to the graph of each equation and passes through the given point.

16. $y = -5x + 1; (2, -1)$

17. $y = 2x - 3; (-5, 3)$

18. $4x + 7y = 3; (-4, -7)$

19. $3x - 4y = 2; (6, 0)$

20. $y = -4x - 2; (4, -4)$

21. $6x + 5y = -3; (-6, 2)$

7–7

NAME ______________________ DATE __________ PERIOD ______

Practice

Student Edition
Pages 322–327

Parallel and Perpendicular Lines

Determine whether the graphs of each pair of equations are parallel, perpendicular,** or **neither.

1. $y = 3x + 4$
   $y = 3x + 7$
   parallel

2. $y = -4x + 1$
   $4y = x + 3$
   perpendicular

3. $y = 2x - 5$
   $y = 5x - 5$
   neither

4. $y = -\frac{1}{3}x + 2$
   $y = 3x - 5$
   perpendicular

5. $y = \frac{3}{5}x - 3$
   $5y = 3x - 10$
   parallel

6. $y = 4$
   $4y = 6$
   parallel

7. $y = 7x + 2$
   $x + 7y = 8$
   perpendicular

8. $y = \frac{5}{6}x - 6$
   $x + 5y = 4$
   neither

9. $y = -\frac{3}{8}x - 9$
   $y = \frac{8}{3}x + 3$
   perpendicular

Write an equation in slope-intercept form of the line that is parallel to the graph of each equation and passes through the given point.

10. $y = 3x + 6$; $(4, 7)$
    $\mathbf{y = 3x - 5}$

11. $y = x - 4$; $(-2, 3)$
    $\mathbf{y = x + 5}$

12. $y = \frac{1}{2}x + 5$; $(4, -5)$
    $\mathbf{y = \frac{1}{2}x - 7}$

13. $y + \frac{2}{3}x = 3$; $(-6, 1)$
    $\mathbf{y = -\frac{2}{3}x - 3}$

14. $y - \frac{2}{5}x = -5$; $(5, 3)$
    $\mathbf{y = \frac{2}{5}x + 1}$

15. $y + 2x = 4$; $(-1, 2)$
    $\mathbf{y = -2x}$

Write an equation in slope-intercept form of the line that is perpendicular to the graph of each equation and passes through the given point.

16. $y = -5x + 1$; $(2, -1)$
    $\mathbf{y = \frac{1}{5}x - \frac{7}{5}}$

17. $y = 2x - 3$; $(-5, 3)$
    $\mathbf{y = -\frac{1}{2}x + \frac{1}{2}}$

18. $4x + 7y = 3$; $(-4, -7)$
    $\mathbf{y = \frac{7}{4}x}$

19. $3x - 4y = 2$; $(6, 0)$
    $\mathbf{y = -\frac{4}{3}x + 8}$

20. $y = -4x - 2$; $(4, -4)$
    $\mathbf{y = \frac{1}{4}x - 5}$

21. $6x + 5y = -3$; $(-6, 2)$
    $\mathbf{y = \frac{5}{6}x + 7}$

8–1

NAME ______________________ DATE __________ PERIOD ______

Practice

Student Edition
Pages 336–340

Powers and Exponents

Write each expression using exponents.

1. $6 \cdot 6 \cdot 6 \cdot 6 \cdot 6$

2. 8

3. $10 \cdot 10 \cdot 10 \cdot 10$

4. $7 \cdot 7 \cdot 7$

5. $(-4) \cdot (-4) \cdot (-4) \cdot (-4)$

6. $b \cdot b \cdot b \cdot b \cdot b \cdot b$

7. $x \cdot x$

8. $m \cdot m \cdot m \cdot m \cdot m \cdot m \cdot m$

9. $3 \cdot 3 \cdot 5 \cdot 5 \cdot 5$

10. $a \cdot a \cdot a \cdot a \cdot c \cdot c \cdot c \cdot c$

11. $7 \cdot 7 \cdot 9 \cdot 7 \cdot 9 \cdot 2 \cdot 2 \cdot 2$

12. $(6)(x)(x)(x)(y)(y)(y)(y)$

Write each power as a multiplication expression.

13. 9^3

14. 13^5

15. 7^2

16. p^4

17. n^6

18. $(-5)^5$

19. $4 \cdot 8^6$

20. $7^3 \cdot 5^2$

21. ab^2

22. m^5n^3

23. $-4c^3$

24. $3x^2y^4$

Evaluate each expression if a = −1, b = 3, and c = 2.

25. b^4

26. a^6

27. $4c^5$

28. $-3b^3$

29. a^5b^2

30. $2bc^3$

31. $-4a^4c^2$

32. $a^2 + b^2$

33. $2(b^2 - c^3)$

8–1 NAME ______________________ DATE __________ PERIOD ______

Practice

Student Edition
Pages 336–340

Powers and Exponents

Write each expression using exponents.

1. $6 \cdot 6 \cdot 6 \cdot 6 \cdot 6$

 6^5

2. 8

 8^1

3. $10 \cdot 10 \cdot 10 \cdot 10$

 10^4

4. $7 \cdot 7 \cdot 7$

 7^3

5. $(-4) \cdot (-4) \cdot (-4) \cdot (-4)$

 $(-4)^4$

6. $b \cdot b \cdot b \cdot b \cdot b \cdot b$

 b^6

7. $x \cdot x$

 x^2

8. $m \cdot m \cdot m \cdot m \cdot m \cdot m \cdot m$

 m^7

9. $3 \cdot 3 \cdot 5 \cdot 5 \cdot 5$

 $3^2 5^3$

10. $a \cdot a \cdot a \cdot a \cdot c \cdot c \cdot c \cdot c$

 a^4c^4

11. $7 \cdot 7 \cdot 9 \cdot 7 \cdot 9 \cdot 2 \cdot 2 \cdot 2$

 $2^3 7^3 9^2$

12. $(6)(x)(x)(x)(y)(y)(y)(y)$

 $6x^3y^4$

Write each power as a multiplication expression.

13. 9^3

 $9 \cdot 9 \cdot 9$

14. 13^5

 $13 \cdot 13 \cdot 13 \cdot 13 \cdot 13$

15. 7^2

 $7 \cdot 7$

16. p^4

 $p \cdot p \cdot p \cdot p$

17. n^6

 $n \cdot n \cdot n \cdot n \cdot n \cdot n$

18. $(-5)^5$

 $(-5)(-5)(-5)(-5)(-5)$

19. $4 \cdot 8^6$

 $4 \cdot 8 \cdot 8 \cdot 8 \cdot 8 \cdot 8 \cdot 8$

20. $7^3 \cdot 5^2$

 $7 \cdot 7 \cdot 7 \cdot 5 \cdot 5$

21. ab^2

 $a \cdot b \cdot b$

22. m^5n^3

 $m \cdot m \cdot m \cdot m \cdot m \cdot n \cdot n \cdot n$

23. $-4c^3$

 $-4 \cdot c \cdot c \cdot c$

24. $3x^2y^4$

 $3 \cdot x \cdot x \cdot y \cdot y \cdot y \cdot y$

Evaluate each expression if a = −1, b = 3, and c = 2.

25. b^4

 81

26. a^6

 1

27. $4c^5$

 128

28. $-3b^3$

 −81

29. a^5b^2

 −9

30. $2bc^3$

 48

31. $-4a^4c^2$

 −16

32. $a^2 + b^2$

 10

33. $2(b^2 - c^3)$

 2

NAME ______________________ DATE __________ PERIOD ______

Practice

Multiplying and Dividing Powers

Simplify each expression.

1. $6^3 \cdot 6^2$

2. $7^6 \cdot 7^4$

3. $y^4 \cdot y^8$

4. $b \cdot b^4$

5. $(g^2)(g^3)(g)$

6. $m(m^8)$

7. $(a^2b^3)(a^4b)$

8. $(xy^5)(x^3y^3)$

9. $(2c^3)(2c)$

10. $(-3x^2)(6x^2)$

11. $(-7xy)(-2x)$

12. $(5m^3n^2)(4m^2n^3)$

13. $(-8ab)(a^2b^5)$

14. $\frac{9^2}{9}$

15. $\frac{12^8}{12^3}$

16. $\frac{y^4}{y^2}$

17. $\frac{k^6}{k^6}$

18. $\frac{x^4y^5}{x^3y^2}$

19. $\frac{a^9b^6}{a^2b}$

20. $\frac{mn^3}{n^2}$

21. $\frac{15a^3}{3a}$

22. $\frac{8x^5y^4}{4x^2y^2}$

23. $\frac{m^2n}{m^2}$

24. $\frac{6a^5b^7}{-2a^3b^7}$

25. $\frac{-20x^3y^2}{-5x^3y}$

26. $\frac{-16ab^4}{4b^3}$

27. $\frac{12x^2y}{2x^2y}$

8–2 NAME ______________________ DATE ________ PERIOD ______

Practice

Student Edition
Pages 341–346

Multiplying and Dividing Powers

Simplify each expression.

1. $6^3 \cdot 6^2$

6^5

2. $7^6 \cdot 7^4$

7^{10}

3. $y^4 \cdot y^8$

y^{12}

4. $b \cdot b^4$

b^5

5. $(g^2)(g^3)(g)$

g^6

6. $m(m^8)$

m^9

7. $(a^2b^3)(a^4b)$

a^6b^4

8. $(xy^5)(x^3y^3)$

x^4y^8

9. $(2c^3)(2c)$

$4c^4$

10. $(-3x^2)(6x^2)$

$-18x^4$

11. $(-7xy)(-2x)$

$14x^2y$

12. $(5m^3n^2)(4m^2n^3)$

$20m^5n^5$

13. $(-8ab)(a^2b^5)$

$-8a^3b^6$

14. $\frac{9^2}{9}$

9

15. $\frac{12^8}{12^3}$

12^5

16. $\frac{y^4}{y^2}$

y^2

17. $\frac{k^6}{k^6}$

1

18. $\frac{x^4y^5}{x^3y^2}$

xy^3

19. $\frac{a^9b^6}{a^2b}$

a^7b^5

20. $\frac{mn^3}{n^2}$

mn

21. $\frac{15a^3}{3a}$

$5a^2$

22. $\frac{8x^5y^4}{4x^2y^2}$

$2x^3y^2$

23. $\frac{m^2n}{m^2}$

n

24. $\frac{6a^5b^7}{-2a^3b^7}$

$-3a^2$

25. $\frac{-20x^3y^2}{-5x^3y}$

$4y$

26. $\frac{-16ab^4}{4b^3}$

$-4ab$

27. $\frac{12x^2y}{2x^2y}$

6

8–3 Practice

NAME ______________________ DATE __________ PERIOD ______

Student Edition
Pages 347–351

Negative Exponents

Write each expression using positive exponents. Then evaluate the expression.

1. 2^{-6}

2. 5^{-1}

3. 8^{-2}

4. 10^{-3}

Simplify each expression.

5. g^{-6}

6. s^{-1}

7. q^0

8. $a^{-2}b^2$

9. m^5n^{-1}

10. $p^{-1}q^{-6}r^3$

11. $x^{-3}y^2z^{-4}$

12. $a^{-2}b^0c^{-1}$

13. $12m^{-6}n^4$

14. $7xy^{-8}z$

15. $x^{-3}(x^2)$

16. $b^3(b^{-5})$

17. $\frac{b^3}{b^6}$

18. $\frac{y^3}{y^{-2}}$

19. $\frac{m^5n^3}{m^6n^2}$

20. $\frac{xy^2}{xy^3}$

21. $\frac{a^7b^4}{a^9b^2}$

22. $\frac{rs^{-3}}{r^2s^4}$

23. $\frac{16c^8}{4c^{10}}$

24. $\frac{9x^{-5}y^5}{36x^4y^3}$

25. $\frac{7p^2q^6}{21p^{-3}q^7}$

26. $\frac{-6m^5n^2q^{-1}}{36m^{-2}n^4q^{-1}}$

27. $\frac{4a^3b^2c^2}{6a^5b^3c}$

28. $\frac{28x^5y^{-3}z}{-4x^4yz^3}$

8–3

NAME ______________________________ DATE __________ PERIOD ________

Practice

Student Edition
Pages 347–351

Negative Exponents

Write each expression using positive exponents. Then evaluate the expression.

1. 2^{-6}

$\frac{1}{2^6} = \frac{1}{64}$

2. 5^{-1}

$\frac{1}{5}$

3. 8^{-2}

$\frac{1}{8^2} = \frac{1}{64}$

4. 10^{-3}

$\frac{1}{10^3} = \frac{1}{1000}$

Simplify each expression.

5. g^{-6}

$\frac{1}{g^6}$

6. s^{-1}

$\frac{1}{s}$

7. q^0

1

8. $a^{-2}b^2$

$\frac{b^2}{a^2}$

9. m^5n^{-1}

$\frac{m^5}{n}$

10. $p^{-1}q^{-6}r^3$

$\frac{r^3}{pq^6}$

11. $x^{-3}y^2z^{-4}$

$\frac{y^2}{x^3z^4}$

12. $a^{-2}b^0c^{-1}$

$\frac{1}{a^2c}$

13. $12m^{-6}n^4$

$\frac{12n^4}{m^6}$

14. $7xy^{-8}z$

$\frac{7xz}{y^8}$

15. $x^{-3}(x^2)$

$\frac{1}{x}$

16. $b^3(b^{-5})$

$\frac{1}{b^2}$

17. $\frac{b^3}{b^6}$

$\frac{1}{b^3}$

18. $\frac{y^3}{y^{-2}}$

y^5

19. $\frac{m^5n^3}{m^6n^2}$

$\frac{n}{m}$

20. $\frac{xy^2}{xy^3}$

$\frac{1}{y}$

21. $\frac{a^7b^4}{a^9b^2}$

$\frac{b^2}{a^2}$

22. $\frac{rs^{-3}}{r^2s^4}$

$\frac{1}{rs^7}$

23. $\frac{16c^8}{4c^{10}}$

$\frac{4}{c^2}$

24. $\frac{9x^{-5}y^5}{36x^4y^3}$

$\frac{y^2}{4x^9}$

25. $\frac{7p^2q^6}{21p^{-3}q^7}$

$\frac{p^5}{3q}$

26. $\frac{-6m^5n^2q^{-1}}{36m^{-2}n^4q^{-1}}$

$-\frac{m^7}{6n^2}$

27. $\frac{4a^3b^2c^2}{6a^5b^3c}$

$\frac{2c}{3a^2b}$

28. $\frac{28x^5y^{-3}z}{-4x^4yz^3}$

$-\frac{7x}{y^4z^2}$

8–4

NAME ______________________ DATE __________ PERIOD __________

Practice

Student Edition
Pages 352–356

Scientific Notation

Express each measure in standard form.

1. 4 gigabytes

2. 78 kilowatts

3. 9 megahertz

4. 7.5 milliamperes

5. 2.3 nanoseconds

6. 3.7 micrograms

Express each number in scientific notation.

7. 6300

8. 4,600,000

9. 92.3

10. 51,200

11. 776,000

12. 68,200,000

13. 0.00013

14. 0.000009

15. 0.026

16. 0.04

17. 0.0055

18. 0.000031

Evaluate each expression. Express each result in scientific notation and in standard form.

19. $(4 \times 10^3)(2 \times 10^4)$

20. $(3 \times 10^2)(1.5 \times 10^{-5})$

21. $(6 \times 10^{-7})(1.5 \times 10^9)$

22. $(7 \times 10^{-3})(2.1 \times 10^{-3})$

23. $\dfrac{5.1 \times 10^5}{1.7 \times 10^7}$

24. $\dfrac{3.6 \times 10^6}{2 \times 10^2}$

25. $\dfrac{8.5 \times 10^{-3}}{2.5 \times 10^6}$

26. $\dfrac{2.7 \times 10^2}{3 \times 10^{-4}}$

27. $\dfrac{3.9 \times 10^4}{3 \times 10^7}$

NAME ______________________ DATE __________ PERIOD ______

Practice

Student Edition
Pages 352–356

Scientific Notation

Express each measure in standard form.

1. 4 gigabytes
4,000,000,000 bytes

2. 78 kilowatts
78,000 watts

3. 9 megahertz
9,000,000 hertz

4. 7.5 milliamperes
0.0075 ampere

5. 2.3 nanoseconds
0.0000000023 second

6. 3.7 micrograms
0.0000037 gram

Express each number in scientific notation.

7. 6300
6.3×10^3

8. 4,600,000
4.6×10^6

9. 92.3
9.23×10

10. 51,200
5.12×10^4

11. 776,000
7.76×10^5

12. 68,200,000
6.82×10^7

13. 0.00013
1.3×10^{-4}

14. 0.000009
9×10^{-6}

15. 0.026
2.6×10^{-2}

16. 0.04
4×10^{-2}

17. 0.0055
5.5×10^{-3}

18. 0.000031
3.1×10^{-5}

Evaluate each expression. Express each result in scientific notation and in standard form.

19. $(4 \times 10^3)(2 \times 10^4)$
$8 \times 10^7 = 80{,}000{,}000$

20. $(3 \times 10^2)(1.5 \times 10^{-5})$
$4.5 \times 10^{-3} = 0.0045$

21. $(6 \times 10^{-7})(1.5 \times 10^9)$
$9 \times 10^2 = 900$

22. $(7 \times 10^{-3})(2.1 \times 10^{-3})$
$1.47 \times 10^{-7} = 0.000000147$

23. $\frac{5.1 \times 10^5}{1.7 \times 10^7}$
$3 \times 10^{-2} = 0.03$

24. $\frac{3.6 \times 10^6}{2 \times 10^2}$
$1.8 \times 10^4 = 18{,}000$

25. $\frac{8.5 \times 10^{-3}}{2.5 \times 10^6}$
$3.4 \times 10^{-9} = 0.0000000034$

26. $\frac{2.7 \times 10^2}{3 \times 10^{-4}}$
$9 \times 10^5 = 900{,}000$

27. $\frac{3.9 \times 10^4}{3 \times 10^7}$
$1.3 \times 10^{-3} = 0.0013$

NAME ______________________ DATE __________ PERIOD __________

8–5 Practice

Student Edition
Pages 357–361

Square Roots

Simplify.

1. $\sqrt{36}$ **2.** $-\sqrt{16}$ **3.** $\sqrt{81}$ **4.** $-\sqrt{144}$

5. $-\sqrt{100}$ **6.** $-\sqrt{121}$ **7.** $\sqrt{169}$ **8.** $-\sqrt{25}$

9. $-\sqrt{529}$ **10.** $\sqrt{256}$ **11.** $\sqrt{324}$ **12.** $-\sqrt{289}$

13. $\sqrt{441}$ **14.** $-\sqrt{225}$ **15.** $\sqrt{196}$ **16.** $\sqrt{400}$

17. $\sqrt{484}$ **18.** $\sqrt{729}$ **19.** $-\sqrt{625}$ **20.** $\sqrt{1225}$

21. $\sqrt{\frac{49}{81}}$ **22.** $-\sqrt{\frac{16}{25}}$ **23.** $\sqrt{\frac{4}{16}}$ **24.** $-\sqrt{\frac{25}{36}}$

25. $-\sqrt{\frac{100}{121}}$ **26.** $\sqrt{\frac{1}{64}}$ **27.** $\sqrt{\frac{36}{64}}$ **28.** $-\sqrt{\frac{144}{36}}$

29. $-\sqrt{\frac{121}{289}}$ **30.** $-\sqrt{\frac{225}{625}}$ **31.** $\sqrt{\frac{400}{100}}$ **32.** $\sqrt{\frac{196}{256}}$

NAME ______________________ DATE __________ PERIOD ________

Practice

Student Edition
Pages 357–361

Square Roots

Simplify.

1. $\sqrt{36}$
6

2. $-\sqrt{16}$
−4

3. $\sqrt{81}$
9

4. $-\sqrt{144}$
−12

5. $-\sqrt{100}$
−10

6. $-\sqrt{121}$
−11

7. $\sqrt{169}$
13

8. $-\sqrt{25}$
−5

9. $-\sqrt{529}$
−23

10. $\sqrt{256}$
16

11. $\sqrt{324}$
18

12. $-\sqrt{289}$
−17

13. $\sqrt{441}$
21

14. $-\sqrt{225}$
−15

15. $\sqrt{196}$
14

16. $\sqrt{400}$
20

17. $\sqrt{484}$
22

18. $\sqrt{729}$
27

19. $-\sqrt{625}$
−25

20. $\sqrt{1225}$
35

21. $\sqrt{\frac{49}{81}}$
$\frac{7}{9}$

22. $-\sqrt{\frac{16}{25}}$
$-\frac{4}{5}$

23. $\sqrt{\frac{4}{16}}$
$\frac{1}{2}$

24. $-\sqrt{\frac{25}{36}}$
$-\frac{5}{6}$

25. $-\sqrt{\frac{100}{121}}$
$-\frac{10}{11}$

26. $\sqrt{\frac{1}{64}}$
$\frac{1}{8}$

27. $\sqrt{\frac{36}{64}}$
$\frac{3}{4}$

28. $-\sqrt{\frac{144}{36}}$
−2

29. $-\sqrt{\frac{121}{289}}$
$-\frac{11}{17}$

30. $-\sqrt{\frac{225}{625}}$
$-\frac{3}{5}$

31. $\sqrt{\frac{400}{100}}$
2

32. $\sqrt{\frac{196}{256}}$
$\frac{7}{8}$

NAME ______________________ DATE __________ PERIOD ______

8-6 Practice

Student Edition
Pages 362–365

Estimating Square Roots

Estimate each square root to the nearest whole number.

1. $\sqrt{10}$

2. $\sqrt{14}$

3. $\sqrt{32}$

4. $\sqrt{19}$

5. $\sqrt{40}$

6. $\sqrt{6}$

7. $\sqrt{53}$

8. $\sqrt{23}$

9. $\sqrt{30}$

10. $\sqrt{21}$

11. $\sqrt{90}$

12. $\sqrt{73}$

13. $\sqrt{72}$

14. $\sqrt{56}$

15. $\sqrt{89}$

16. $\sqrt{135}$

17. $\sqrt{152}$

18. $\sqrt{110}$

19. $\sqrt{162}$

20. $\sqrt{129}$

21. $\sqrt{181}$

22. $\sqrt{174}$

23. $\sqrt{223}$

24. $\sqrt{195}$

25. $\sqrt{240}$

26. $\sqrt{271}$

27. $\sqrt{312}$

28. $\sqrt{380}$

29. $\sqrt{335}$

30. $\sqrt{300}$

NAME ______________________ DATE __________ PERIOD _______

Practice

Estimating Square Roots

Estimate each square root to the nearest whole number.

1. $\sqrt{10}$
3

2. $\sqrt{14}$
4

3. $\sqrt{32}$
6

4. $\sqrt{19}$
4

5. $\sqrt{40}$
6

6. $\sqrt{6}$
2

7. $\sqrt{53}$
7

8. $\sqrt{23}$
5

9. $\sqrt{30}$
5

10. $\sqrt{21}$
5

11. $\sqrt{90}$
9

12. $\sqrt{73}$
9

13. $\sqrt{72}$
8

14. $\sqrt{56}$
7

15. $\sqrt{89}$
9

16. $\sqrt{135}$
12

17. $\sqrt{152}$
12

18. $\sqrt{110}$
10

19. $\sqrt{162}$
13

20. $\sqrt{129}$
11

21. $\sqrt{181}$
13

22. $\sqrt{174}$
13

23. $\sqrt{223}$
15

24. $\sqrt{195}$
14

25. $\sqrt{240}$
15

26. $\sqrt{271}$
16

27. $\sqrt{312}$
18

28. $\sqrt{380}$
19

29. $\sqrt{335}$
18

30. $\sqrt{300}$
17

NAME ______________________ DATE ____________ PERIOD ________

Practice

Student Edition
Pages 366–371

The Pythagorean Theorem

If c is the measure of the hypotenuse and a and b are the measures of the legs, find each missing measure. Round to the nearest tenth if necessary.

1.

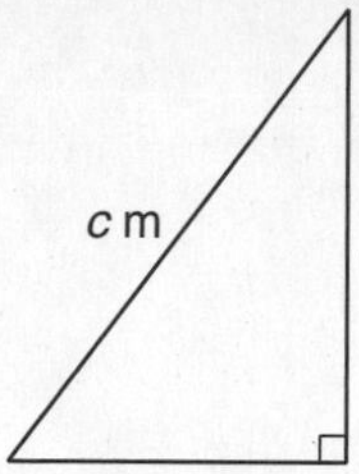

2.

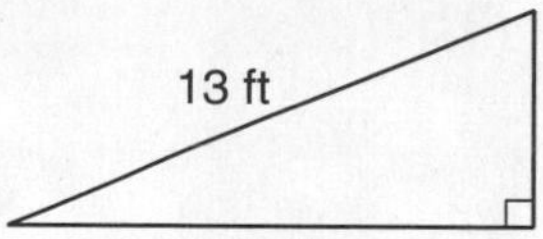

3.

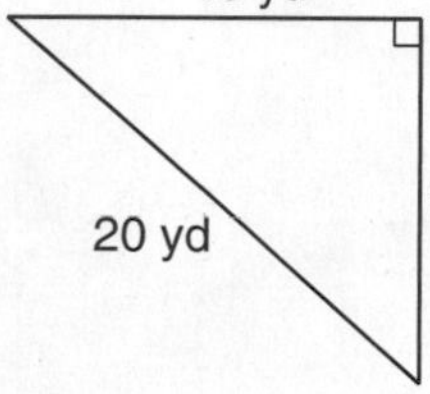

4.

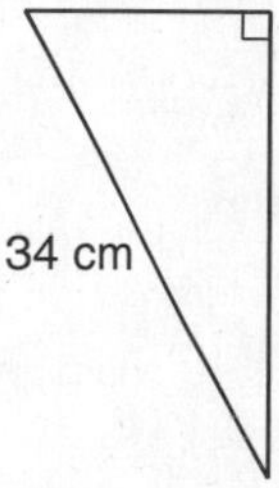

5.

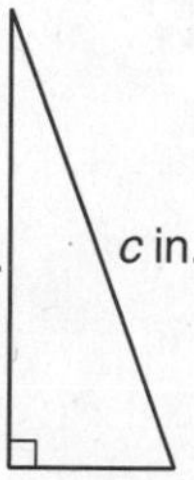

6.

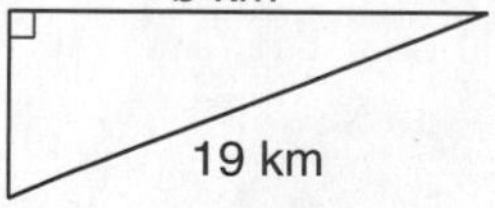

7. $a = 8, b = 10, c = ?$

8. $b = 20, c = 22, a = ?$

9. $c = 26, a = 10, b = ?$

10. $a = 21, c = 35, b = ?$

The lengths of three sides of a triangle are given. Determine whether each triangle is a right triangle.

11. 12 m, 16 m, 20 m

12. 8 cm, 12 cm, 14 cm

13. 6 in., 15 in., 16 in.

14. 7 ft, 24 ft, 25 ft

NAME ______________________ DATE __________ PERIOD ______

Practice

The Pythagorean Theorem

If c is the measure of the hypotenuse and a and b are the measures of the legs, find each missing measure. Round to the nearest tenth if necessary.

1. **15**

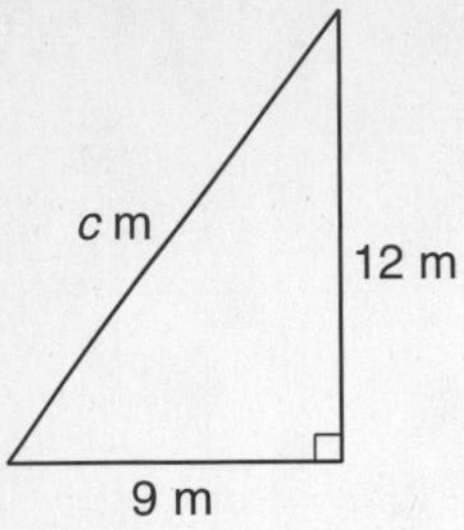

2. **5**

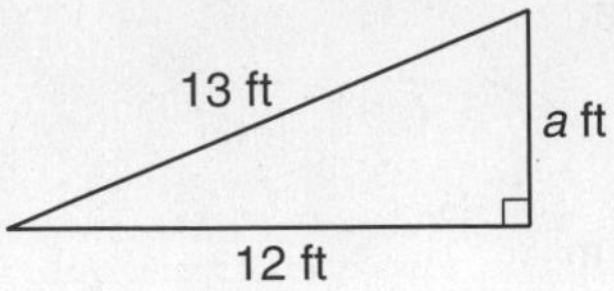

3. **13.2**

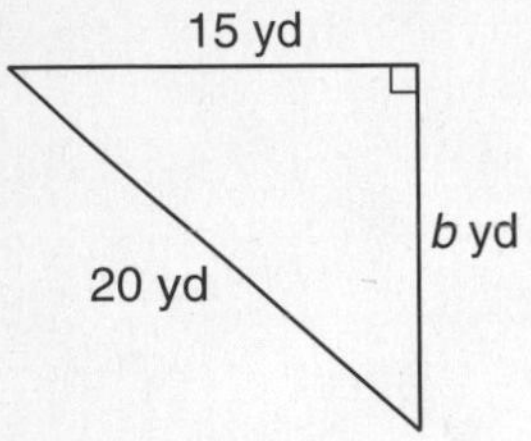

4. **16**

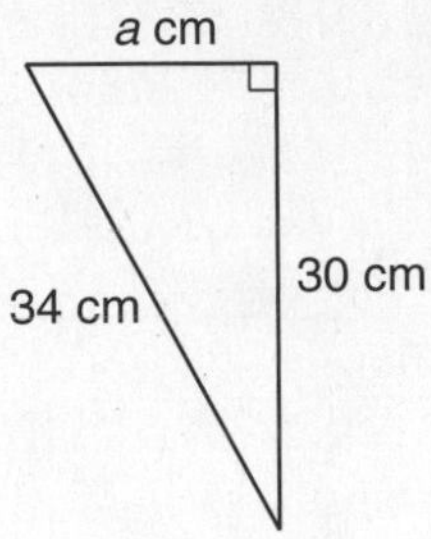

5. **11.7**

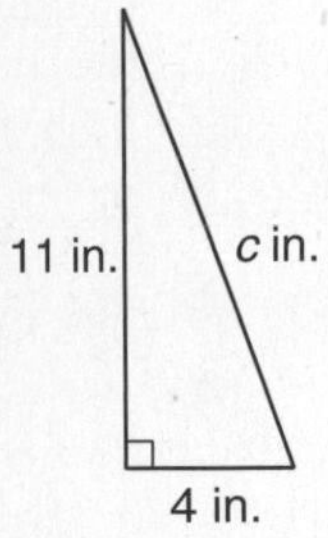

6. **17.7**

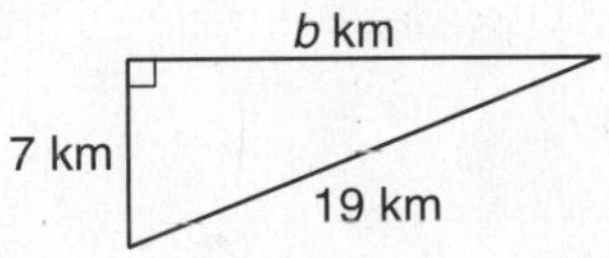

7. $a = 8, b = 10, c = ?$ **12.8**

8. $b = 20, c = 22, a = ?$ **9.2**

9. $c = 26, a = 10, b = ?$ **24**

10. $a = 21, c = 35, b = ?$ **28**

The lengths of three sides of a triangle are given. Determine whether each triangle is a right triangle.

11. 12 m, 16 m, 20 m **yes**

12. 8 cm, 12 cm, 14 cm **no**

13. 6 in., 15 in., 16 in. **no**

14. 7 ft, 24 ft, 25 ft **yes**

NAME ______________________ DATE __________ PERIOD _______

Practice

Student Edition
Pages 382–387

Polynomials

Determine whether each expression is a monomial. Explain why or why not.

1. $8y^2$
2. $3m^{-4}$
3. $\frac{6}{p}$
4. -9
5. $2x^2 + 5$
6. $-7a^3b$

State whether each expression is a polynomial. If it is a polynomial, identify it as a monomial, binomial, or trinomial.

7. $4h + 8$
8. 13
9. $3xy$
10. $\frac{2}{c} + 4$
11. $m^2 + 2 - m$
12. $5a + b^{-2}$
13. $7 - \frac{1}{2}d$
14. n^2
15. $2a^2 + 8a + 9 - 3$
16. $x^3 + 4x^3$
17. $m^2 + 2mn + n^2$
18. $6 - y$

Find the degree of each polynomial.

19. 8
20. $3a^2$
21. $5m + n^2$
22. $16cd$
23. $3g^4 + 2h^3$
24. $4a^2b + 3ab^3$
25. $c^2 + 2c - 8$
26. $2p^3 - 7p^2 - 4p$
27. $9y^3z + 15y^5z$
28. $7s^2 - 4s^2t + 2st$
29. $6x^3 + x^3y^2 - 3$
30. $2ab^3 - 5abc$

NAME ______________________ DATE __________ PERIOD _____

Practice

Student Edition
Pages 382–387

Polynomials

Determine whether each expression is a monomial. Explain why or why not.

1. $8y^2$ **yes; product of numbers and variables**
2. $3m^{-4}$ **no; has a negative exponent**
3. $\frac{6}{p}$ **no; includes division**
4. -9 **yes; a number**
5. $2x^2 + 5$ **no; includes addition**
6. $-7a^3b$ **yes; product of numbers and variables**

State whether each expression is a polynomial. If it is a polynomial, identify it as a monomial, binomial, or trinomial.

7. $4h + 8$ **yes; binomial**
8. 13 **yes; monomial**
9. $3xy$ **yes; monomial**
10. $\frac{2}{c} + 4$ **no**
11. $m^2 + 2 - m$ **yes; trinomial**
12. $5a + b^{-2}$ **no**
13. $7 - \frac{1}{2}d$ **yes; binomial**
14. n^2 **yes; monomial**
15. $2a^2 + 8a + 9 - 3$ **yes; trinomial**
16. $x^3 + 4x^3$ **yes; monomial**
17. $m^2 + 2mn + n^2$ **yes; trinomial**
18. $6 - y$ **yes; binomial**

Find the degree of each polynomial.

19. 8 **0**
20. $3a^2$ **2**
21. $5m + n^2$ **2**
22. $16cd$ **2**
23. $3g^4 + 2h^3$ **4**
24. $4a^2b + 3ab^3$ **4**
25. $c^2 + 2c - 8$ **2**
26. $2p^3 - 7p^2 - 4p$ **3**
27. $9y^3z + 15y^5z$ **6**
28. $7s^2 - 4s^2t + 2st$ **3**
29. $6x^3 + x^3y^2 - 3$ **5**
30. $2ab^3 - 5abc$ **4**

9–2

NAME ______________________ DATE __________ PERIOD ______

Practice

Student Edition
Pages 388–393

Adding and Subtracting Polynomials

Find each sum.

1. $\begin{array}{r} 5x - 2 \\ \underline{(+)\ 4x + 6} \end{array}$

2. $\begin{array}{r} 2y + 4 \\ \underline{(+)\ y - 1} \end{array}$

3. $\begin{array}{r} 4x - 8 \\ \underline{(+)\ 2x + 5} \end{array}$

4. $\begin{array}{r} 2x^2 - 7x - 4 \\ \underline{(+)\ x^2 + 3x + 2} \end{array}$

5. $\begin{array}{r} n^2 + 4n + 3 \\ \underline{(+)\ 3n^2 + 4n - 4} \end{array}$

6. $\begin{array}{r} 2x^2 + 3xy - y^2 \\ \underline{(+)\ 2x^2 - 2xy - 4y^2} \end{array}$

7. $(2x^2 - 2x - 4) + (x^2 - 3x + 2)$

8. $(x^2 + 2x + 1) + (3x^2 + 4x + 1)$

9. $(2a^2 + 8a + 6) + (a^2 + 3a - 4)$

10. $(x^2 + x - 12) + (x^2 - 3x)$

11. $(3x^2 + 8x + 4) + (4x^2 - 1)$

12. $(x^2 - 4x - 5) + (x^2 + 4x)$

Find each difference.

13. $\begin{array}{r} 7n + 2 \\ \underline{(-)\ n + 1} \end{array}$

14. $\begin{array}{r} 3x - 3 \\ \underline{(-)\ 2x + 2} \end{array}$

15. $\begin{array}{r} 2y + 5 \\ \underline{(-)\ y - 1} \end{array}$

16. $\begin{array}{r} 4x^2 + 7x - 2 \\ \underline{(-)\ 2x^2 - 6x + 4} \end{array}$

17. $\begin{array}{r} 2x^2 - 9x - 5 \\ \underline{(-)\ x^2 - 5x - 6} \end{array}$

18. $\begin{array}{r} 5m^2 - 4m - 1 \\ \underline{(-)\ 4m^2 + 8m + 4} \end{array}$

19. $(6x - 2) - (8x + 3)$

20. $(3x^2 + 3x - 6) - (2x^2 - 2x - 4)$

21. $(6x^2 + 2x - 8) - (4x^2 + 8x + 4)$

22. $(2a^2 + 6a + 4) - (a^2 - 3)$

23. $(2x^2 - 8x + 3) - (-x^2 + 2x)$

24. $(3x^2 - 5xy - 2y^2) - (2x^2 + y^2)$

NAME ______________________ DATE __________ PERIOD ______

Practice

Student Edition
Pages 388–393

Adding and Subtracting Polynomials

Find each sum.

1. $5x - 2$ (+) $4x + 6$ — **$9x + 4$**

2. $2y + 4$ (+) $y - 1$ — **$3y + 3$**

3. $4x - 8$ (+) $2x + 5$ — **$6x - 3$**

4. $2x^2 - 7x - 4$ (+) $x^2 + 3x + 2$ — **$3x^2 - 4x - 2$**

5. $n^2 + 4n + 3$ (+) $3n^2 + 4n - 4$ — **$4n^2 + 8n - 1$**

6. $2x^2 + 3xy - y^2$ (+) $2x^2 - 2xy - 4y^2$ — **$4x^2 + xy - 5y^2$**

7. $(2x^2 - 2x - 4) + (x^2 - 3x + 2)$
$3x^2 - 5x - 2$

8. $(x^2 + 2x + 1) + (3x^2 + 4x + 1)$
$4x^2 + 6x + 2$

9. $(2a^2 + 8a + 6) + (a^2 + 3a - 4)$
$3a^2 + 11a + 2$

10. $(x^2 + x - 12) + (x^2 - 3x)$
$2x^2 - 2x - 12$

11. $(3x^2 + 8x + 4) + (4x^2 - 1)$
$7x^2 + 8x + 3$

12. $(x^2 - 4x - 5) + (x^2 + 4x)$
$2x^2 - 5$

Find each difference.

13. $7n + 2$ (−) $n + 1$ — **$6n + 1$**

14. $3x - 3$ (−) $2x + 2$ — **$x - 5$**

15. $2y + 5$ (−) $y - 1$ — **$y + 6$**

16. $4x^2 + 7x - 2$ (−) $2x^2 - 6x + 4$ — **$2x^2 + 13x - 6$**

17. $2x^2 - 9x - 5$ (−) $x^2 - 5x - 6$ — **$x^2 - 4x + 1$**

18. $5m^2 - 4m - 1$ (−) $4m^2 + 8m + 4$ — **$m^2 - 12m - 5$**

19. $(6x - 2) - (8x + 3)$
$-2x - 5$

20. $(3x^2 + 3x - 6) - (2x^2 - 2x - 4)$
$x^2 + 5x - 2$

21. $(6x^2 + 2x - 8) - (4x^2 + 8x + 4)$
$2x^2 - 6x - 12$

22. $(2a^2 + 6a + 4) - (a^2 - 3)$
$a^2 + 6a + 7$

23. $(2x^2 - 8x + 3) - (-x^2 + 2x)$
$3x^2 - 10x + 3$

24. $(3x^2 - 5xy - 2y^2) - (2x^2 + y^2)$
$x^2 - 5xy - 3y^2$

9–3

NAME ______________________ DATE __________ PERIOD ______

Practice

Student Edition
Pages 394–398

Multiplying a Polynomial by a Monomial

Find each product.

1. $3(y + 4)$

2. $-2(n + 3)$

3. $5(3a - 4)$

4. $7(-2c + 3)$

5. $x(x + 6)$

6. $8y(2y - 3)$

7. $y(9 + 2y)$

8. $-3b(b - 1)$

9. $6(a^2 + 5)$

10. $-4m(-2 + 2m)$

11. $-7n(-4n + 2)$

12. $2q(3q - 1)$

13. $p(3p^2 + 7)$

14. $4x(5 - 2x^2)$

15. $5b(b^2 + 5b)$

16. $-3y(-9 + 3y^2)$

17. $2(8a^2 - 4a + 9)$

18. $6(z^2 + 2z - 6)$

19. $x(x^2 - x + 3)$

20. $-4b(1 - 7b + b^2)$

21. $5m^2(3m^2 - m - 7)$

22. $-7y(-2 + 7y + 3y^2)$

23. $-3n^2(n^2 - 2n + 3)$

24. $9c(2c^3 + c^2 - 4)$

Solve each equation.

25. $5(y + 2) = 25$

26. $7(x - 2) = -7$

27. $2(a - 5) + 4 = a + 9$

28. $3(2x + 6) - 10 = 4(x + 3)$

29. $-6(2n - 2) + 12 = 4(2n - 9)$

30. $b(b + 8) = b(b + 7) + 5$

31. $y(y + 7) + 3y = y(y + 3) - 14$

32. $m(m - 5) + 14 = m(m + 2) - 14$

Practice

Multiplying a Polynomial by a Monomial

Find each product.

1. $3(y + 4)$ **$3y + 12$**
2. $-2(n + 3)$ **$-2n - 6$**
3. $5(3a - 4)$ **$15a - 20$**
4. $7(-2c + 3)$ **$-14c + 21$**
5. $x(x + 6)$ **$x^2 + 6x$**
6. $8y(2y - 3)$ **$16y^2 - 24y$**
7. $y(9 + 2y)$ **$9y + 2y^2$**
8. $-3b(b - 1)$ **$-3b^2 + 3b$**
9. $6(a^2 + 5)$ **$6a^2 + 30$**
10. $-4m(-2 + 2m)$ **$8m - 8m^2$**
11. $-7n(-4n + 2)$ **$28n^2 - 14n$**
12. $2q(3q - 1)$ **$6q^2 - 2q$**
13. $p(3p^2 + 7)$ **$3p^3 + 7p$**
14. $4x(5 - 2x^2)$ **$20x - 8x^3$**
15. $5b(b^2 + 5b)$ **$5b^3 + 25b^2$**
16. $-3y(-9 + 3y^2)$ **$27y - 9y^3$**
17. $2(8a^2 - 4a + 9)$ **$16a^2 - 8a + 18$**
18. $6(z^2 + 2z - 6)$ **$6z^2 + 12z - 36$**
19. $x(x^2 - x + 3)$ **$x^3 - x^2 + 3x$**
20. $-4b(1 - 7b + b^2)$ **$-4b + 28b^2 - 4b^3$**
21. $5m^2(3m^2 - m - 7)$ **$15m^4 - 5m^3 - 35m^2$**
22. $-7y(-2 + 7y + 3y^2)$ **$14y - 49y^2 - 21y^3$**
23. $-3n^2(n^2 - 2n + 3)$ **$-3n^4 + 6n^3 - 9n^2$**
24. $9c(2c^3 + c^2 - 4)$ **$18c^4 + 9c^3 - 36c$**

Solve each equation.

25. $5(y + 2) = 25$ **3**
26. $7(x - 2) = -7$ **1**
27. $2(a - 5) + 4 = a + 9$ **15**
28. $3(2x + 6) - 10 = 4(x + 3)$ **2**
29. $-6(2n - 2) + 12 = 4(2n - 9)$ **3**
30. $b(b + 8) = b(b + 7) + 5$ **5**
31. $y(y + 7) + 3y = y(y + 3) - 14$ **−2**
32. $m(m - 5) + 14 = m(m + 2) - 14$ **4**

NAME ______________________ DATE __________ PERIOD ______

Practice

Student Edition
Pages 399–404

Multiplying Binomials

Find each product. Use the Distributive Property or the FOIL method.

1. $(y + 4)(y + 3)$

2. $(x + 2)(x + 1)$

3. $(b + 5)(b - 2)$

4. $(a - 6)(a - 4)$

5. $(z - 5)(z + 3)$

6. $(n - 1)(n - 8)$

7. $(x + 7)(x - 4)$

8. $(y - 3)(y + 9)$

9. $(b + 2)(b + 3)$

10. $(2c + 5)(c - 4)$

11. $(4x - 7)(x + 3)$

12. $(x - 1)(5x - 4)$

13. $(3y + 1)(3y + 2)$

14. $(2n + 4)(5n - 3)$

15. $(7h - 3)(4h - 1)$

16. $(2m - 6)(3m + 2)$

17. $(6a + 2)(2a + 3)$

18. $(4c + 5)(2c - 2)$

19. $(x + y)(2x + y)$

20. $(3a+ 4b)(a - 3b)$

21. $(3m - 3n)(3m - 2n)$

22. $(7p - 4q)(2p + 3q)$

23. $(2r + 2s)(2r + 3s)$

24. $(3y - 5z)(3y + 3z)$

25. $(x^2 + 1)(x - 3)$

26. $(y - 4)(y^2 + 2)$

27. $(2c^2 - 5)(c - 4)$

28. $(a^3 - 3a)(a + 4)$

29. $(b^2 + 2)(b^2 + 3)$

30. $(x^3 - 3)(4x + 1)$

NAME ______________________________ DATE __________ PERIOD ______

Practice

Multiplying Binomials

Find each product. Use the Distributive Property or the FOIL method.

1. $(y + 4)(y + 3)$
$y^2 + 7y + 12$

2. $(x + 2)(x + 1)$
$x^2 + 3x + 2$

3. $(b + 5)(b - 2)$
$b^2 + 3b - 10$

4. $(a - 6)(a - 4)$
$a^2 - 10a + 24$

5. $(z - 5)(z + 3)$
$z^2 - 2z - 15$

6. $(n - 1)(n - 8)$
$n^2 - 9n + 8$

7. $(x + 7)(x - 4)$
$x^2 + 3x - 28$

8. $(y - 3)(y + 9)$
$y^2 + 6y - 27$

9. $(b + 2)(b + 3)$
$b^2 + 5b + 6$

10. $(2c + 5)(c - 4)$
$2c^2 - 3c - 20$

11. $(4x - 7)(x + 3)$
$4x^2 + 5x - 21$

12. $(x - 1)(5x - 4)$
$5x^2 - 9x + 4$

13. $(3y + 1)(3y + 2)$
$9y^2 + 9y + 2$

14. $(2n + 4)(5n - 3)$
$10n^2 + 14n - 12$

15. $(7h - 3)(4h - 1)$
$28h^2 - 19h + 3$

16. $(2m - 6)(3m + 2)$
$6m^2 - 14m - 12$

17. $(6a + 2)(2a + 3)$
$12a^2 + 22a + 6$

18. $(4c + 5)(2c - 2)$
$8c^2 + 2c - 10$

19. $(x + y)(2x + y)$
$2x^2 + 3xy + y^2$

20. $(3a+ 4b)(a - 3b)$
$3a^2 - 5ab - 12b^2$

21. $(3m - 3n)(3m - 2n)$
$9m^2 - 15mn + 6n^2$

22. $(7p - 4q)(2p + 3q)$
$14p^2 + 13pq - 12q^2$

23. $(2r + 2s)(2r + 3s)$
$4r^2 + 10rs + 6s^2$

24. $(3y - 5z)(3y + 3z)$
$9y^2 - 6yz - 15z^2$

25. $(x^2 + 1)(x - 3)$
$x^3 - 3x^2 + x - 3$

26. $(y - 4)(y^2 + 2)$
$y^3 - 4y^2 + 2y - 8$

27. $(2c^2 - 5)(c - 4)$
$2c^3 - 8c^2 - 5c + 20$

28. $(a^3 - 3a)(a + 4)$
$a^4 + 4a^3 - 3a^2 - 12a$

29. $(b^2 + 2)(b^2 + 3)$
$b^4 + 5b^2 + 6$

30. $(x^3 - 3)(4x + 1)$
$4x^4 + x^3 - 12x - 3$

NAME ______________________ DATE __________ PERIOD ______

Practice

Student Edition
Pages 405–409

Special Products

Find each product.

1. $(y + 4)^2$

2. $(x + 3)^2$

3. $(m + 6)^2$

4. $(2b + c)^2$

5. $(x + 3y)^2$

6. $(4r + s)^2$

7. $(2m + 2n)^2$

8. $(4a + 2b)^2$

9. $(3g + 3h)^2$

10. $(b - 3)^2$

11. $(p - 4)^2$

12. $(s - 5)^2$

13. $(3x - 3)^2$

14. $(2y - 3)^2$

15. $(c - 6d)^2$

16. $(m - 2n)^2$

17. $(5x - y)^2$

18. $(a - 4b)^2$

19. $(3p - 5q)^2$

20. $(2j - 4k)^2$

21. $(2r - 2s)^2$

22. $(y + 3)(y - 3)$

23. $(x + 6)(x - 6)$

24. $(a + 9)(a - 9)$

25. $(3a + b)(3a - b)$

26. $(4r + s)(4r - s)$

27. $(2y + 6)(2y - 6)$

28. $(5x + 4)(5x - 4)$

29. $(2c + 4d)(2c - 4d)$

30. $(3m + 6n)(3m - 6n)$

NAME ______________________ DATE __________ PERIOD ______

9–5 Practice

Student Edition
Pages 405–409

Special Products

Find each product.

1. $(y + 4)^2$
$y^2 + 8y + 16$

2. $(x + 3)^2$
$x^2 + 6x + 9$

3. $(m + 6)^2$
$m^2 + 12m + 36$

4. $(2b + c)^2$
$4b^2 + 4bc + c^2$

5. $(x + 3y)^2$
$x^2 + 6xy + 9y^2$

6. $(4r + s)^2$
$16r^2 + 8rs + s^2$

7. $(2m + 2n)^2$
$4m^2 + 8mn + 4n^2$

8. $(4a + 2b)^2$
$16a^2 + 16ab + 4b^2$

9. $(3g + 3h)^2$
$9g^2 + 18gh + 9h^2$

10. $(b - 3)^2$
$b^2 - 6b + 9$

11. $(p - 4)^2$
$p^2 - 8p + 16$

12. $(s - 5)^2$
$s^2 - 10s + 25$

13. $(3x - 3)^2$
$9x^2 - 18x + 9$

14. $(2y - 3)^2$
$4y^2 - 12y + 9$

15. $(c - 6d)^2$
$c^2 - 12cd + 36d^2$

16. $(m - 2n)^2$
$m^2 - 4mn + 4n^2$

17. $(5x - y)^2$
$25x^2 - 10xy + y^2$

18. $(a - 4b)^2$
$a^2 - 8ab + 16b^2$

19. $(3p - 5q)^2$
$9p^2 - 30pq + 25q^2$

20. $(2j - 4k)^2$
$4j^2 - 16jk + 16k^2$

21. $(2r - 2s)^2$
$4r^2 - 8rs + 4s^2$

22. $(y + 3)(y - 3)$
$y^2 - 9$

23. $(x + 6)(x - 6)$
$x^2 - 36$

24. $(a + 9)(a - 9)$
$a^2 - 81$

25. $(3a + b)(3a - b)$
$9a^2 - b^2$

26. $(4r + s)(4r - s)$
$16r^2 - s^2$

27. $(2y + 6)(2y - 6)$
$4y^2 - 36$

28. $(5x + 4)(5x - 4)$
$25x^2 - 16$

29. $(2c + 4d)(2c - 4d)$
$4c^2 - 16d^2$

30. $(3m + 6n)(3m - 6n)$
$9m^2 - 36n^2$

10–1

NAME ______________________ DATE __________ PERIOD ______

Practice

Student Edition
Pages 420–425

Factors

Find the factors of each number. Then classify each number as prime or composite.

1. 36

2. 31

3. 28

4. 70

5. 43

6. 27

7. 28

8. 97

Factor each monomial.

9. $30m^2n$

10. $-12x^2y^3$

11. $-21ab^2$

12. $36r^3s$

13. $63x^3yz^2$

14. $-40pq^2r^2$

Find the GCF of each set of numbers or monomials.

15. 27, 18

16. 9, 12

17. 45, 56

18. 4, 8, 16

19. 32, 36, 38

20. 24, 36, 48

21. $6x$, $9x$

22. $5y^2$, $15y$

23. $14c^2$, $-13d$

24. $25mn^2$, $20m$

25. $12ab^2$, $18ab$

26. $-28x^2y^3$, $21xy^2$

27. $6xy$, $18y^2$

28. $18c^2d$, $27cd^2$

29. $7m$, mn

NAME ______________________ DATE ________ PERIOD ______

Practice

Student Edition
Pages 420–425

Factors

Find the factors of each number. Then classify each number as prime or composite.

1. 36
1, 2, 3, 4, 6, 9, 12, 18, 36; C

2. 31
1, 31; P

3. 28
1, 2, 4, 7, 14, 28; C

4. 70
1, 2, 5, 7, 10, 14, 35, 70; C

5. 43
1, 43; P

6. 27
1, 3, 9, 27; C

7. 28
1, 2, 4, 7, 14; C

8. 97
1, 97; P

Factor each monomial.

9. $30m^2n$
$2 \cdot 3 \cdot 5 \cdot m \cdot m \cdot n$

10. $-12x^2y^3$
$-1 \cdot 2 \cdot 2 \cdot 3 \cdot x \cdot x \cdot y \cdot y \cdot y$

11. $-21ab^2$
$-1 \cdot 3 \cdot 7 \cdot a \cdot b \cdot b$

12. $36r^3s$
$2 \cdot 2 \cdot 3 \cdot 3 \cdot r \cdot r \cdot r \cdot s$

13. $63x^3yz^2$
$3 \cdot 3 \cdot 7 \cdot x \cdot x \cdot x \cdot y \cdot z \cdot z$

14. $-40pq^2r^2$
$-1 \cdot 2 \cdot 2 \cdot 2 \cdot 5 \cdot p \cdot q \cdot q \cdot r \cdot r$

Find the GCF of each set of numbers or monomials.

15. 27, 18
9

16. 9, 12
3

17. 45, 56
1

18. 4, 8, 16
4

19. 32, 36, 38
2

20. 24, 36, 48
12

21. $6x$, $9x$
$3x$

22. $5y^2$, $15y$
$5y$

23. $14c^2$, $-13d$
1

24. $25mn^2$, $20m$
$5m$

25. $12ab^2$, $18ab$
$6ab$

26. $-28x^2y^3$, $21xy^2$
$7xy^2$

27. $6xy$, $18y^2$
$6y$

28. $18c^2d$, $27cd^2$
$9cd$

29. $7m$, mn
m

NAME ______________________ DATE __________ PERIOD ______

Practice

Student Edition
Pages 428–433

Factoring Using the Distributive Property

Factor each polynomial. If the polynomial cannot be factored, write prime.

1. $4x + 16$
2. $3y^2 + 12y$
3. $10x + 5x^2y$
4. $7yz + 3x$
5. $15r + 20rs$
6. $14ab + 21a$
7. $9xy - 3xy^2$
8. $12m^2n - 18mn^2$
9. $8ab + 2a^2b^2$
10. $16a^2bc - 36ab^2$
11. $3x^2y + 25m^2$
12. $8x^2y^3 - 10xy$
13. $4xy^2 + 18xy + 14y$
14. $7m^2 + 28mn + 14n^2$
15. $2x^2y + 4xy - 2xy^2$
16. $3a^3b - 9a^2b + 15b^2$
17. $18a^2bc + 24ac^2 + 36a^3c$
18. $8x^3y^2 + 16xy + 28x^2y^3$

Find each quotient.

19. $(6m^2 + 4) \div 2$
20. $(14x^2 - 21x) \div 7x$
21. $(10x^2 + 15y^2) \div 5$
22. $(2c^2 + 4c) \div 2c$
23. $(12xy + 9y) \div 3y$
24. $(9a^2b - 27ab) \div 9ab$
25. $(25m^2n^2 + 15mn) \div 5mn$
26. $(3a^2b - 9abc^2) \div 3ab$

10–2

NAME ______________________ DATE __________ PERIOD ______

Practice

Student Edition
Pages 428–433

Factoring Using the Distributive Property

Factor each polynomial. If the polynomial cannot be factored, write prime.

1. $4x + 16$
$4(x + 4)$

2. $3y^2 + 12y$
$3y(y + 4)$

3. $10x + 5x^2y$
$5x(2 + xy)$

4. $7yz + 3x$
prime

5. $15r + 20rs$
$5r(3 + 4s)$

6. $14ab + 21a$
$7a(2b + 3)$

7. $9xy - 3xy^2$
$3xy(3 - y)$

8. $12m^2n - 18mn^2$
$6mn(2m - 3n)$

9. $8ab + 2a^2b^2$
$2ab(4 + ab)$

10. $16a^2bc - 36ab^2$
$4ab(4ac - 9b)$

11. $3x^2y + 25m^2$
prime

12. $8x^2y^3 - 10xy$
$2xy(4xy^2 - 5)$

13. $4xy^2 + 18xy + 14y$
$2y(2xy + 9x + 7)$

14. $7m^2 + 28mn + 14n^2$
$7(m^2 + 4mn + 2n^2)$

15. $2x^2y + 4xy - 2xy^2$
$2xy(x + 2 - y)$

16. $3a^3b - 9a^2b + 15b^2$
$3b(a^3 - 3a^2 + 5b)$

17. $18a^2bc + 24ac^2 + 36a^3c$
$6ac(3ab + 4c + 6a^2)$

18. $8x^3y^2 + 16xy + 28x^2y^3$
$4xy(2x^2y + 4 + 7xy^2)$

Find each quotient.

19. $(6m^2 + 4) \div 2$
$3m^2 + 2$

20. $(14x^2 - 21x) \div 7x$
$2x - 3$

21. $(10x^2 + 15y^2) \div 5$
$2x^2 + 3y^2$

22. $(2c^2 + 4c) \div 2c$
$c + 2$

23. $(12xy + 9y) \div 3y$
$4x + 3$

24. $(9a^2b - 27ab) \div 9ab$
$a - 3$

25. $(25m^2n^2 + 15mn) \div 5mn$
$5mn + 3$

26. $(3a^2b - 9abc^2) \div 3ab$
$a - 3c^2$

NAME ______________________ DATE __________ PERIOD ______

Practice

Student Edition
Pages 434–439

Factoring Trinomials: $x^2 + bx + c$

Factor each trinomial. If the trinomial cannot be factored, write prime.

1. $x^2 + 5x + 6$

2. $y^2 + 5y + 4$

3. $m^2 + 12m + 35$

4. $p^2 + 8p + 15$

5. $a^2 + 8a + 12$

6. $n^2 + 4n + 4$

7. $x^2 + 9x + 18$

8. $x^2 + x + 3$

9. $y^2 - 6y + 8$

10. $c^2 - 8c + 15$

11. $m^2 - 2m + 1$

12. $b^2 - 9b + 20$

13. $x^2 - 8x + 7$

14. $n^2 - 5n + 6$

15. $y^2 - 8y + 12$

16. $c^2 - 4c + 5$

17. $x^2 - x - 12$

18. $m^2 + 5m - 6$

19. $a^2 + 4a - 12$

20. $y^2 - y - 6$

21. $b^2 - 3b - 10$

22. $x^2 + 3x - 4$

23. $c^2 + 2c - 15$

24. $2x^2 + 10x + 8$

25. $3y^2 - 15y + 18$

26. $5m^2 - 10m - 40$

27. $3b^2 + 6b - 9$

28. $4n^2 + 12n + 8$

29. $2x^2 + 8x - 24$

30. $3y^2 - 15y + 12$

NAME ______________________________ DATE __________ PERIOD ______

Practice

Student Edition
Pages 434–439

Factoring Trinomials: $x^2 + bx + c$

Factor each trinomial. If the trinomial cannot be factored, write prime.

1. $x^2 + 5x + 6$
   $(x + 2)(x + 3)$
2. $y^2 + 5y + 4$
   $(y + 4)(y + 1)$
3. $m^2 + 12m + 35$
   $(m + 5)(m + 7)$
4. $p^2 + 8p + 15$
   $(p + 5)(p + 3)$
5. $a^2 + 8a + 12$
   $(a + 6)(a + 2)$
6. $n^2 + 4n + 4$
   $(n + 2)(n + 2)$
7. $x^2 + 9x + 18$
   $(x + 3)(x + 6)$
8. $x^2 + x + 3$
   prime
9. $y^2 - 6y + 8$
   $(y - 2)(y - 4)$
10. $c^2 - 8c + 15$
    $(c - 5)(c - 3)$
11. $m^2 - 2m + 1$
    $(m - 1)(m - 1)$
12. $b^2 - 9b + 20$
    $(b - 4)(b - 5)$
13. $x^2 - 8x + 7$
    $(x - 1)(x - 7)$
14. $n^2 - 5n + 6$
    $(n - 3)(n - 2)$
15. $y^2 - 8y + 12$
    $(y - 6)(y - 2)$
16. $c^2 - 4c + 5$
    prime
17. $x^2 - x - 12$
    $(x + 3)(x - 4)$
18. $m^2 + 5m - 6$
    $(m - 1)(m + 6)$
19. $a^2 + 4a - 12$
    $(a - 2)(a + 6)$
20. $y^2 - y - 6$
    $(y + 2)(y - 3)$
21. $b^2 - 3b - 10$
    $(b - 5)(b + 2)$
22. $x^2 + 3x - 4$
    $(x + 4)(x - 1)$
23. $c^2 + 2c - 15$
    $(c + 5)(c - 3)$
24. $2x^2 + 10x + 8$
    $2(x + 4)(x + 1)$
25. $3y^2 - 15y + 18$
    $3(y - 2)(y - 3)$
26. $5m^2 - 10m - 40$
    $5(m + 2)(m - 4)$
27. $3b^2 + 6b - 9$
    $3(b - 1)(b + 3)$
28. $4n^2 + 12n + 8$
    $4(n + 2)(n + 1)$
29. $2x^2 + 8x - 24$
    $2(x - 2)(x + 6)$
30. $3y^2 - 15y + 12$
    $3(y - 4)(y - 1)$

NAME ______________________ DATE __________ PERIOD ______

Practice

Factoring Trinomials: $ax^2 + bx + c$

Factor each trinomial. If the trinomial cannot be factored, write prime.

1. $2y^2 + 8y + 6$

2. $2x^2 + 5x + 2$

3. $3a^2 - 4a - 4$

4. $5m^2 - 4m - 1$

5. $2c^2 + 6c - 8$

6. $4q^2 + 2q + 3$

7. $3x^2 - 13x + 4$

8. $4y^2 - 14y + 6$

9. $2b^2 - b - 10$

10. $6a^2 + 8a + 2$

11. $3n^2 + 7n - 6$

12. $3x^2 - 3x - 6$

13. $2c^2 + 3c - 7$

14. $5y^2 - 17y + 6$

15. $2b^2 + 2b - 12$

16. $2x^2 + 10x + 8$

17. $3m^2 - 19m + 6$

18. $4a^2 + 10a - 6$

19. $7b^2 - 16b + 4$

20. $3y^2 - y - 10$

21. $6c^2 + 11c + 4$

22. $10x^2 - x - 2$

23. $12m^2 - 11m + 2$

24. $9y^2 - 3y - 6$

25. $8b^2 + 12b + 4$

26. $6x^2 + 8x - 8$

27. $4n^2 - 14n + 12$

28. $6x^2 + 18x + 12$

29. $4a^2 + 18a - 10$

30. $9y^2 - 15y + 6$

10–4

NAME ______________________________ DATE ____________ PERIOD ________

Practice

Student Edition
Pages 440–444

Factoring Trinomials: $ax^2 + bx + c$

Factor each trinomial. If the trinomial cannot be factored, write prime.

1. $2y^2 + 8y + 6$
   $2(y + 1)(y + 3)$

2. $2x^2 + 5x + 2$
   $(2x + 1)(x + 2)$

3. $3a^2 - 4a - 4$
   $(3a + 2)(a - 2)$

4. $5m^2 - 4m - 1$
   $(5m + 1)(m - 1)$

5. $2c^2 + 6c - 8$
   $2(c - 1)(c + 4)$

6. $4q^2 + 2q + 3$
   prime

7. $3x^2 - 13x + 4$
   $(3x - 1)(x - 4)$

8. $4y^2 - 14y + 6$
   $2(2y - 1)(y - 3)$

9. $2b^2 - b - 10$
   $(2b - 5)(b + 2)$

10. $6a^2 + 8a + 2$
    $2(3a + 1)(a + 1)$

11. $3n^2 + 7n - 6$
    $(3n - 2)(n + 3)$

12. $3x^2 - 3x - 6$
    $3(x + 1)(x - 2)$

13. $2c^2 + 3c - 7$
    prime

14. $5y^2 - 17y + 6$
    $(5y - 2)(y - 3)$

15. $2b^2 + 2b - 12$
    $2(b + 3)(b - 2)$

16. $2x^2 + 10x + 8$
    $2(x + 1)(x + 4)$

17. $3m^2 - 19m + 6$
    $(3m - 1)(m - 6)$

18. $4a^2 + 10a - 6$
    $2(2a - 1)(a + 3)$

19. $7b^2 - 16b + 4$
    $(7b - 2)(b - 2)$

20. $3y^2 - y - 10$
    $(3y + 5)(y - 2)$

21. $6c^2 + 11c + 4$
    $(2c + 1)(3c + 4)$

22. $10x^2 - x - 2$
    $(5x + 2)(2x - 1)$

23. $12m^2 - 11m + 2$
    $(4m - 1)(3m - 2)$

24. $9y^2 - 3y - 6$
    $3(y - 1)(3y + 2)$

25. $8b^2 + 12b + 4$
    $4(b + 1)(2b + 1)$

26. $6x^2 + 8x - 8$
    $2(3x - 2)(x + 2)$

27. $4n^2 - 14n + 12$
    $2(2n - 3)(n - 2)$

28. $6x^2 + 18x + 12$
    $6(x + 2)(x + 1)$

29. $4a^2 + 18a - 10$
    $2(2a - 1)(a + 5)$

30. $9y^2 - 15y + 6$
    $3(3y - 2)(y - 1)$

10–5

NAME ______________________ DATE __________ PERIOD ______

Practice

Student Edition
Pages 445–449

Special Factors

Determine whether each trinomial is a perfect square trinomial. If so, factor it.

1. $y^2 + 6y + 9$

2. $x^2 - 4x + 4$

3. $n^2 + 6n + 3$

4. $m^2 - 12m + 36$

5. $y^2 - 10y + 20$

6. $4a^2 + 16a + 16$

7. $9x^2 + 6x + 1$

8. $4n^2 - 20n + 25$

9. $4y^2 + 9y + 9$

Determine whether each binomial is the difference of squares. If so, factor it.

10. $x^2 - 49$

11. $b^2 + 16$

12. $y^2 - 81$

13. $4m^2 - 9$

14. $9a^2 - 16$

15. $25r^2 + 9$

16. $18n^2 - 18$

17. $3x^2 - 12y^2$

18. $8m^2 - 18n^2$

Factor each polynomial. If the polynomial cannot be factored, write prime.

19. $4a - 24$

20. $6x + 9$

21. $x^2 + 5x - 10$

22. $2y^2 + 6y - 20$

23. $m^2 - 9n^2$

24. $a^2 - 8a + 16$

25. $5b^2 + 10b$

26. $9y^2 + 12y + 4$

27. $3x^2 - 3x - 18$

NAME ______________________________ DATE __________ PERIOD ______

Practice

Student Edition
Pages 445–449

Special Factors

Determine whether each trinomial is a perfect square trinomial. If so, factor it.

1. $y^2 + 6y + 9$
   $(y + 3)^2$
2. $x^2 - 4x + 4$
   $(x - 2)^2$
3. $n^2 + 6n + 3$
   no
4. $m^2 - 12m + 36$
   $(m - 6)^2$
5. $y^2 - 10y + 20$
   no
6. $4a^2 + 16a + 16$
   $(2a + 4)^2$
7. $9x^2 + 6x + 1$
   $(3x + 1)^2$
8. $4n^2 - 20n + 25$
   $(2n - 5)^2$
9. $4y^2 + 9y + 9$
   no

Determine whether each binomial is the difference of squares. If so, factor it.

10. $x^2 - 49$
    $(x - 7)(x + 7)$
11. $b^2 + 16$
    no
12. $y^2 - 81$
    $(y - 9)(y + 9)$
13. $4m^2 - 9$
    $(2m - 3)(2m + 3)$
14. $9a^2 - 16$
    $(3a - 4)(3a + 4)$
15. $25r^2 + 9$
    no
16. $18n^2 - 18$
    $18(n - 1)(n + 1)$
17. $3x^2 - 12y^2$
    $3(x - 2y)(x + 2y)$
18. $8m^2 - 18n^2$
    $2(2m - 3n)(2m + 3n)$

Factor each polynomial. If the polynomial cannot be factored, write prime.

19. $4a - 24$
    $4(a - 6)$
20. $6x + 9$
    $3(2x + 3)$
21. $x^2 + 5x - 10$
    prime
22. $2y^2 + 6y - 20$
    $2(y - 2)(y + 5)$
23. $m^2 - 9n^2$
    $(m - 3n)(m + 3n)$
24. $a^2 - 8a + 16$
    $(a - 4)^2$
25. $5b^2 + 10b$
    $5b(b + 2)$
26. $9y^2 + 12y + 4$
    $(3y + 2)^2$
27. $3x^2 - 3x - 18$
    $(3x + 6)(x - 3)$

NAME ______________________________ DATE __________ PERIOD ________

Practice

Student Edition
Pages 458–463

Graphing Quadratic Functions

Graph each quadratic equation by making a table of values.

1. $y = x^2 + 2x$

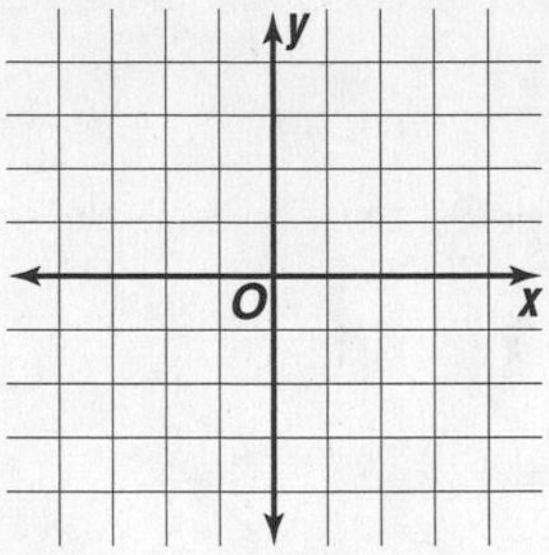

2. $y = -x^2 + 4$

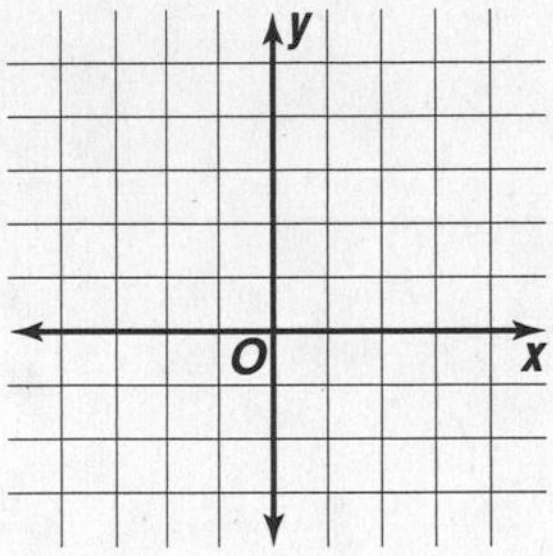

3. $y = -2x^2 + 5$

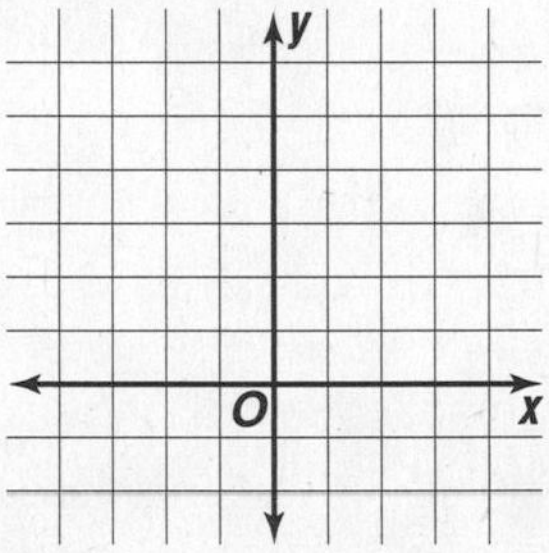

4. $y = x^2 - 2x - 6$

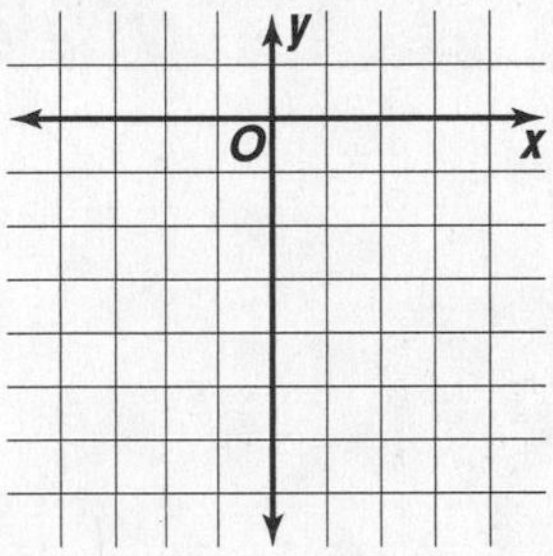

Write the equation of the axis of symmetry and the coordinates of the vertex of the graph of each quadratic function. Then graph the function.

5. $y = x^2 - 1$

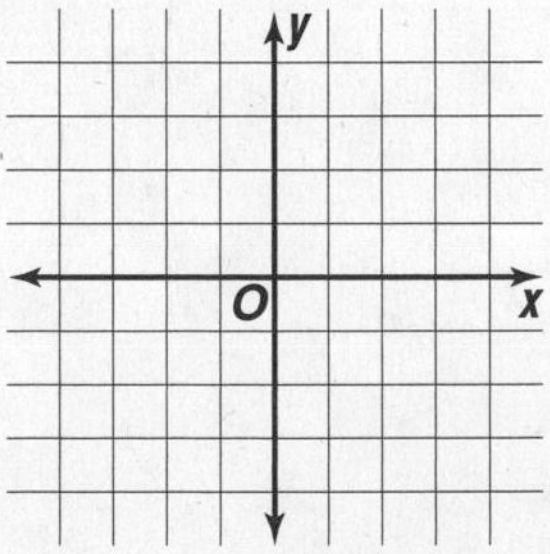

6. $y = x^2 + 4x + 2$

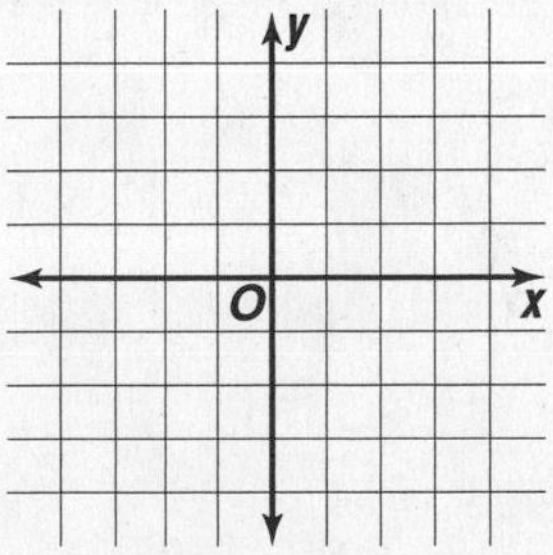

7. $y = -x^2 + 2x + 6$

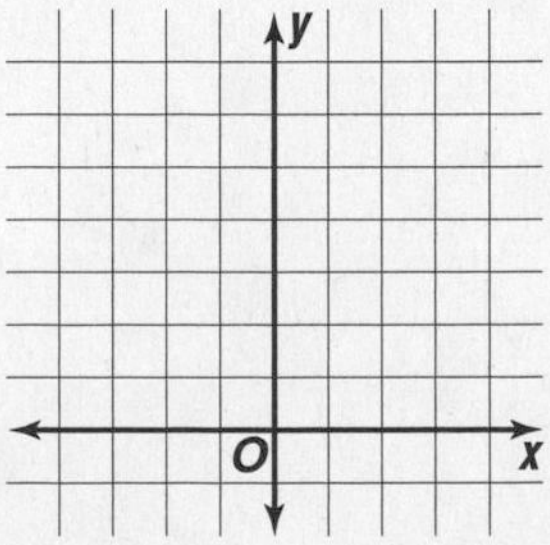

8. $y = -x^2 + 4x$

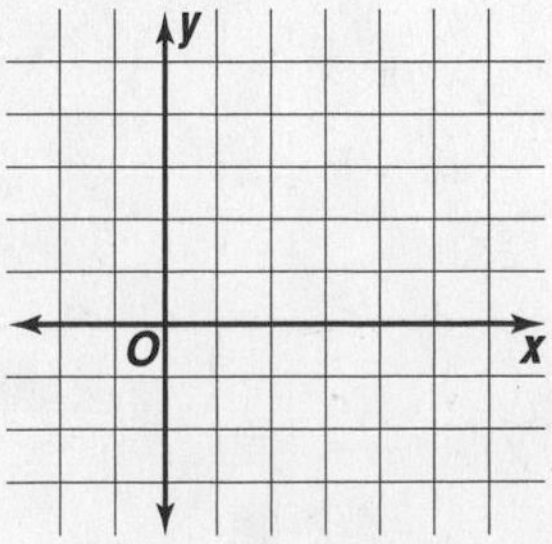

NAME ______________________ DATE __________ PERIOD ______

Practice

Student Edition
Pages 458–463

Graphing Quadratic Functions

Graph each quadratic equation by making a table of values.

1. $y = x^2 + 2x$

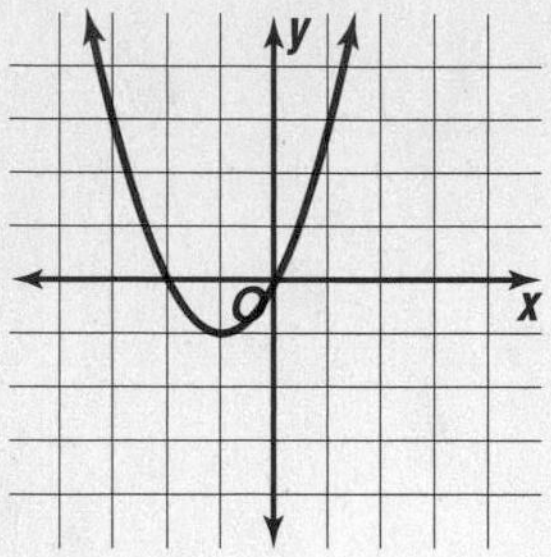

2. $y = -x^2 + 4$

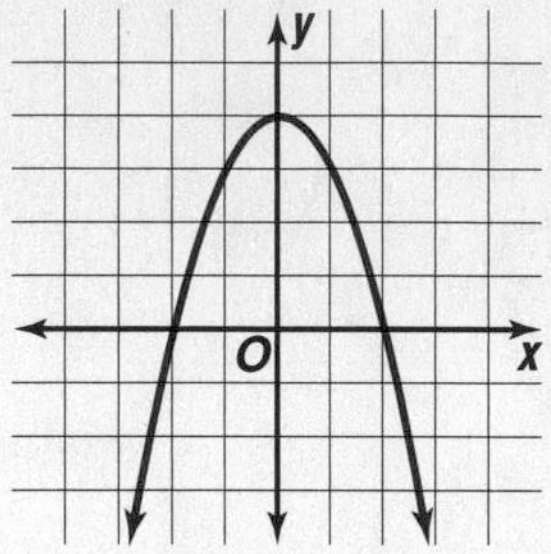

3. $y = -2x^2 + 5$

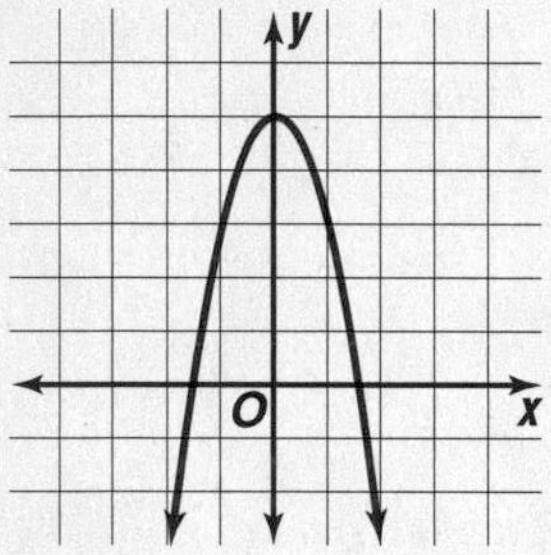

4. $y = x^2 - 2x - 6$

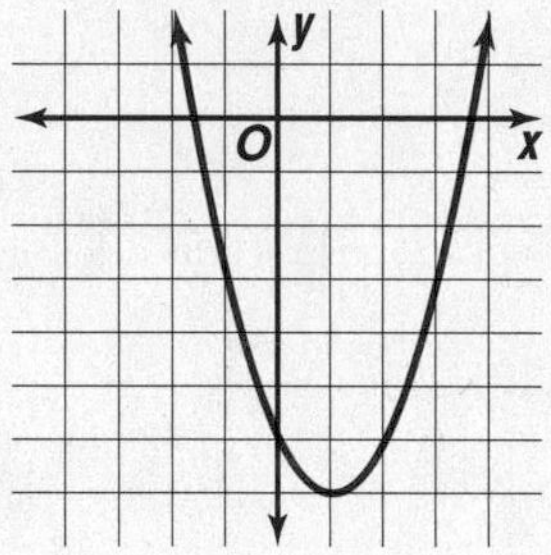

Write the equation of the axis of symmetry and the coordinates of the vertex of the graph of each quadratic function. Then graph the function.

5. $y = x^2 - 1$ **x = 0, (0, – 1)**

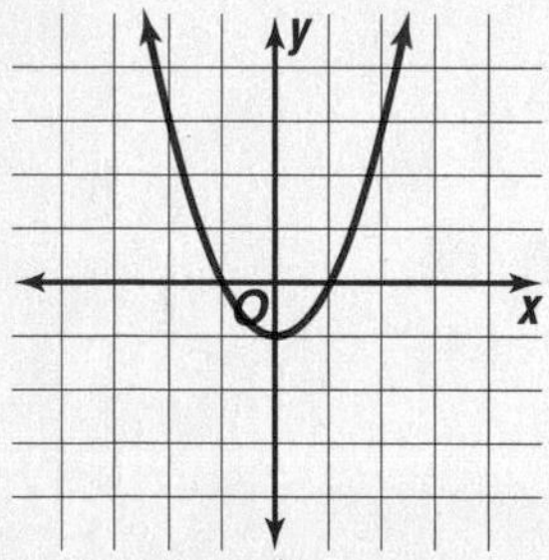

6. $y = x^2 + 4x + 2$ **x = –2, (–2, –2)**

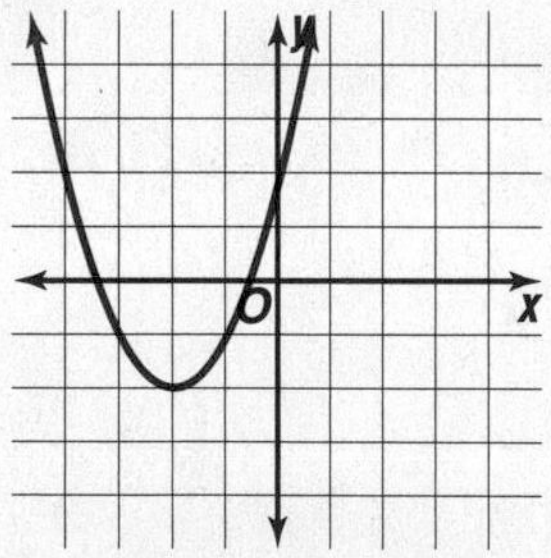

7. $y = -x^2 + 2x + 6$ **x = 1, (1, 7)**

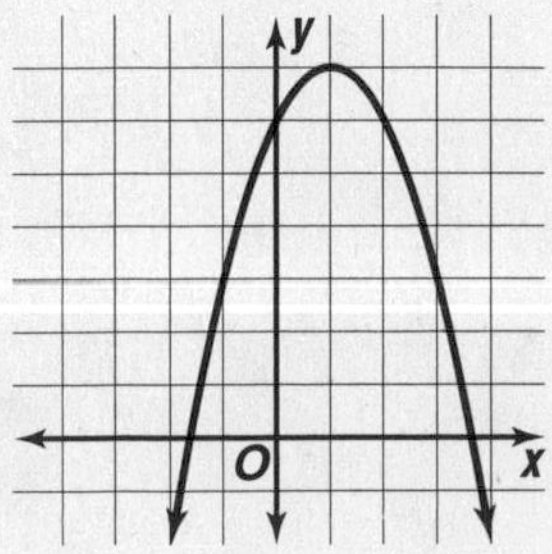

8. $y = -x^2 + 4x$ **x = 2, (2, 4)**

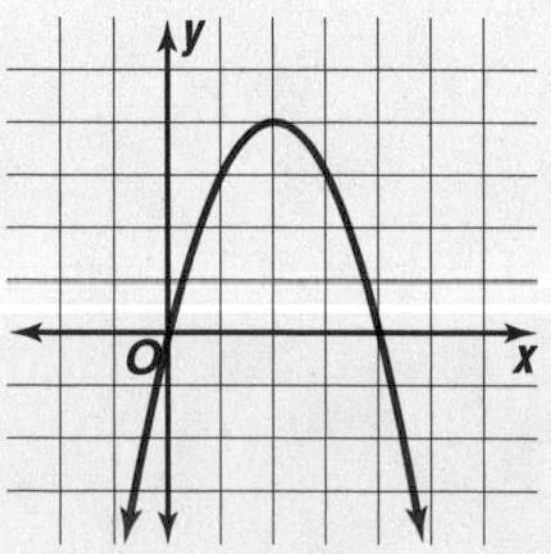

NAME ______________________ DATE __________ PERIOD ______

Practice

Student Edition
Pages 464–467

Families of Quadratic Functions

Graph each group of equations on the same axes. Compare and contrast the graphs.

1. $y = -x^2 + 1$
$y = -x^2 + 3$
$y = -x^2 + 5$

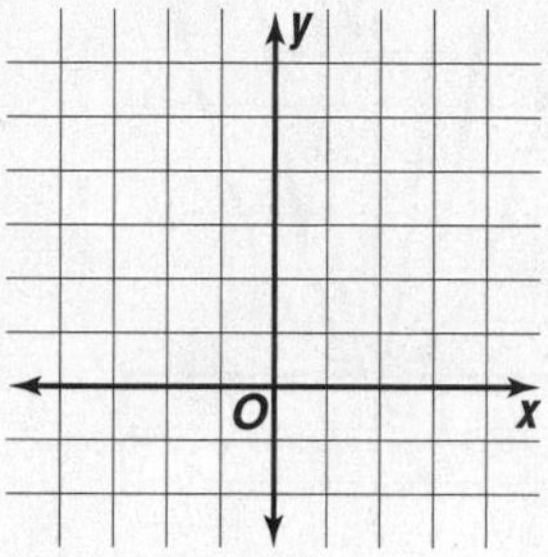

2. $y = (x + 1)^2$
$y = (x - 1)^2$
$y = (x - 3)^2$

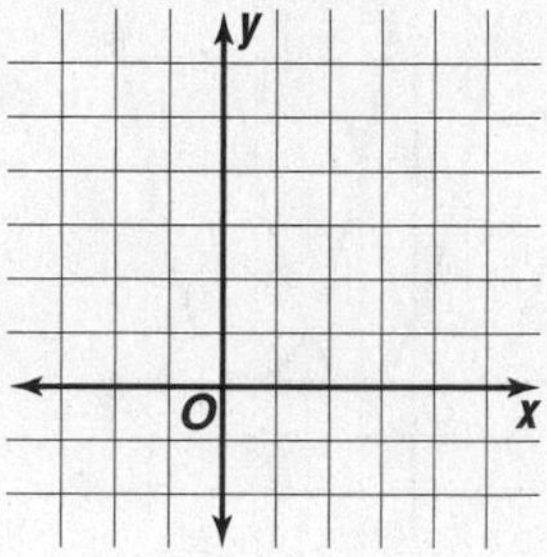

3. $y = 5.5x^2$
$y = 1.5x^2$
$y = 0.5x^2$

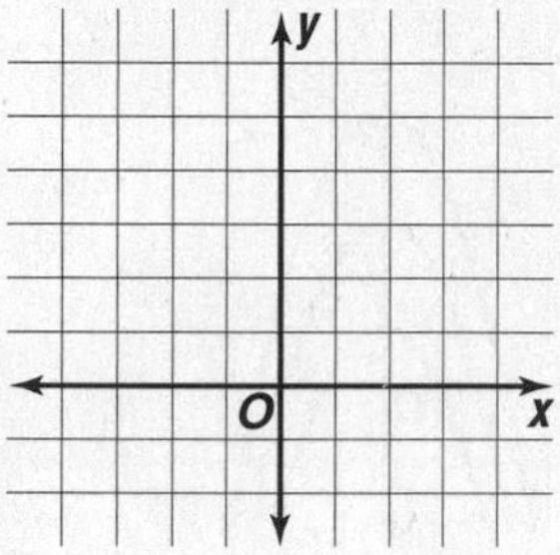

Describe how each graph changes from the parent graph of $y = x^2$. Then name the vertex of each graph.

4. $y = 2x^2$

5. $y = x^2 + 3$

6. $y = -x^2 + 5$

7. $y = -0.2x^2$

8. $y = (x + 1)^2$

9. $y = (x - 9)^2$

10. $y = -4x^2 - 1$

11. $y = (x - 6)^2 + 5$

12. $y = -0.5x^2 + 4$

13. $y = 5x^2 + 8$

14. $y = (x - 2)^2 - 3$

15. $y = -(x + 1)^2 + 8$

16. $y = -(x + 3)^2 - 7$

17. $y = -(x - 4)^2 + 5$

18. $y = (x + 6)^2 + 2$

NAME ______________________ DATE __________ PERIOD ______

11–2 Practice

Student Edition
Pages 464–467

Families of Quadratic Functions

Graph each group of equations on the same axes. Compare and contrast the graphs.

1. $y = -x^2 + 1$
$y = -x^2 + 3$
$y = -x^2 + 5$

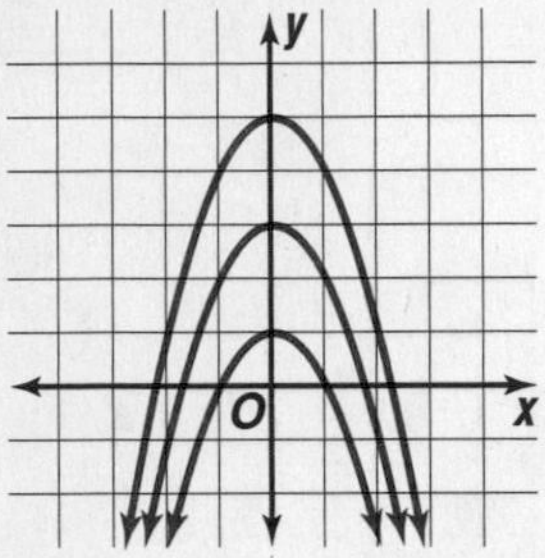

All open down; graphs shift up 2 units.

2. $y = (x + 1)^2$
$y = (x - 1)^2$
$y = (x - 3)^2$

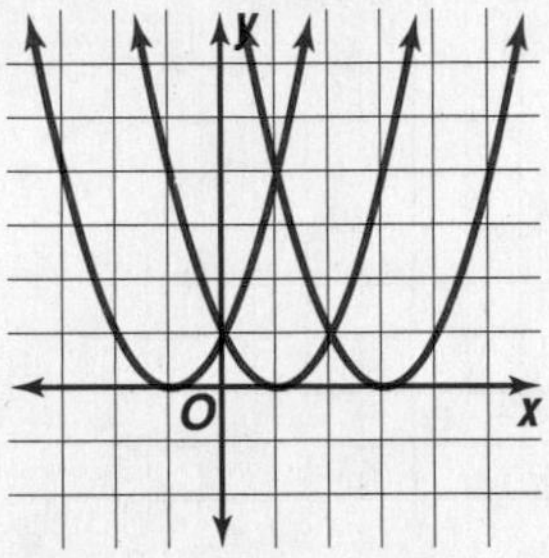

All open up; graphs shift right 2 units.

3. $y = 5.5x^2$
$y = 1.5x^2$
$y = 0.5x^2$

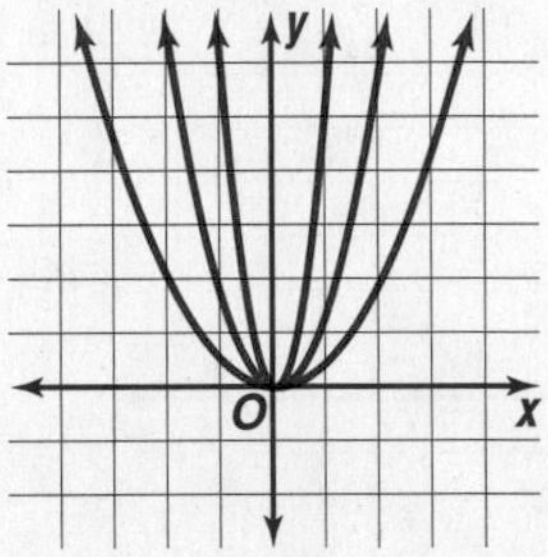

All open up; graphs get wider the smaller the coefficient of x^2.

Describe how each graph changes from the parent graph of $y = x^2$. Then name the vertex of each graph.

4. $y = 2x^2$
narrows; (0, 0)

5. $y = x^2 + 3$
up 3 units; (0, 3)

6. $y = -x^2 + 5$
opens down, up 5 units; (0, 5)

7. $y = -0.2x^2$
open down; widens (0, 0)

8. $y = (x + 1)^2$
left 1 unit; (−1, 0)

9. $y = (x - 9)^2$
right 9 units; (9, 0)

10. $y = -4x^2 - 1$
opens down, narrows, down 1 unit; (0, −1)

11. $y = (x - 6)^2 + 5$
right 6 units, up 5 units; (6, 5)

12. $y = -0.5x^2 + 4$
opens down, widens, up 4 units; (0, 4)

13. $y = 5x^2 + 8$
narrows, up 8 units; (0, 8)

14. $y = (x - 2)^2 - 3$
right 2 units, down 3 units; (2, −3)

15. $y = -(x + 1)^2 + 8$
opens down, left 1 unit, up 8 units; (−1, 8)

16. $y = -(x + 3)^2 - 7$
opens down, left 3 units, down 7 units; (−3, −7)

17. $y = -(x - 4)^2 + 5$
opens down, right 4 units, up 5 units; (4, 5)

18. $y = (x + 6)^2 + 2$
left 6 units, up 2 units; (−6, 2)

11–3

NAME ______________________ DATE __________ PERIOD ______

Practice

Student Edition
Pages 468–473

Solving Quadratic Equations by Graphing

Solve each equation by graphing the related function. If exact roots cannot be found, state the consecutive integers between which the roots are located.

1. $x^2 - 2x + 1 = 0$

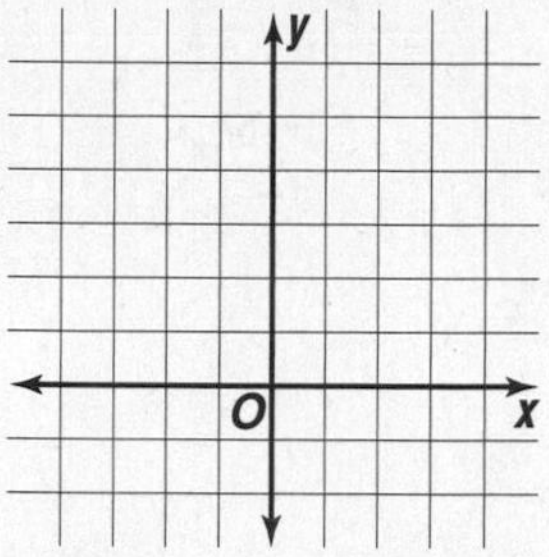

2. $x^2 + 6x + 5 = 0$

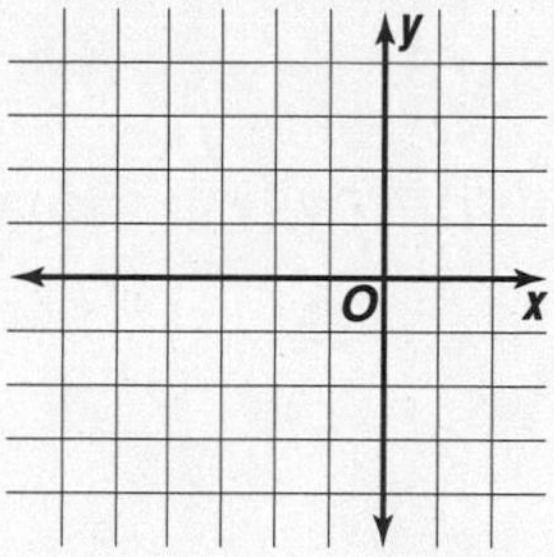

3. $x^2 - 3x - 4 = 0$

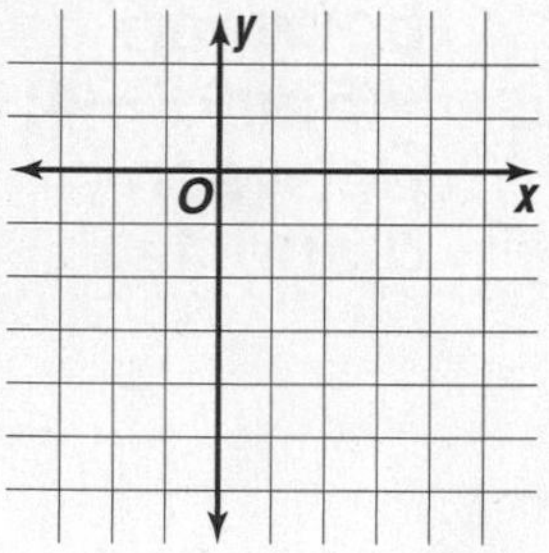

4. $x^2 + 4x - 3 = 0$

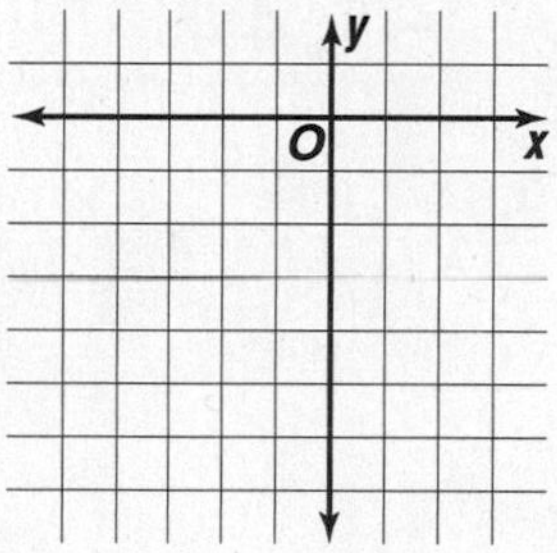

5. $x^2 - 7x + 10 = 0$

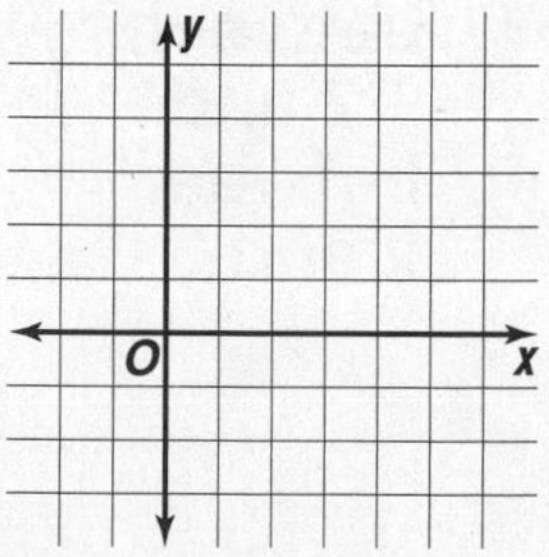

6. $2x^2 - 3x - 6 = 0$

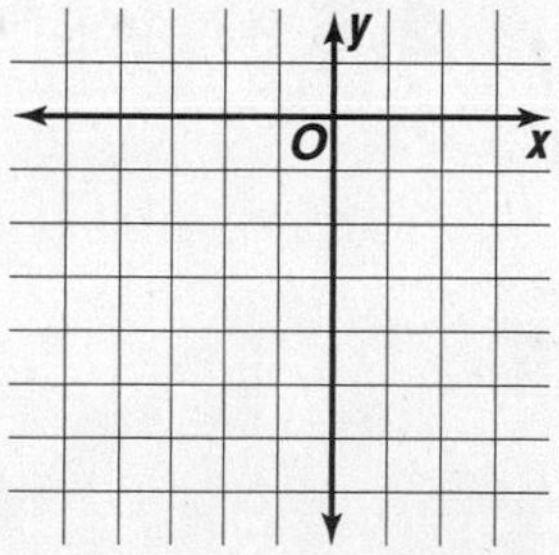

7. $2x^2 - 6x + 3 = 0$

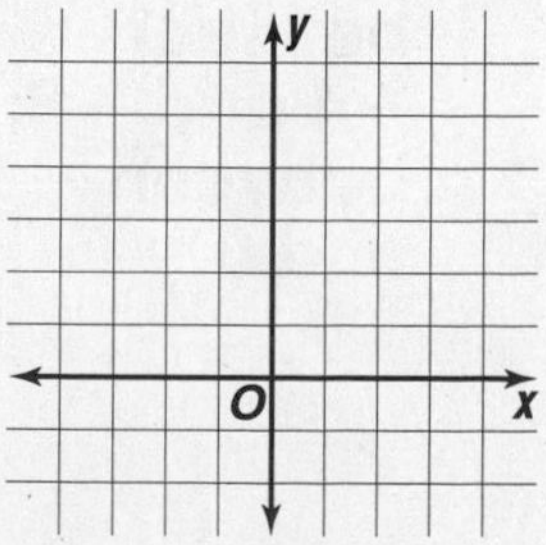

8. $2x^2 + 8x + 2 = 0$

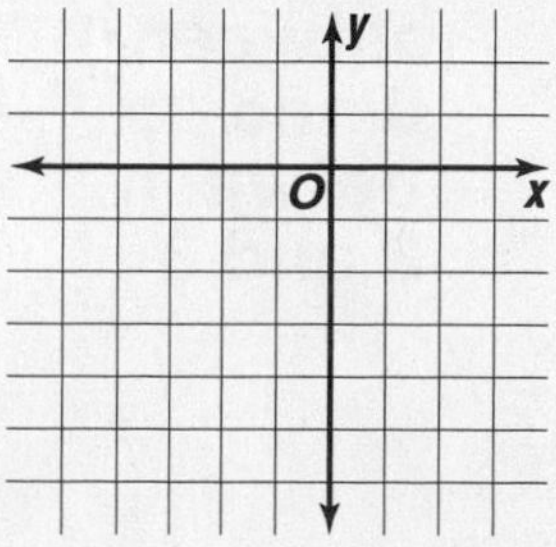

NAME ______________________ DATE __________ PERIOD ______

Practice

Student Edition
Pages 468–473

Solving Quadratic Equations by Graphing

Solve each equation by graphing the related function. If exact roots cannot be found, state the consecutive integers between which the roots are located.

1. $x^2 - 2x + 1 = 0$

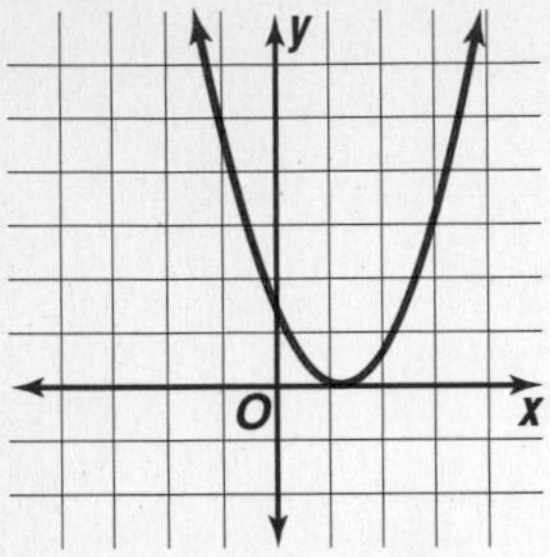

1

2. $x^2 + 6x + 5 = 0$

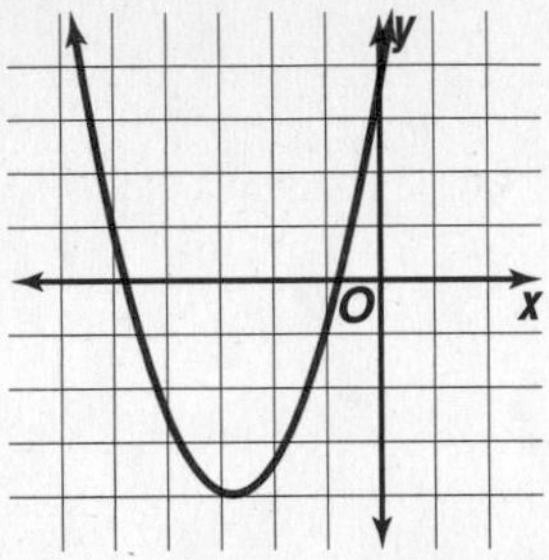

−5, −1

3. $x^2 - 3x - 4 = 0$

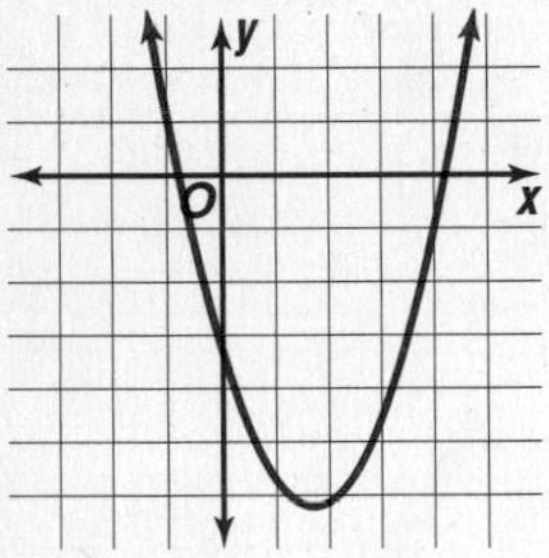

−1, 4

4. $x^2 + 4x - 3 = 0$

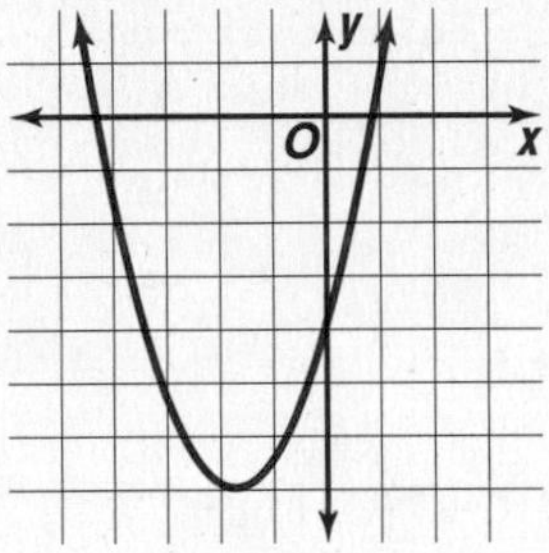

between −5 and −4; between 0 and 1

5. $x^2 - 7x + 10 = 0$

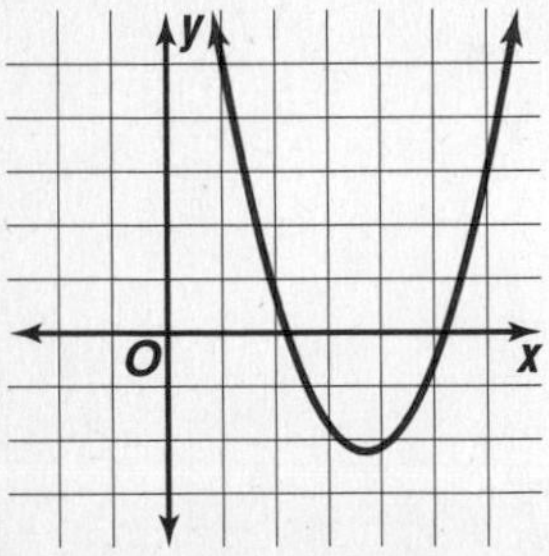

2, 5

6. $2x^2 - 3x - 6 = 0$

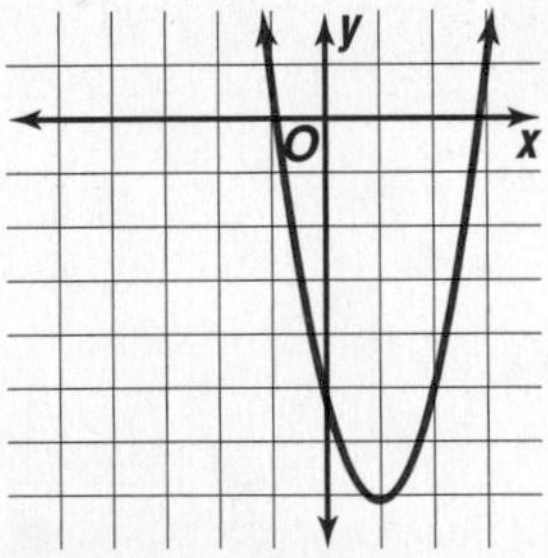

between −2 and −1; between 2 and 3

7. $2x^2 - 6x + 3 = 0$

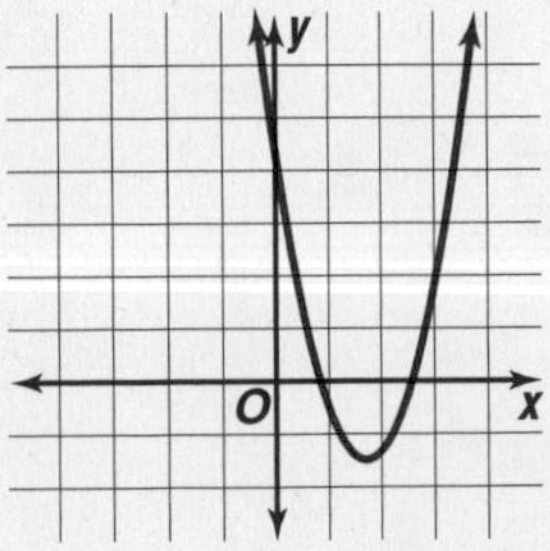

between 0 and 1; between 2 and 3

8. $2x^2 + 8x + 2 = 0$

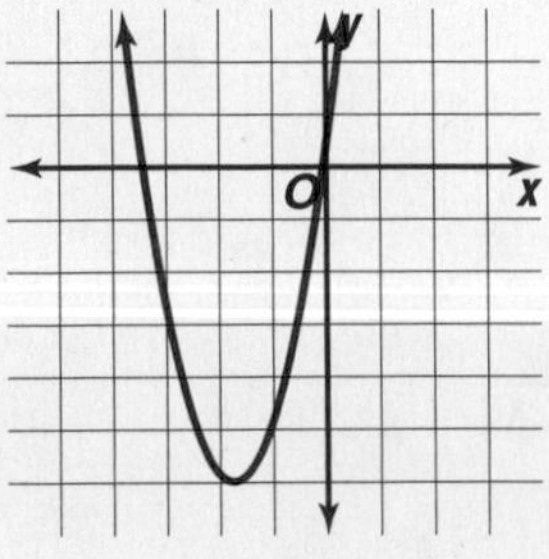

between −4 and −3; between −1 and 0

NAME ______________________________ DATE __________ PERIOD ________

Practice

Solving Quadratic Equations by Factoring

Solve each equation. Check your solution.

1. $s(s + 3) = 0$

2. $4a(a - 6) = 0$

3. $3m(m + 5) = 0$

4. $6t(t - 2) = 0$

5. $(y + 4)(y - 5) = 0$

6. $(p - 2)(p + 3) = 0$

7. $(x + 5)(x - 6) = 0$

8. $(3r + 2)(r - 1) = 0$

9. $(2n - 2)(n + 1) = 0$

10. $(x - 3)(3x + 6) = 0$

11. $(y + 4)(2y - 8) = 0$

12. $(4c + 3)(c - 7) = 0$

13. $x^2 + 3x - 10 = 0$

14. $x^2 - 6x + 8 = 0$

15. $x^2 + 11x + 30 = 0$

16. $x^2 + 4x = 21$

17. $x^2 - 5x = 36$

18. $x^2 - 5x = 0$

19. $2a^2 = 6a$

20. $2x^2 - 10x + 8 = 0$

21. $3x^2 - 7x - 6 = 0$

22. $5x^2 - x = 4$

23. $3x^2 + 13x = -4$

24. $4x^2 + 7x = 2$

NAME ______________________ DATE __________ PERIOD ______

Practice

Student Edition
Pages 474–477

Solving Quadratic Equations by Factoring

Solve each equation. Check your solution.

1. $s(s + 3) = 0$
   0, −3

2. $4a(a - 6) = 0$
   0, 6

3. $3m(m + 5) = 0$
   0, −5

4. $6t(t - 2) = 0$
   0, 2

5. $(y + 4)(y - 5) = 0$
   −4, 5

6. $(p - 2)(p + 3) = 0$
   2, −3

7. $(x + 5)(x - 6) = 0$
   −5, 6

8. $(3r + 2)(r - 1) = 0$
   $-\frac{2}{3}, 1$

9. $(2n - 2)(n + 1) = 0$
   1, −1

10. $(x - 3)(3x + 6) = 0$
    3, −2

11. $(y + 4)(2y - 8) = 0$
    −4, 4

12. $(4c + 3)(c - 7) = 0$
    $-\frac{3}{4}, 7$

13. $x^2 + 3x - 10 = 0$
    −5, 2

14. $x^2 - 6x + 8 = 0$
    2, 4

15. $x^2 + 11x + 30 = 0$
    −6, −5

16. $x^2 + 4x = 21$
    −7, 3

17. $x^2 - 5x = 36$
    −4, 9

18. $x^2 - 5x = 0$
    0, 5

19. $2a^2 = 6a$
    0, 3

20. $2x^2 - 10x + 8 = 0$
    1, 4

21. $3x^2 - 7x - 6 = 0$
    $-\frac{2}{3}, 3$

22. $5x^2 - x = 4$
    $-\frac{4}{5}, 1$

23. $3x^2 + 13x = -4$
    $-\frac{1}{3}, -4$

24. $4x^2 + 7x = 2$
    $\frac{1}{4}, -2$

NAME ______________________ DATE __________ PERIOD ______

Practice

Student Edition
Pages 478–482

Solving Quadratic Equations by Completing the Square

Find the value of c that makes each trinomial a perfect square.

1. $x^2 + 12x + c$

2. $b^2 - 4b + c$

3. $g^2 - 16g + c$

4. $n^2 + 6n + c$

5. $q^2 + 20q + c$

6. $s^2 - 8s + c$

7. $a^2 + 10a + c$

8. $m^2 - 26m + c$

9. $r^2 + 5r + c$

10. $y^2 + y + c$

11. $p^2 - 7p + c$

12. $z^2 + 11z + c$

Solve each equation by completing the square.

13. $x^2 + 10x - 11 = 0$

14. $p^2 - 8p + 12 = 0$

15. $r^2 - 2r - 15 = 0$

16. $c^2 - 4c - 12 = 0$

17. $t^2 - 4t = 0$

18. $x^2 + 6x - 7 = 0$

19. $n^2 + 6n = 16$

20. $w^2 - 14w + 24 = 0$

21. $m^2 - 2m - 5 = 0$

22. $f^2 + 10f + 15 = 0$

23. $s^2 - 6s - 4 = 0$

24. $h^2 - 4h = 2$

25. $y^2 - 12y + 7 = 0$

26. $k^2 - 8k + 13 = 0$

27. $d^2 + 8d + 9 = 0$

NAME ______________________ DATE ____________ PERIOD ________

Practice

Student Edition
Pages 478–482

Solving Quadratic Equations by Completing the Square

Find the value of c that makes each trinomial a perfect square.

1. $x^2 + 12x + c$ **36**
2. $b^2 - 4b + c$ **4**
3. $g^2 - 16g + c$ **64**
4. $n^2 + 6n + c$ **9**
5. $q^2 + 20q + c$ **100**
6. $s^2 - 8s + c$ **16**
7. $a^2 + 10a + c$ **25**
8. $m^2 - 26m + c$ **169**
9. $r^2 + 5r + c$ $\mathbf{\frac{25}{4}}$
10. $y^2 + y + c$ $\mathbf{\frac{1}{4}}$
11. $p^2 - 7p + c$ $\mathbf{\frac{49}{4}}$
12. $z^2 + 11z + c$ $\mathbf{\frac{121}{4}}$

Solve each equation by completing the square.

13. $x^2 + 10x - 11 = 0$ **−11, 1**
14. $p^2 - 8p + 12 = 0$ **2, 6**
15. $r^2 - 2r - 15 = 0$ **−3, 5**
16. $c^2 - 4c - 12 = 0$ **−2, 6**
17. $t^2 - 4t = 0$ **0, 4**
18. $x^2 + 6x - 7 = 0$ **−7, 1**
19. $n^2 + 6n = 16$ **−8, 2**
20. $w^2 - 14w + 24 = 0$ **2, 12**
21. $m^2 - 2m - 5 = 0$ $\mathbf{1 \pm \sqrt{6}}$
22. $f^2 + 10f + 15 = 0$ $\mathbf{-5 \pm \sqrt{10}}$
23. $s^2 - 6s - 4 = 0$ $\mathbf{3 \pm \sqrt{13}}$
24. $h^2 - 4h = 2$ $\mathbf{2 \pm \sqrt{6}}$
25. $y^2 - 12y + 7 = 0$ $\mathbf{6 \pm \sqrt{29}}$
26. $k^2 - 8k + 13 = 0$ $\mathbf{4 \pm \sqrt{3}}$
27. $d^2 + 8d + 9 = 0$ $\mathbf{-4 \pm \sqrt{7}}$

11–6

NAME ______________________ DATE __________ PERIOD ______

Practice

Student Edition
Pages 483–488

The Quadratic Formula

Use the Quadratic Formula to solve each equation.

1. $y^2 - 49 = 0$

2. $x^2 + 7x + 6 = 0$

3. $k^2 - 7k + 12 = 0$

4. $n^2 + 5n - 14 = 0$

5. $b^2 - 5b - 6 = 0$

6. $z^2 + 8z + 12 = 0$

7. $-q^2 + 5q - 4 = 0$

8. $a^2 - 9a + 22 = 0$

9. $c^2 - 4c = -3$

10. $x^2 + 9x = -14$

11. $h^2 - 2h = 8$

12. $m^2 + m = -4$

13. $-z^2 - 8z - 15 = 0$

14. $r^2 + 6r = -5$

15. $-h^2 + 6h = -7$

16. $g^2 + 12x + 20 = 0$

17. $w^2 + 10w = -9$

18. $2y^2 + 6y + 4 = 0$

19. $-2m^2 + 4m + 6 = 0$

20. $2x^2 + 8x = 10$

21. $2b^2 - 3b = -1$

22. $2p^2 + 6p + 8 = 0$

23. $3k^2 + 6k = 9$

24. $-3x^2 - 4x + 4 = 0$

NAME ______________________ DATE __________ PERIOD ______

Practice

Student Edition
Pages 483–488

The Quadratic Formula

Use the Quadratic Formula to solve each equation.

1. $y^2 - 49 = 0$
±7

2. $x^2 + 7x + 6 = 0$
−1, −6

3. $k^2 - 7k + 12 = 0$
3, 4

4. $n^2 + 5n - 14 = 0$
2, −7

5. $b^2 - 5b - 6 = 0$
−1, 6

6. $z^2 + 8z + 12 = 0$
−6, −2

7. $-q^2 + 5q - 4 = 0$
1, 4

8. $a^2 - 9a + 22 = 0$
no real solutions

9. $c^2 - 4c = -3$
1, 3

10. $x^2 + 9x = -14$
−7, −2

11. $h^2 - 2h = 8$
−2, 4

12. $m^2 + m = -4$
no real solutions

13. $-z^2 - 8z - 15 = 0$
−5, −3

14. $r^2 + 6r = -5$
−5, −1

15. $-h^2 + 6h = -7$
−1, 7

16. $g^2 + 12x + 20 = 0$
−10, −2

17. $w^2 + 10w = -9$
−9, −1

18. $2y^2 + 6y + 4 = 0$
−2, −1

19. $-2m^2 + 4m + 6 = 0$
−1, 3

20. $2x^2 + 8x = 10$
−5, 1

21. $2b^2 - 3b = -1$
$\frac{1}{2}$, **1**

22. $2p^2 + 6p + 8 = 0$
no real solutions

23. $3k^2 + 6k = 9$
−3, 1

24. $-3x^2 - 4x + 4 = 0$
−2, $\frac{2}{3}$

NAME ______________________	DATE __________	PERIOD ______

11–7 Practice

Student Edition
Pages 489–493

Exponential Functions

Graph each exponential function. Then state the y-intercept.

1. $y = 2^x + 3$

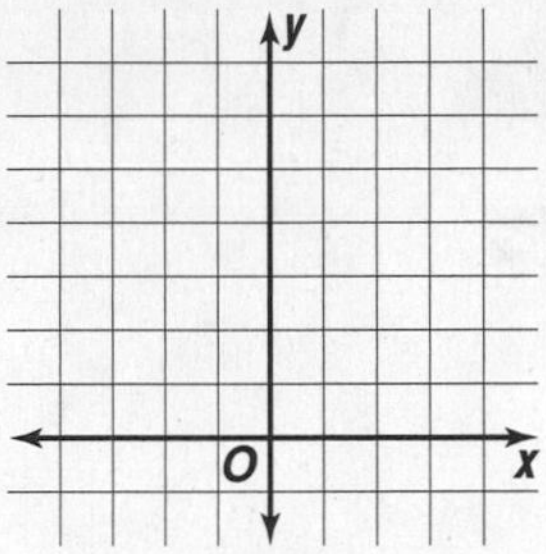

2. $y = 2^x - 2$

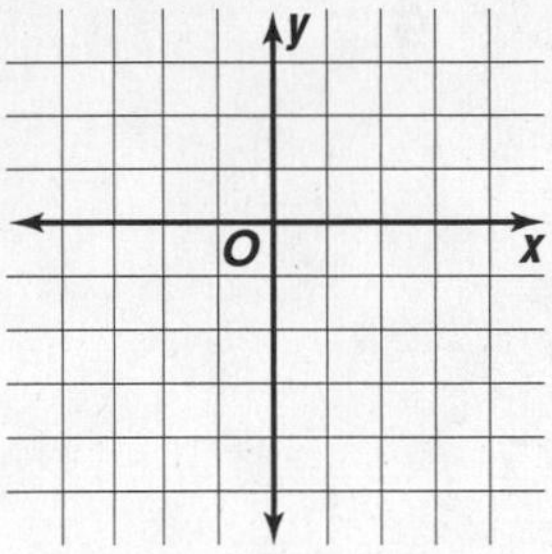

3. $y = 3^x - 4$

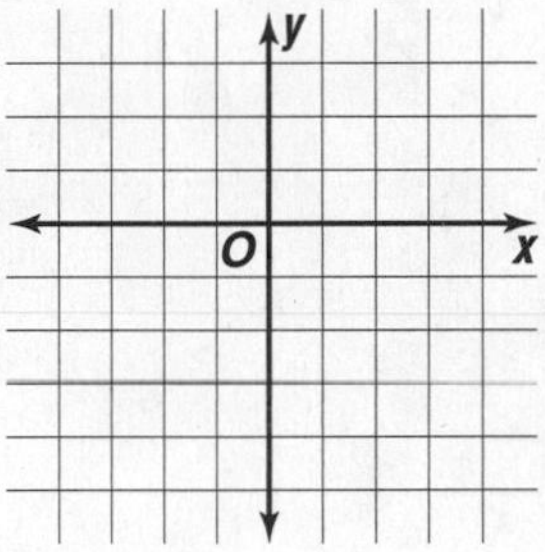

4. $y = 2^x + 4$

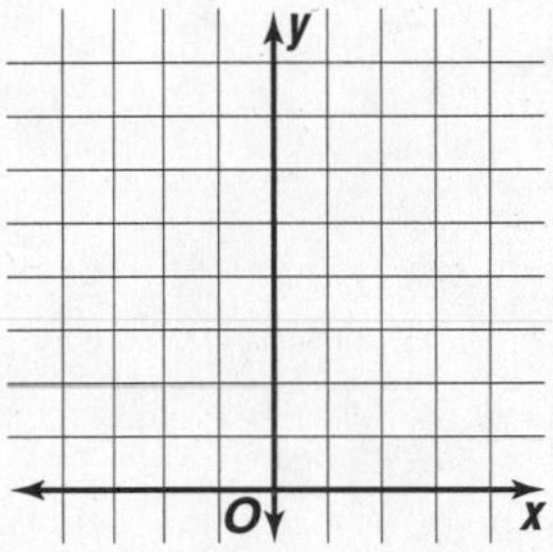

5. $y = 3^x + 1$

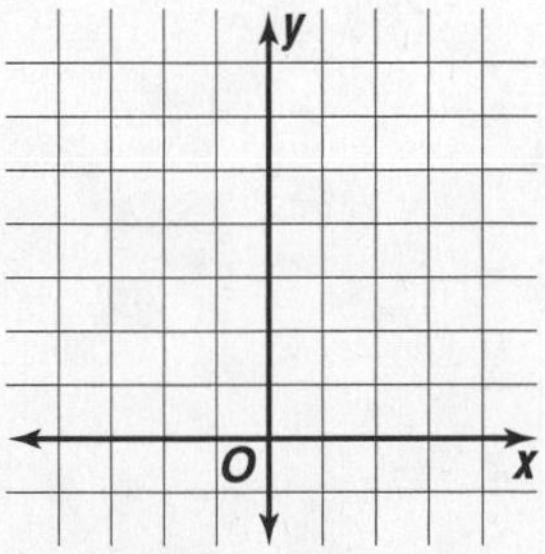

6. $y = 4^x + 2$

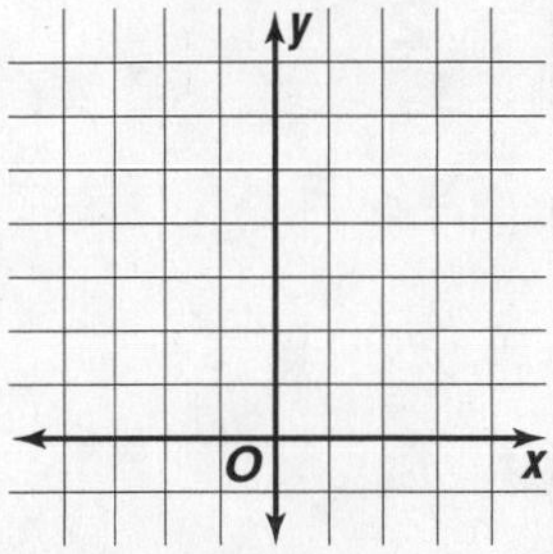

7. $y = 3^x - 2$

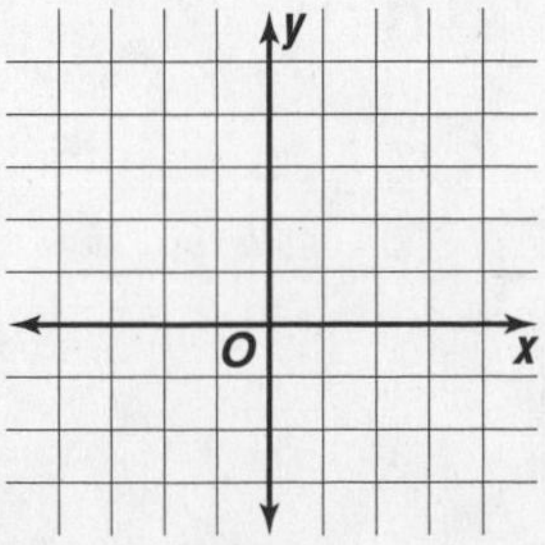

8. $y = 2^x - 1$

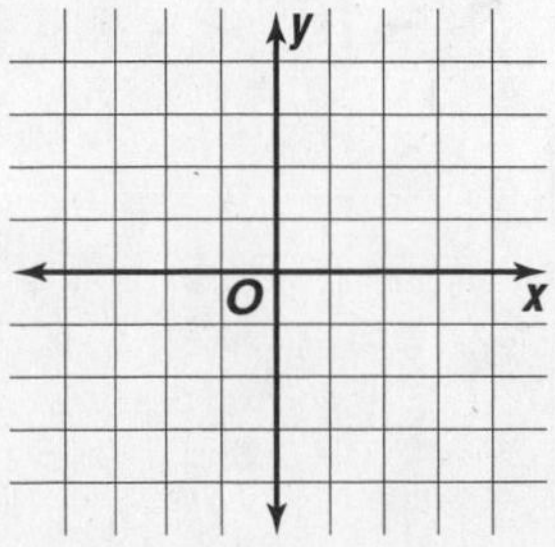

11–7

NAME ______________________ DATE __________ PERIOD ______

Practice

Student Edition
Pages 489–493

Exponential Functions

Graph each exponential function. Then state the y-intercept.

1. $y = 2^x + 3$

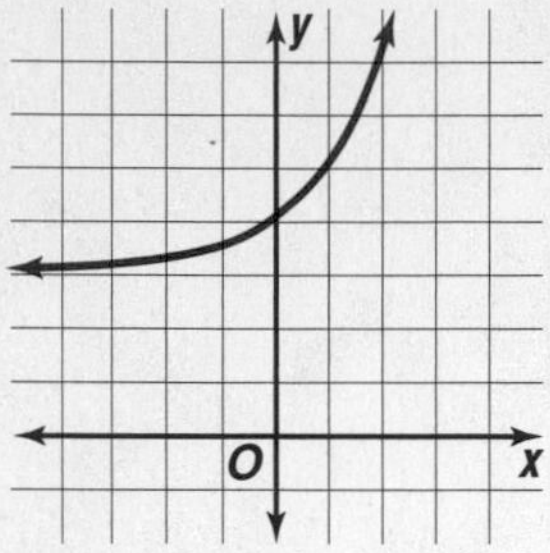

4

2. $y = 2^x - 2$

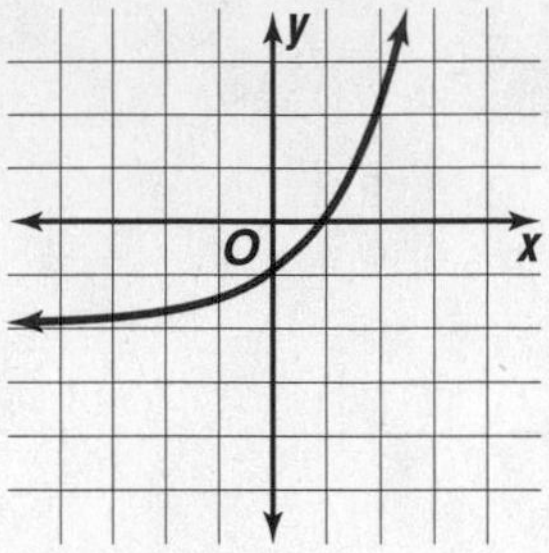

−1

3. $y = 3^x - 4$

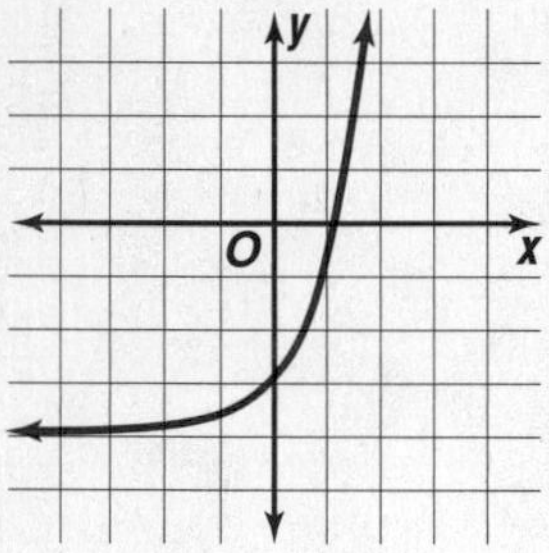

−3

4. $y = 2^x + 4$

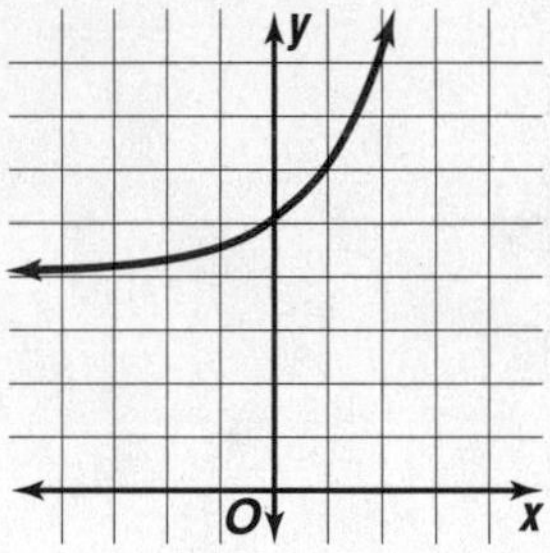

5

5. $y = 3^x + 1$

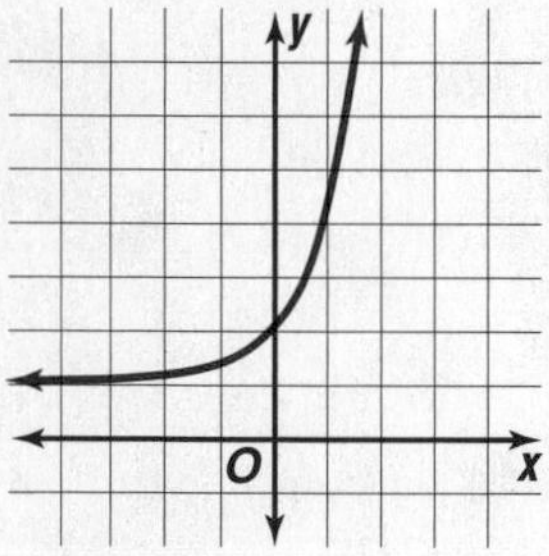

2

6. $y = 4^x + 2$

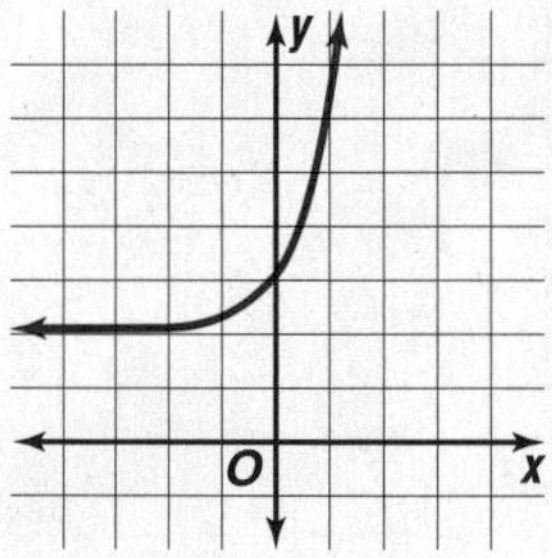

3

7. $y = 3^x - 2$

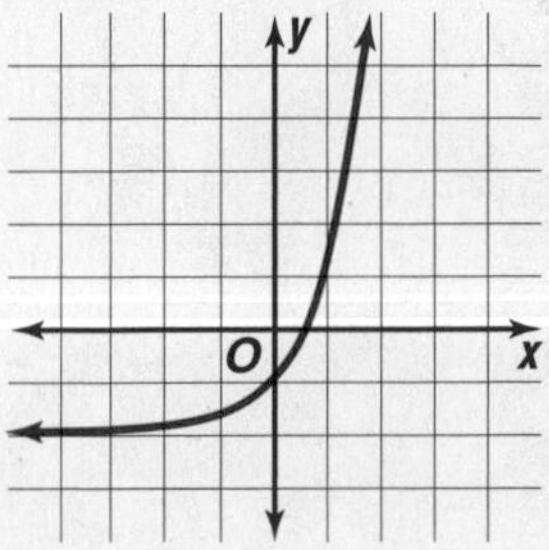

−1

8. $y = 2^x - 1$

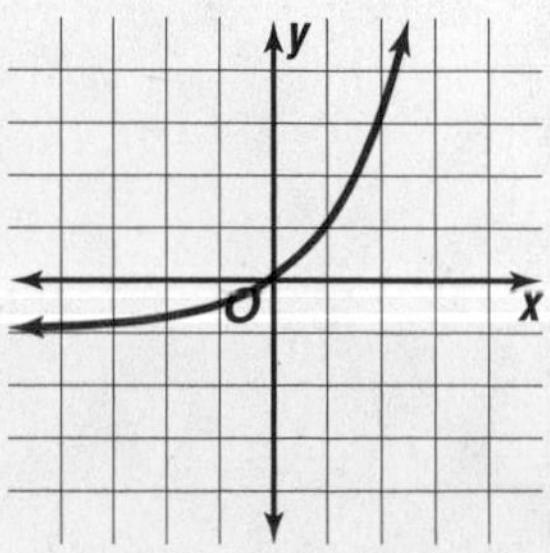

0

12–1 NAME ______________________ DATE __________ PERIOD ______

Practice

Student Edition
Pages 504–508

Inequalities and Their Graphs

Write an inequality to describe each number.

1. a number less than or equal to 11
2. a number greater than 3
3. a number that is at least 6
4. a number that is no less than -7
5. a maximum number of 9
6. a number that is less than -2

Graph each inequality on a number line.

7. $x < 4$

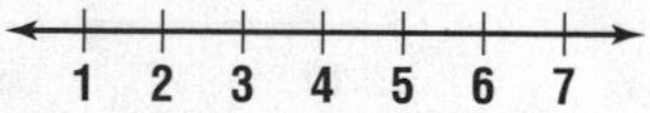

8. $x \geq 8$

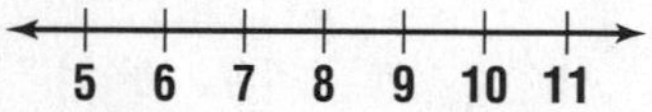

9. $y > 9$

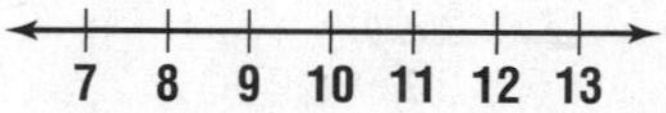

10. $-5 \leq x$

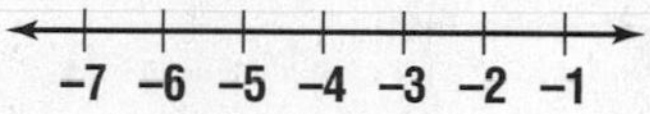

11. $p > -2$

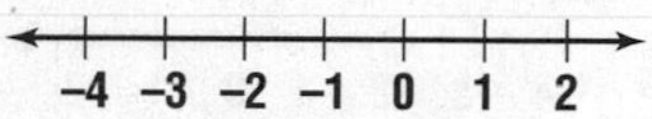

12. $7 \geq g$

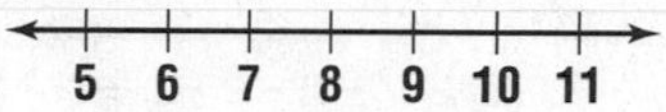

13. $y < 1.5$

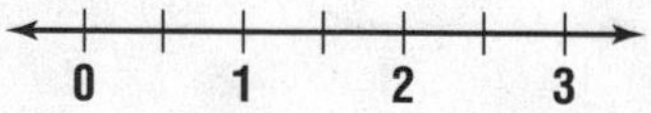

14. $x \geq 0.5$

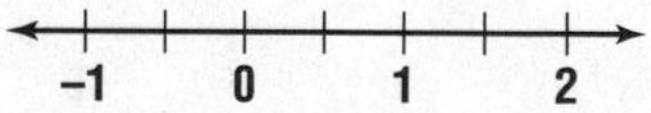

15. $-2.5 > h$

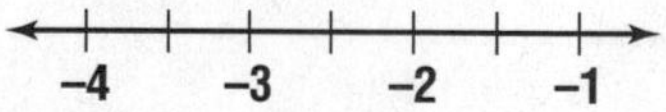

16. $x \leq \frac{1}{3}$

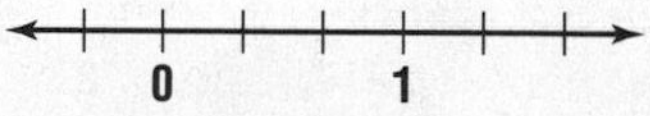

17. $m < -\frac{1}{2}$

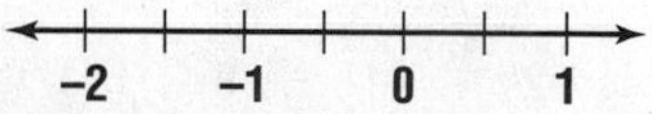

18. $2\frac{1}{4} > x$

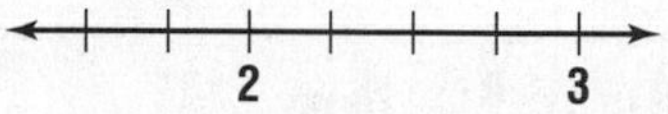

Write an inequality for each graph.

19. 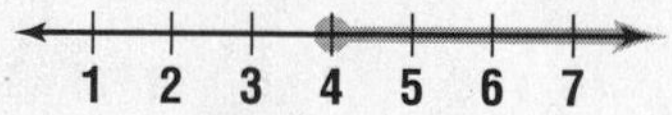

20. 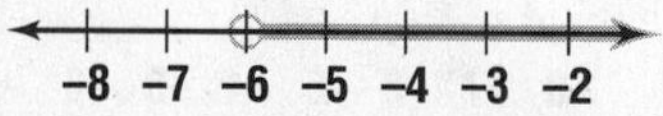

21. 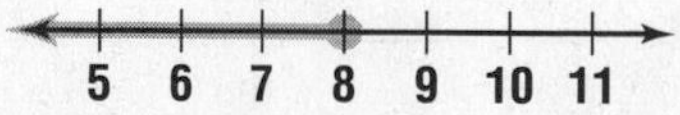

22. 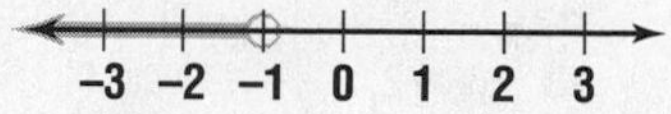

23. 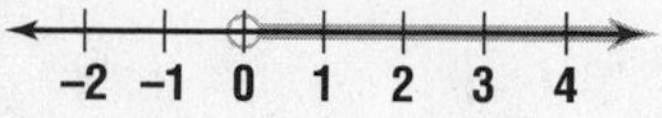

24. 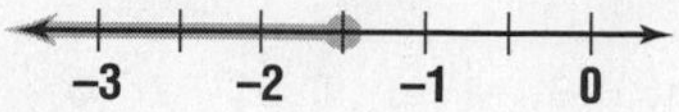

25. 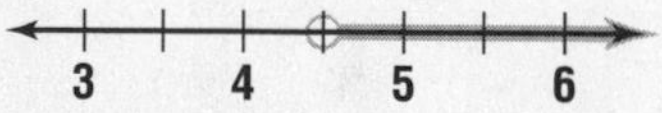

26. 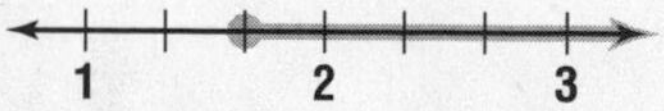

27. 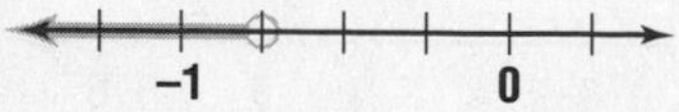

12–1

NAME ______________________ DATE __________ PERIOD ______

Practice

Student Edition
Pages 504–508

Inequalities and Their Graphs

Write an inequality to describe each number.

1. a number less than or equal to 11
$x \leq 11$

2. a number greater than 3
$x > 3$

3. a number that is at least 6
$x \geq 6$

4. a number that is no less than -7
$x \geq -7$

5. a maximum number of 9
$x \leq 9$

6. a number that is less than -2
$x < -2$

Graph each inequality on a number line.

7. $x < 4$
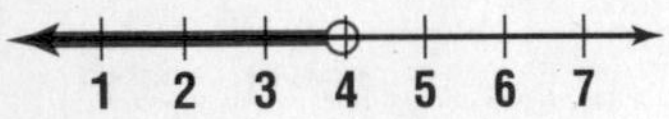

8. $x \geq 8$

9. $y > 9$
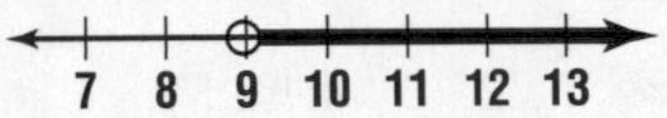

10. $-5 \leq x$
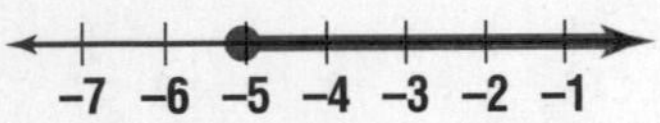

11. $p > -2$
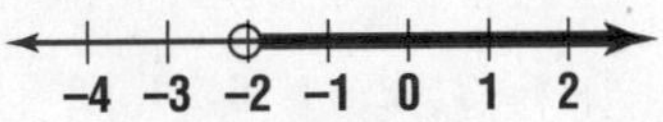

12. $7 \geq g$
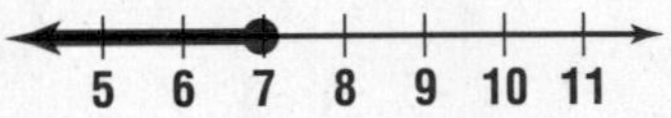

13. $y < 1.5$
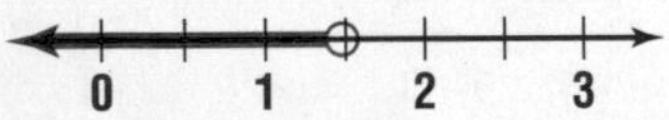

14. $x \geq 0.5$

15. $-2.5 > h$
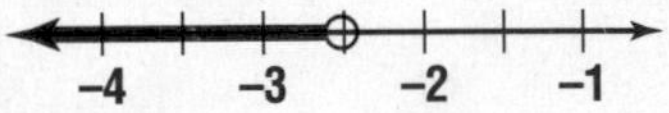

16. $x \leq \frac{1}{3}$
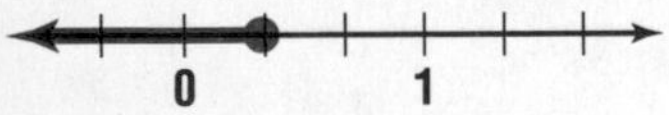

17. $m < -\frac{1}{2}$
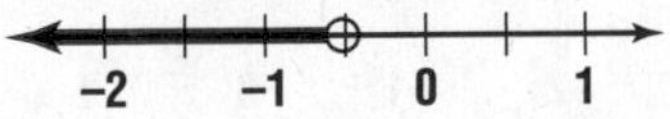

18. $2\frac{1}{4} > x$

Write an inequality for each graph.

19.

$x \geq 4$

20.
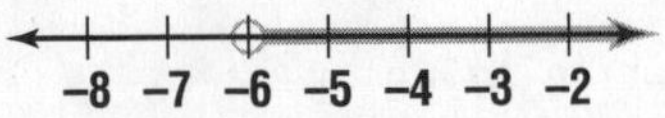

$x > -6$

21.
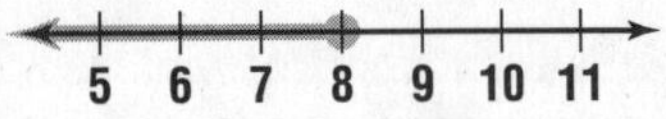

$x \leq 8$

22.
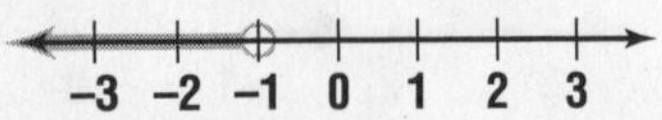

$x < -1$

23.
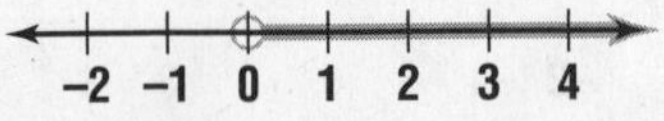

$x > 0$

24.
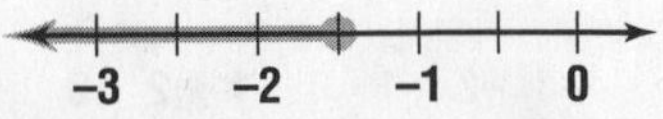

$x \leq -1.5$

25.
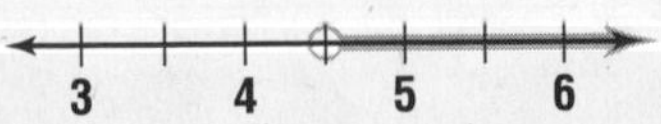

$x > 4.5$

26.
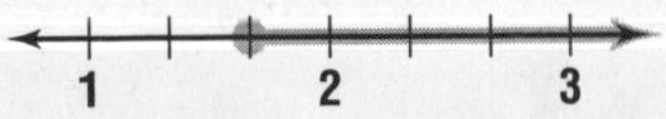

$x \geq 1\frac{2}{3}$

27.
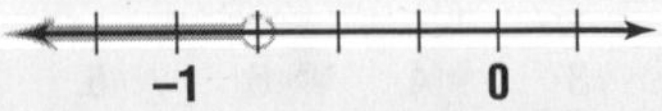

$x < -\frac{3}{4}$

NAME ______________________ DATE __________ PERIOD ______

12-2 Practice

Student Edition
Pages 509–513

Solving Addition and Subtraction Inequalities

Solve each inequality. Check your solution.

1. $x + 7 > 16$

2. $b - 4 < 3$

3. $y - 6 \geq -12$

4. $f + 9 < 24$

5. $a - 2 \leq 9$

6. $3 + w > -1$

7. $n - 1 \leq 7$

8. $10 + c \geq 13$

9. $q - 9 < 4$

10. $-5 \geq d - 7$

11. $17 \geq v + 11$

12. $14 > h - 9$

13. $x + 1.7 \leq 5.8$

14. $2.9 + s < 5.7$

15. $0.3 \leq g - 4.4$

16. $y + \frac{1}{2} \geq 2\frac{3}{4}$

17. $1\frac{1}{4} + m \leq 4\frac{5}{8}$

18. $2\frac{1}{6} > r - \frac{2}{3}$

Solve each inequality. Graph the solution.

19. $5x - 2 > 6x$

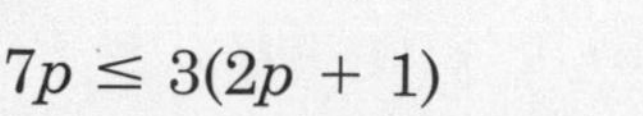

20. $n + 7 \leq 2n - 1$

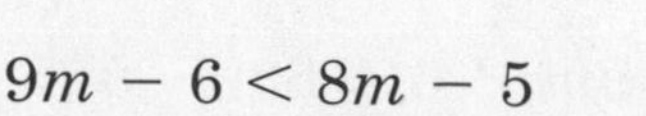

21. $2y + 6 < 3y + 9$

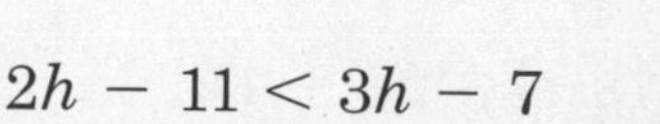

22. $7p \leq 3(2p + 1)$

23. $9m - 6 < 8m - 5$

24. $2h - 11 < 3h - 7$

NAME ____________________ DATE __________ PERIOD ______

Practice

Student Edition
Pages 509–513

Solving Addition and Subtraction Inequalities

Solve each inequality. Check your solution.

1. $x + 7 > 16$
   $\{x|x > 9\}$

2. $b - 4 < 3$
   $\{b|b < 7\}$

3. $y - 6 \geq -12$
   $\{y|y \geq -6\}$

4. $f + 9 < 24$
   $\{f|f < 15\}$

5. $a - 2 \leq 9$
   $\{a|a \leq 11\}$

6. $3 + w > -1$
   $\{w|w > -4\}$

7. $n - 1 \leq 7$
   $\{n|n \leq 8\}$

8. $10 + c \geq 13$
   $\{c|c \geq 3\}$

9. $q - 9 < 4$
   $\{q|q < 13\}$

10. $-5 \geq d - 7$
    $\{d|d \leq 2\}$

11. $17 \geq v + 11$
    $\{v|v \leq 6\}$

12. $14 > h - 9$
    $\{h|h < 23\}$

13. $x + 1.7 \leq 5.8$
    $\{x|x \leq 4.1\}$

14. $2.9 + s < 5.7$
    $\{s|s < 2.8\}$

15. $0.3 \leq g - 4.4$
    $\{g|g \geq 4.7\}$

16. $y + \frac{1}{2} \geq 2\frac{3}{4}$
    $\left\{y|y \geq 2\frac{1}{4}\right\}$

17. $1\frac{1}{4} + m \leq 4\frac{5}{8}$
    $\left\{m|m \leq 3\frac{3}{8}\right\}$

18. $2\frac{1}{6} > r - \frac{2}{3}$
    $\left\{r|r < 2\frac{5}{6}\right\}$

Solve each inequality. Graph the solution.

19. $5x - 2 > 6x$
    $\{x|x < -2\}$

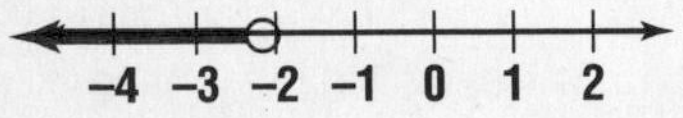

20. $n + 7 \leq 2n - 1$
    $\{n|n \geq 8\}$

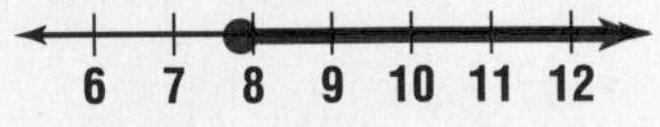

21. $2y + 6 < 3y + 9$
    $\{y|y > -3\}$

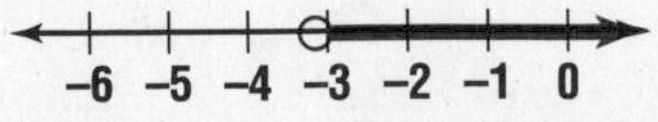

22. $7p \leq 3(2p + 1)$
    $\{p|p \leq 3\}$

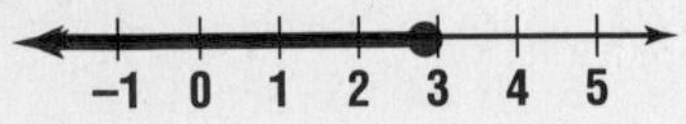

23. $9m - 6 < 8m - 5$
    $\{m|m < 1\}$

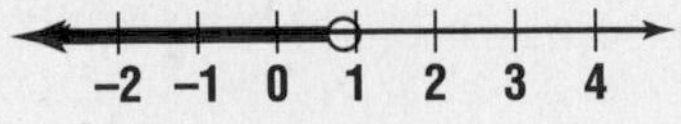

24. $2h - 11 < 3h - 7$
    $\{h|h > -4\}$

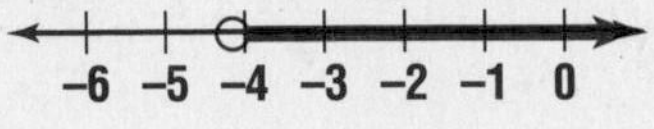

12–3 NAME ______________________ DATE __________ PERIOD ________

Practice

Student Edition
Pages 514–518

Solving Multiplication and Division Inequalities

Solve each inequality. Check your solution.

1. $4y < 16$

2. $-3q \leq 18$

3. $9g \leq -27$

4. $\frac{p}{5} > 5$

5. $\frac{a}{2} < -4$

6. $-\frac{m}{7} \geq 7$

7. $-6x \leq 30$

8. $-4z > -28$

9. $16 \geq 2e$

10. $-\frac{n}{3} \geq -3$

11. $4 \leq \frac{f}{6}$

12. $-\frac{w}{5} > 8$

13. $-81 < 9v$

14. $6r \leq -42$

15. $-12a \leq -60$

16. $-4 > \frac{u}{9}$

17. $-\frac{d}{6} < -8.1$

18. $\frac{l}{8} > -8$

19. $4k \leq 6$

20. $-0.9b \geq -2.7$

21. $-1.6 < 4t$

22. $\frac{2}{3}y > 6$

23. $-\frac{3}{5}c < 15$

24. $-\frac{5}{8}j \geq -10$

NAME ______________________ DATE __________ PERIOD ______

Practice

Student Edition
Pages 514–518

Solving Multiplication and Division Inequalities

Solve each inequality. Check your solution.

1. $4y < 16$

   $\{y|y < 4\}$

2. $-3q \leq 18$

   $\{q|q \geq -6\}$

3. $9g \leq -27$

   $\{g|g \leq -3\}$

4. $\frac{p}{5} > 5$

   $\{p|p > 25\}$

5. $\frac{a}{2} < -4$

   $\{a|a < -8\}$

6. $-\frac{m}{7} \geq 7$

   $\{m|m \leq -49\}$

7. $-6x \leq 30$

   $\{x|x \geq -5\}$

8. $-4z > -28$

   $\{z|z < 7\}$

9. $16 \geq 2e$

   $\{e|e \leq 8\}$

10. $-\frac{n}{3} \geq -3$

    $\{n|n \leq 9\}$

11. $4 \leq \frac{f}{6}$

    $\{f|f \geq 24\}$

12. $-\frac{w}{5} > 8$

    $\{w|w < -40\}$

13. $-81 < 9v$

    $\{v|v > -9\}$

14. $6r \leq -42$

    $\{r|r \leq -7\}$

15. $-12a \leq -60$

    $\{a|a \leq 5\}$

16. $-4 > \frac{u}{9}$

    $\{u|u < -36\}$

17. $-\frac{d}{6} < -8.1$

    $\{d|d > 48.6\}$

18. $\frac{l}{8} > -8$

    $\{l|l > -64\}$

19. $4k \leq 6$

    $\{k|k \leq 1.5\}$

20. $-0.9b \geq -2.7$

    $\{b|b \leq 3\}$

21. $-1.6 < 4t$

    $\{t|t > -0.4\}$

22. $\frac{2}{3}y > 6$

    $\{y|y > 9\}$

23. $-\frac{3}{5}c < 15$

    $\{c|c > -25\}$

24. $-\frac{5}{8}j \geq -10$

    $\{j|j \leq 16\}$

NAME ______________________ DATE __________ PERIOD ______

Practice

Student Edition
Pages 519–523

Solving Multi-Step Inequalities

Solve each inequality. Check your solution.

1. $3x + 5 < 14$

2. $3t - 6 > 15$

3. $-5y + 2 \geq 32$

4. $-2n - 3 \geq -11$

5. $6 \leq 4a + 10$

6. $-28 < 7 + 7w$

7. $5 - 1.3z \leq 31$

8. $1.7b - 1.1 < 2.3$

9. $6.4 \geq 8 + 2g$

10. $-6 < \frac{k}{2} - 1$

11. $-\frac{c}{6} + 9 \leq 3$

12. $\frac{5m - 5}{3} \geq -15$

13. $\frac{-2n + 6}{4} > 8$

14. $\frac{6 - 3n}{6} \leq -5$

15. $9 - 5j < j - 3$

16. $7p - 4 \geq 3p + 12$

17. $2f - 5 \leq 4f + 13$

18. $5(7 - 2a) \geq -15$

19. $2(q + 2) > 3(q - 6)$

20. $3(h + 5) < -6(h - 4)$

21. $-2(b - 3) \leq 4(b - 9)$

12–4

NAME ______________________ DATE __________ PERIOD ______

Practice

Student Edition
Pages 519–523

Solving Multi-Step Inequalities

Solve each inequality. Check your solution.

1. $3x + 5 < 14$

$\{x|x < 3\}$

2. $3t - 6 > 15$

$\{t|t > 7\}$

3. $-5y + 2 \geq 32$

$\{y|y \leq -6\}$

4. $-2n - 3 \geq -11$

$\{n|n \leq 4\}$

5. $6 \leq 4a + 10$

$\{a|a \geq -1\}$

6. $-28 < 7 + 7w$

$\{w|w > -5\}$

7. $5 - 1.3z \leq 31$

$\{z|z \geq -20\}$

8. $1.7b - 1.1 < 2.3$

$\{b|b < 2\}$

9. $6.4 \geq 8 + 2g$

$\{g|g \leq -0.8\}$

10. $-6 < \frac{k}{2} - 1$

$\{k|k > -10\}$

11. $-\frac{c}{6} + 9 \leq 3$

$\{c|c \geq 36\}$

12. $\frac{5m - 5}{3} \geq -15$

$\{m|m \geq -8\}$

13. $\frac{-2n + 6}{4} > 8$

$\{n|n < -13\}$

14. $\frac{6 - 3n}{6} \leq -5$

$\{n|n \geq 12\}$

15. $9 - 5j < j - 3$

$\{j|j > 2\}$

16. $7p - 4 \geq 3p + 12$

$\{p|p \geq 4\}$

17. $2f - 5 \leq 4f + 13$

$\{f|f \geq -9\}$

18. $5(7 - 2a) \geq -15$

$\{a|a \leq 5\}$

19. $2(q + 2) > 3(q - 6)$

$\{q|q < 22\}$

20. $3(h + 5) < -6(h - 4)$

$\{h|h < 1\}$

21. $-2(b - 3) \leq 4(b - 9)$

$\{b|b \geq 7\}$

NAME ______________________ DATE __________ PERIOD ______

12–5 Practice

Student Edition
Pages 524–529

Solving Compound Inequalities

Write each compound inequality without using and.

1. $a > 2$ and $a < 7$

2. $b \leq 9$ and $b \geq 6$

3. $w \leq 4$ and $w > -3$

4. $k \geq -4$ and $k < 1$

5. $z < 0$ and $z > -6$

6. $p \geq -8$ and $p < 5$

Graph the solution of each compound inequality.

7. $f > -1$ and $f < 5$

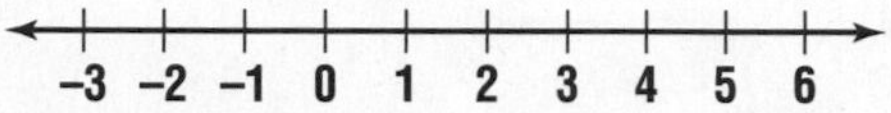

8. $x < 7$ and $x \geq 4$

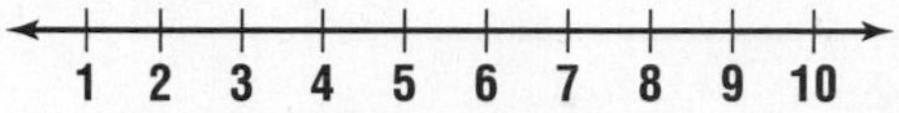

9. $y \leq -3$ or $y \geq 1$

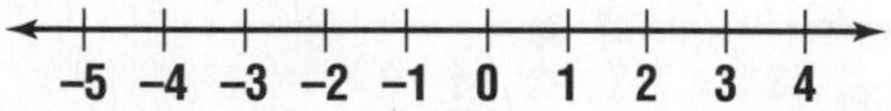

10. $h < -3$ or $h \geq -2$

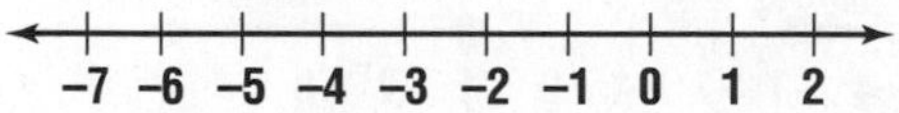

Solve each compound inequality. Graph the solution.

11. $4 > c + 6 \geq 2$

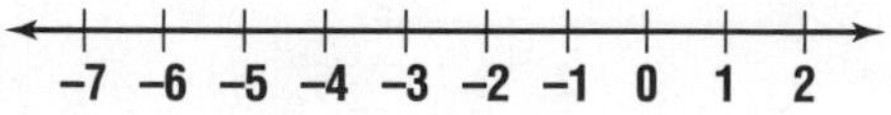

12. $-6 < u - 5 < 0$

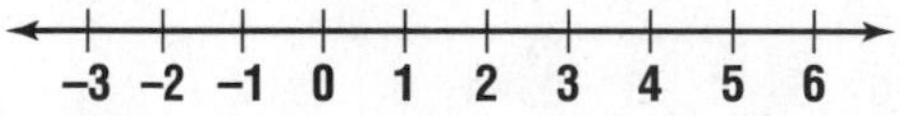

13. $6 < -2m < 10$

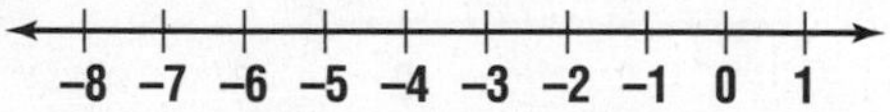

14. $10 > 4n > -2$

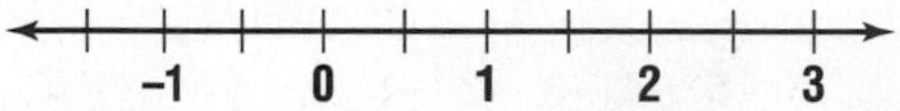

15. $0 \leq \frac{t}{3} \leq 2$

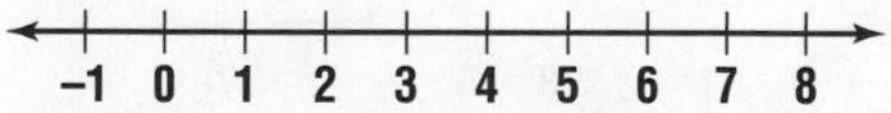

16. $r - 2 < -3$ or $5r > 25$

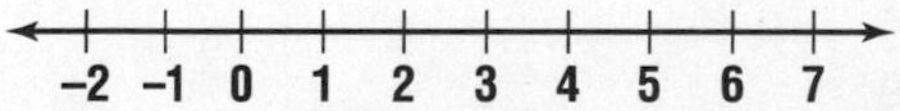

17. $v + 2 \leq -4$ or $v + 7 > 2$

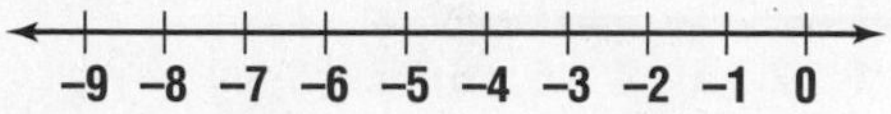

18. $a - 5 < -3$ or $-5a \geq -30$

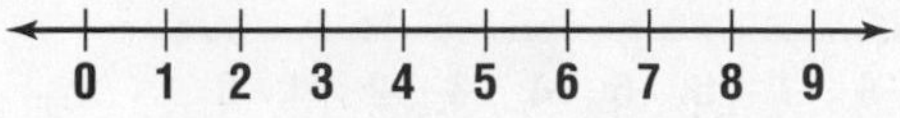

19. $-4y > -6$ or $2.5y > 5$

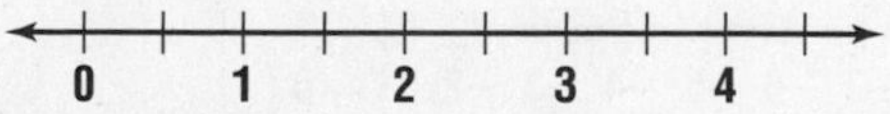

20. $\frac{w}{2} < -1$ or $\frac{w}{3} \leq -2$

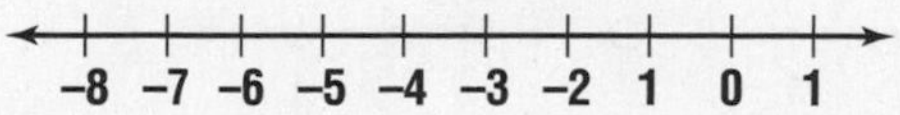

12-5 Practice

NAME ______________________ DATE __________ PERIOD ______

Student Edition
Pages 524–529

Solving Compound Inequalities

Write each compound inequality without using and.

1. $a > 2$ and $a < 7$
   $2 < a < 7$

2. $b \leq 9$ and $b \geq 6$
   $6 \leq b \leq 9$

3. $w \leq 4$ and $w > -3$
   $-3 < w \leq 4$

4. $k \geq -4$ and $k < 1$
   $-4 \leq k < 1$

5. $z < 0$ and $z > -6$
   $-6 < z < 0$

6. $p \geq -8$ and $p < 5$
   $-8 \leq p < 5$

Graph the solution of each compound inequality.

7. $f > -1$ and $f < 5$

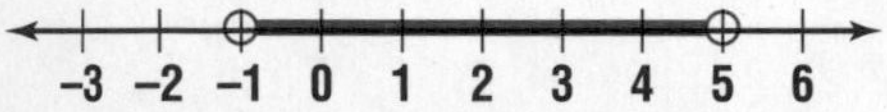

8. $x < 7$ and $x \geq 4$

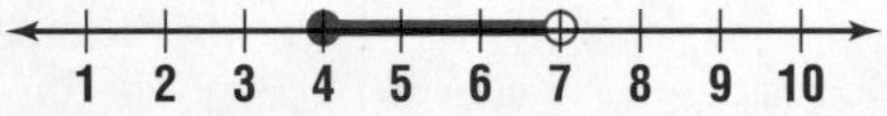

9. $y \leq -3$ or $y \geq 1$

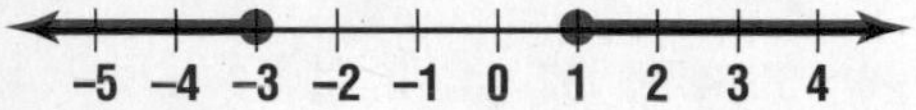

10. $h < -3$ or $h \geq -2$

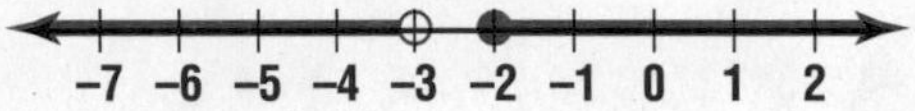

Solve each compound inequality. Graph the solution.

11. $4 > c + 6 \geq 2$
    $\{c \mid -4 \leq c < -2\}$

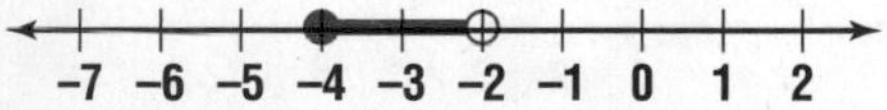

12. $-6 < u - 5 < 0$
    $\{u \mid -1 < u < 5\}$

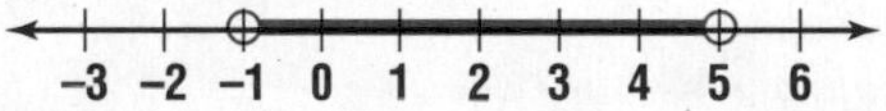

13. $6 < -2m < 10$
    $\{m \mid -5 < m < -3\}$

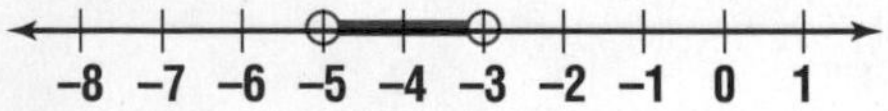

14. $10 > 4n > -2$
    $\{n \mid -0.5 < n < 2.5\}$

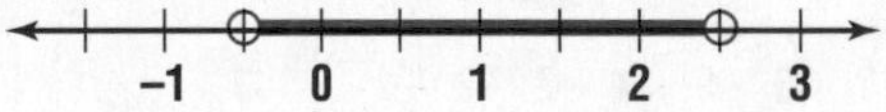

15. $0 \leq \frac{t}{3} \leq 2$
    $\{t \mid 0 \leq t \leq 6\}$

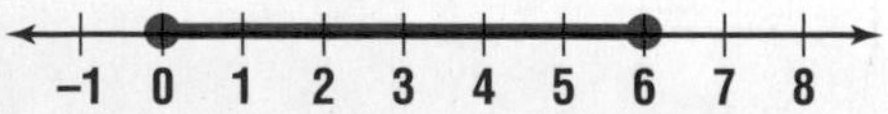

16. $r - 2 < -3$ or $5r > 25$
    $\{r \mid r < -1 \text{ or } r > 5\}$

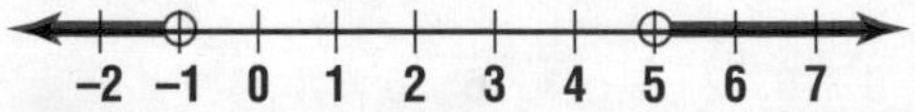

17. $v + 2 \leq -4$ or $v + 7 > 2$
    $\{v \mid v \leq -6 \text{ or } v > -5\}$

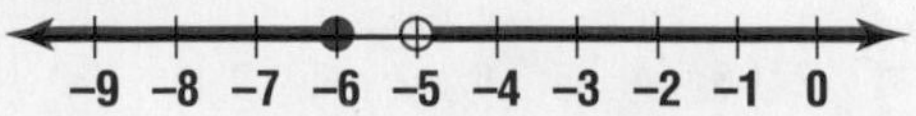

18. $a - 5 < -3$ or $-5a \geq -30$
    $\{a \mid a \leq 6\}$

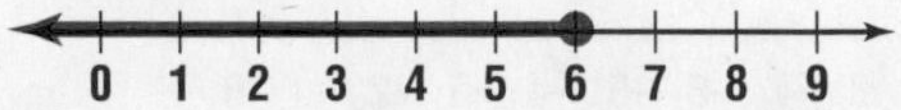

19. $-4y > -6$ or $2.5y > 5$
    $\{y \mid y < 1.5 \text{ or } y > 2\}$

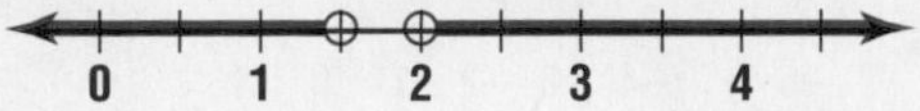

20. $\frac{w}{2} < -1$ or $\frac{w}{3} \leq -2$
    $\{w \mid w < -2\}$

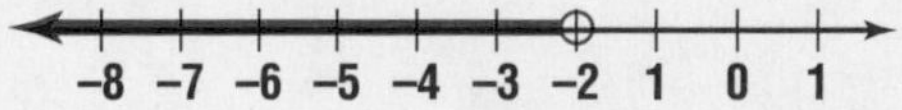

NAME ______________________ DATE __________ PERIOD _______

Practice

Student Edition
Pages 530–534

Solving Inequalities Involving Absolute Value

Solve each inequality. Graph the solution.

1. $|k + 2| < 1$

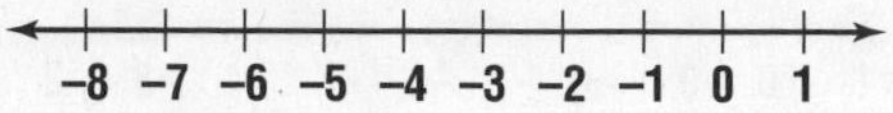

2. $|m + 7| \leq 4$

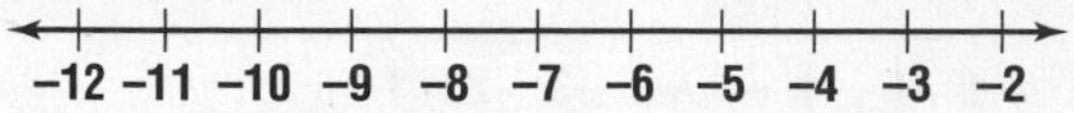

3. $|4p| < 16$

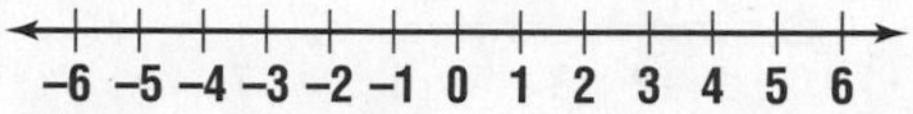

4. $|w - 3| < 3$

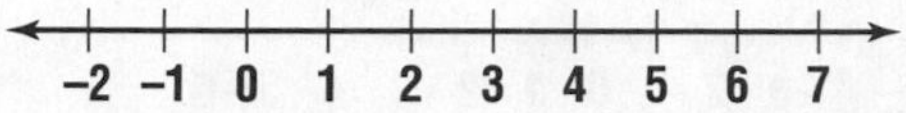

5. $|a - 5| \leq 4$

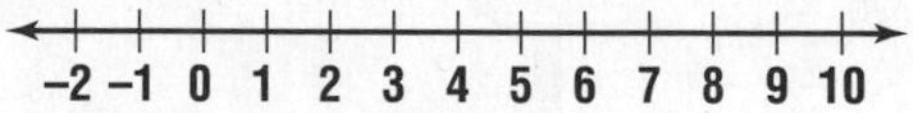

6. $|6t| < 12$

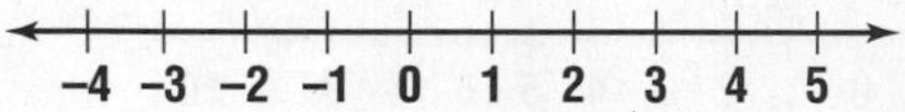

7. $|v + 9| \leq 3$

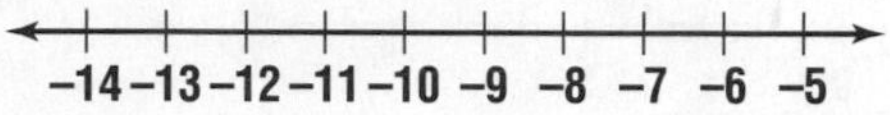

8. $|q - 2| < 2.5$

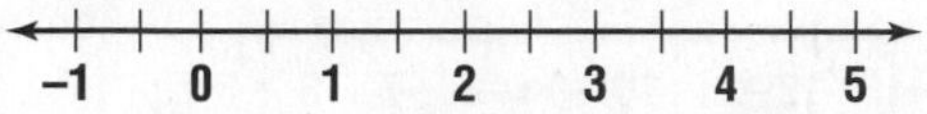

9. $|b - 8| > 2$

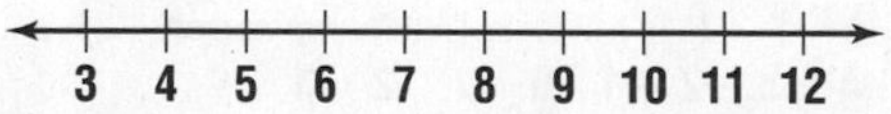

10. $|y + 1| \geq 3$

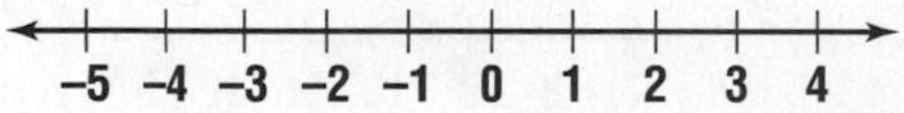

11. $|x + 4| \geq 4$

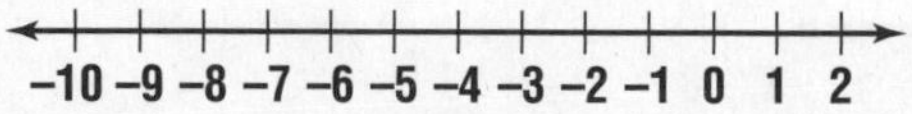

12. $|z + 7| > 2$

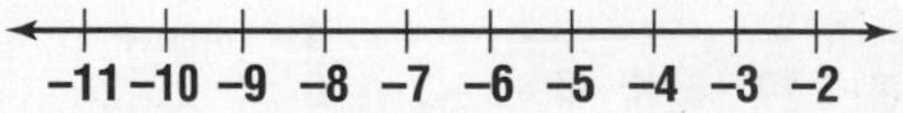

13. $|5c| > 25$

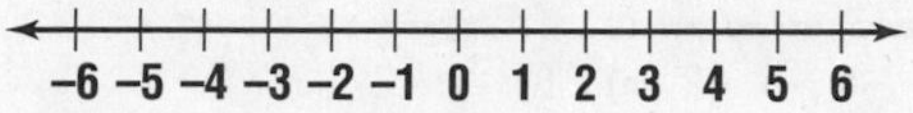

14. $|2g| \geq 2$

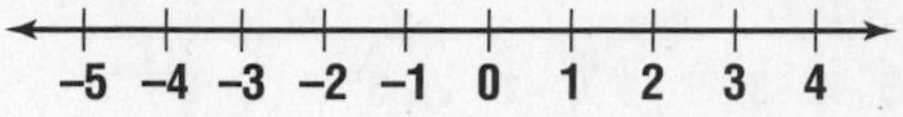

15. $|f - 5| \geq 2$

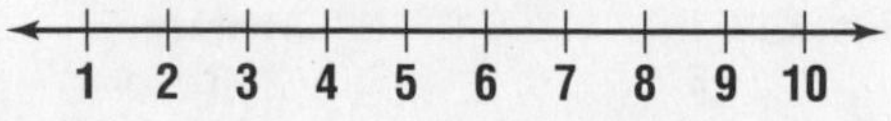

16. $|s - 6| > 1.5$

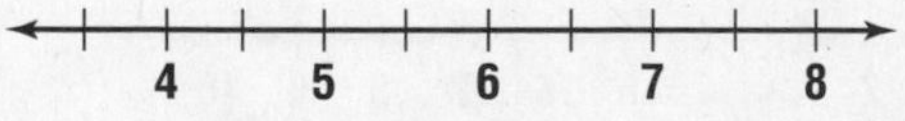

NAME ______________________ DATE __________ PERIOD ______

Practice

Solving Inequalities Involving Absolute Value

Solve each inequality. Graph the solution.

1. $|k + 2| < 1$

$\{k|-3 < k < -1\}$

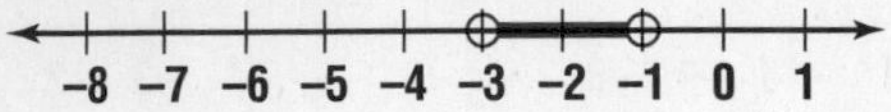

2. $|m + 7| \leq 4$

$\{m|-11 \leq m \leq -3\}$

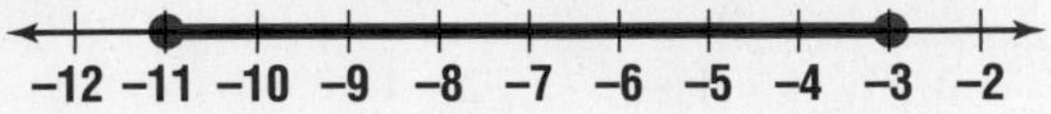

3. $|4p| < 16$

$\{p|-4 < p < 4\}$

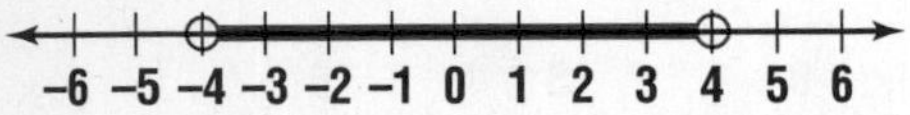

4. $|w - 3| < 3$

$\{w|0 < w < 6\}$

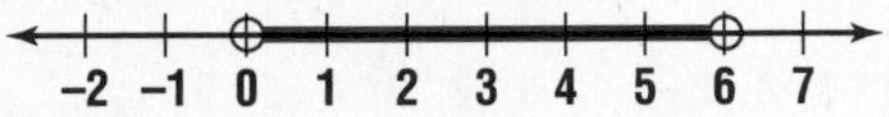

5. $|a - 5| \leq 4$

$\{a|-1 \leq a \leq 9\}$

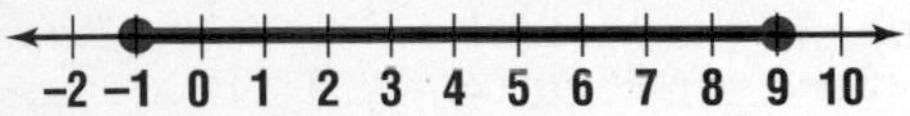

6. $|6t| < 12$

$\{t|-2 < t < 2\}$

7. $|v + 9| \leq 3$

$\{v|-12 \leq v \leq -6\}$

8. $|q - 2| < 2.5$

$\{q|-0.5 < q < 4.5\}$

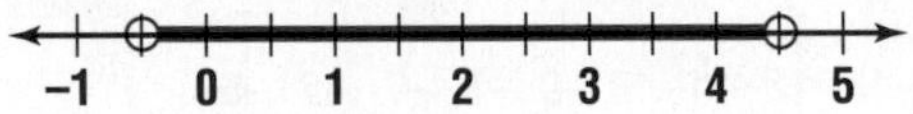

9. $|b - 8| > 2$

$\{b|b > 10 \text{ or } b < 6\}$

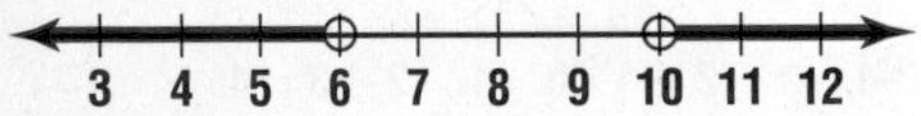

10. $|y + 1| \geq 3$

$\{y|y \geq 2 \text{ or } y \leq -4\}$

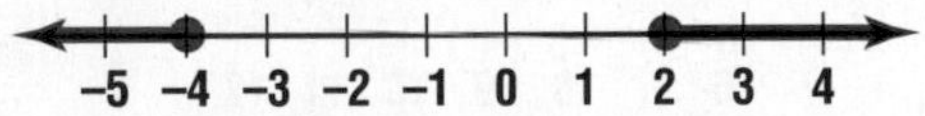

11. $|x + 4| \geq 4$

$\{x|x \geq 0 \text{ or } x \leq -8\}$

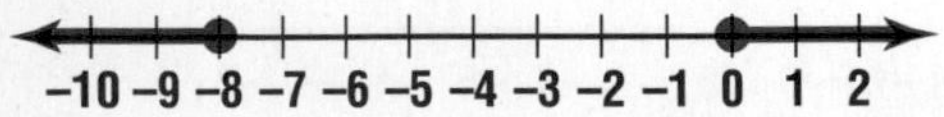

12. $|z + 7| > 2$

$\{z|z > -5 \text{ or } z < -9\}$

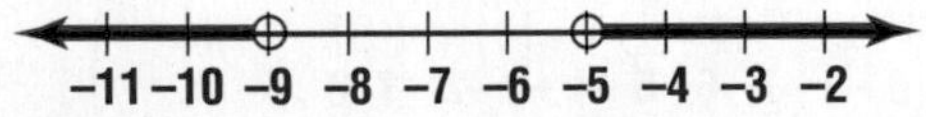

13. $|5c| > 25$

$\{c|c > 5 \text{ or } c < -5\}$

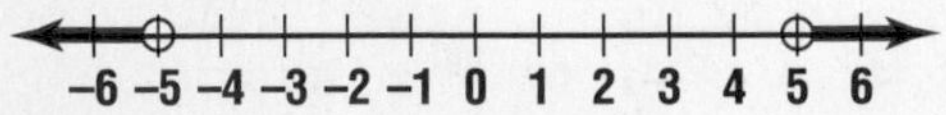

14. $|2g| \geq 2$

$\{g|g \geq 1 \text{ or } g \leq -1\}$

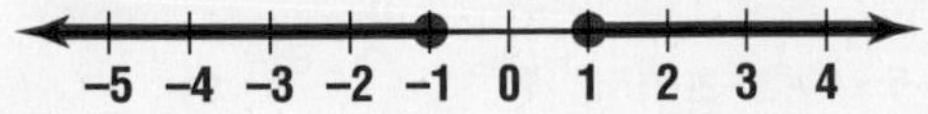

15. $|f - 5| \geq 2$

$\{f|f \geq 7 \text{ or } f \leq 3\}$

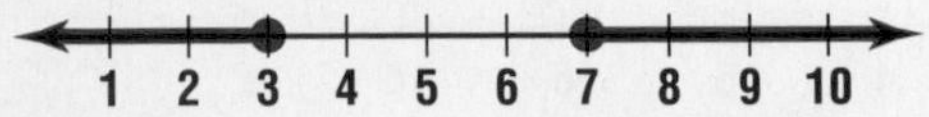

16. $|s - 6| > 1.5$

$\{s|s > 7.5 \text{ or } s < 4.5\}$

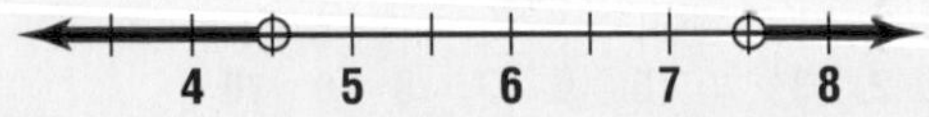

NAME ______________________ DATE ________ PERIOD ______

12-7 Practice

Student Edition
Pages 535–539

Graphing Inequalities in Two Variables

Graph each inequality.

1. $y > -2$

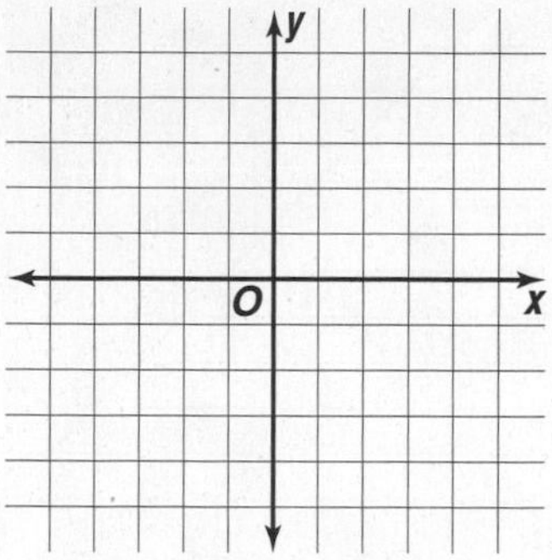

2. $y \leq x + 3$

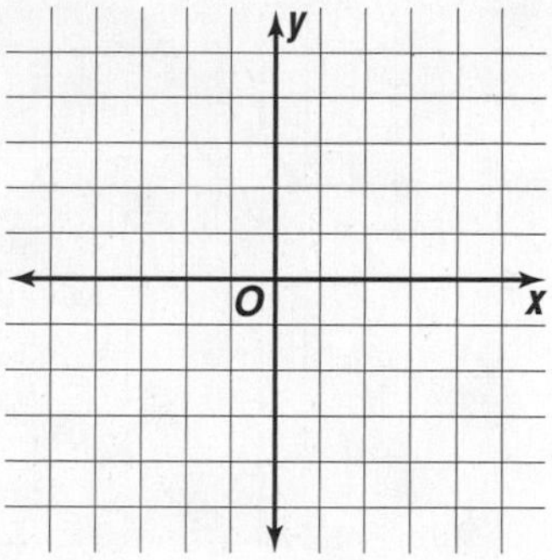

3. $y \geq -x + 1$

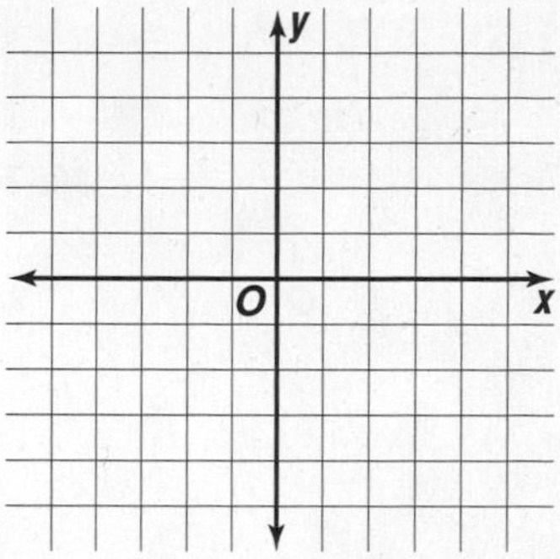

4. $y < 3x + 3$

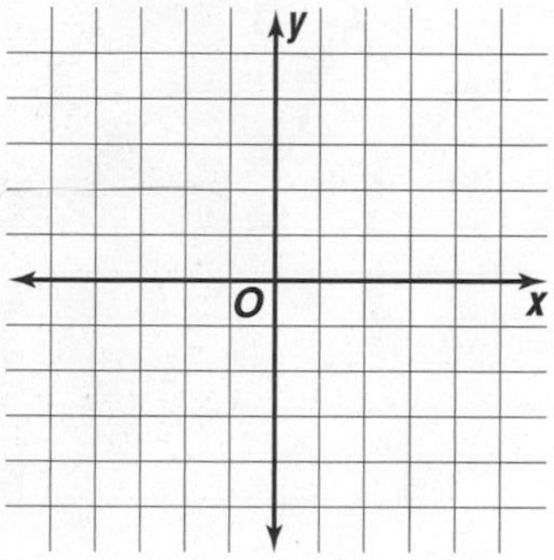

5. $x + y \leq -4$

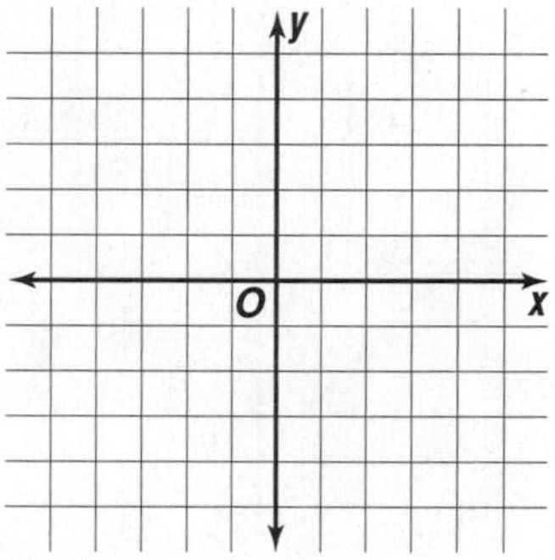

6. $2x + y > 2$

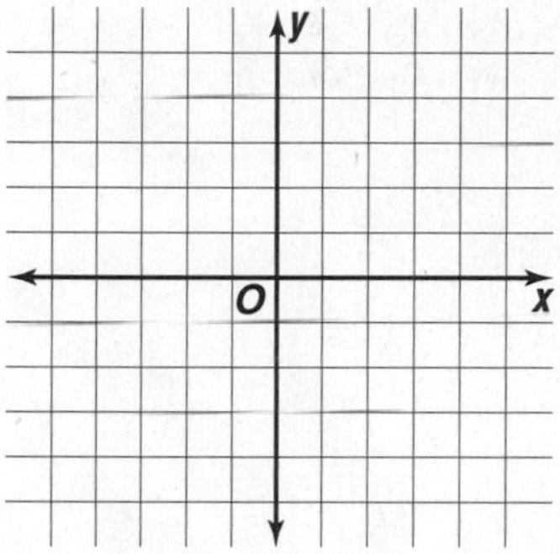

7. $2x - y \geq 10$

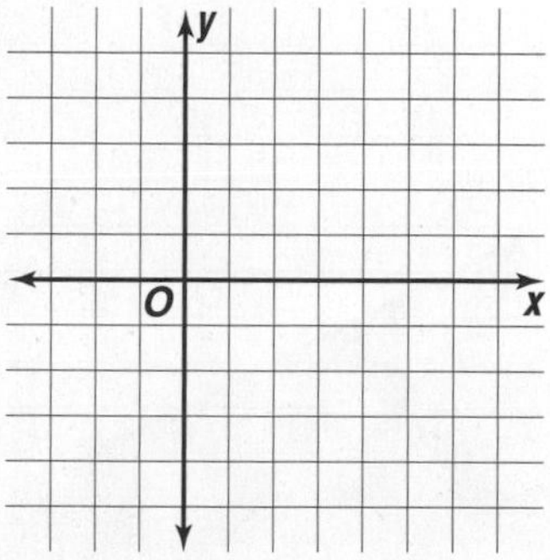

8. $-3x + y > 9$

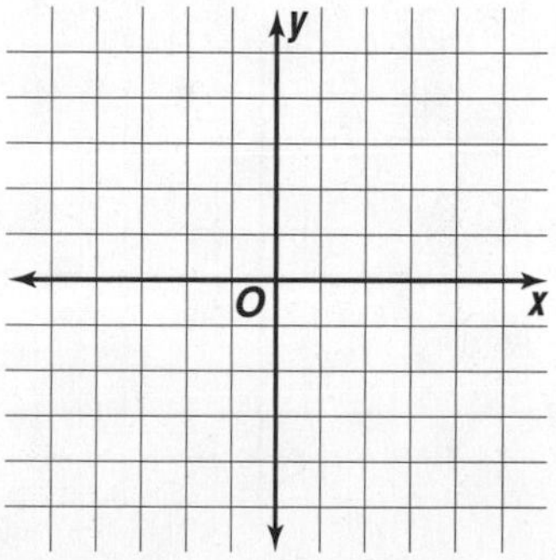

9. $x + 2y \leq -6$

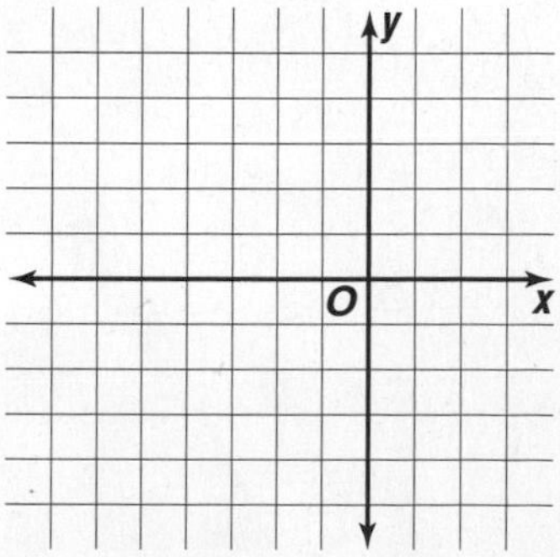

10. $x - 4y < 8$

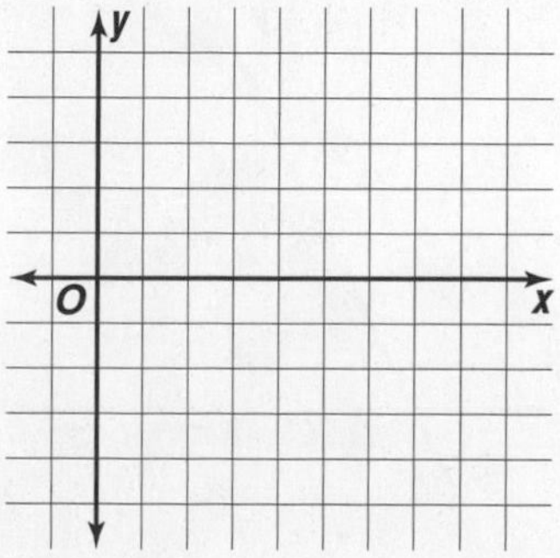

11. $2x + 2y \geq 6$

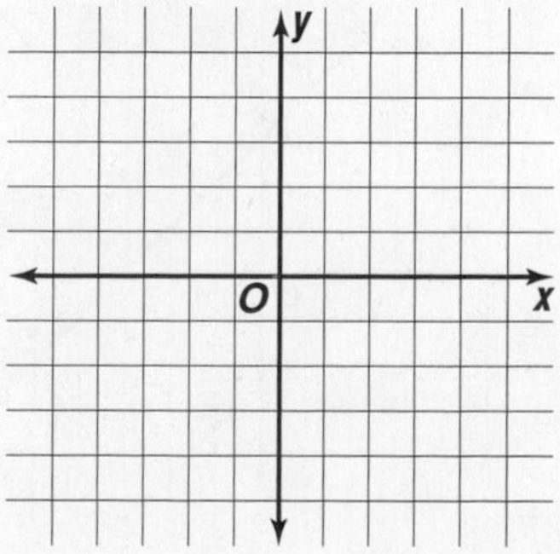

12. $-4x + 2y \leq 12$

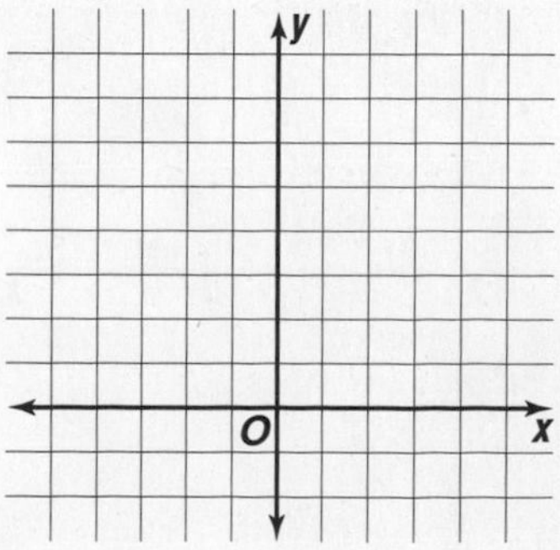

12–7 Practice

NAME ______________________ DATE __________ PERIOD ______

Student Edition
Pages 535–539

Graphing Inequalities in Two Variables

Graph each inequality.

1. $y > -2$

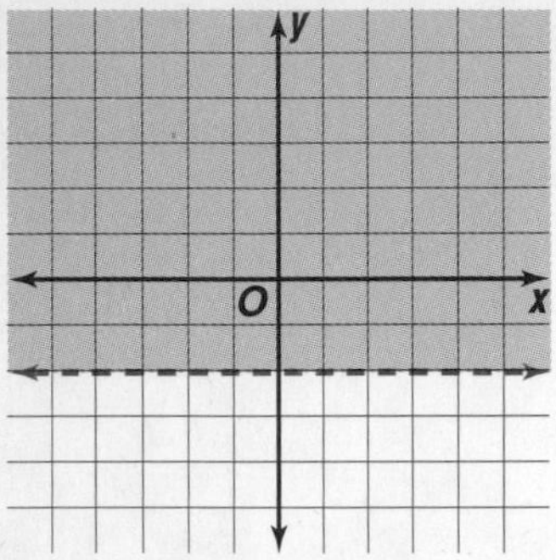

2. $y \leq x + 3$

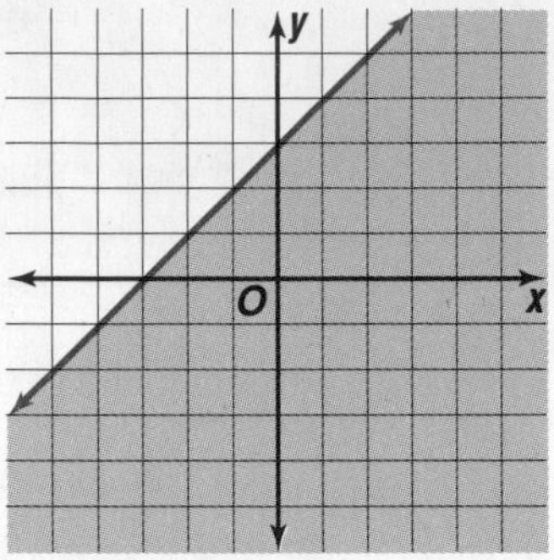

3. $y \geq -x + 1$

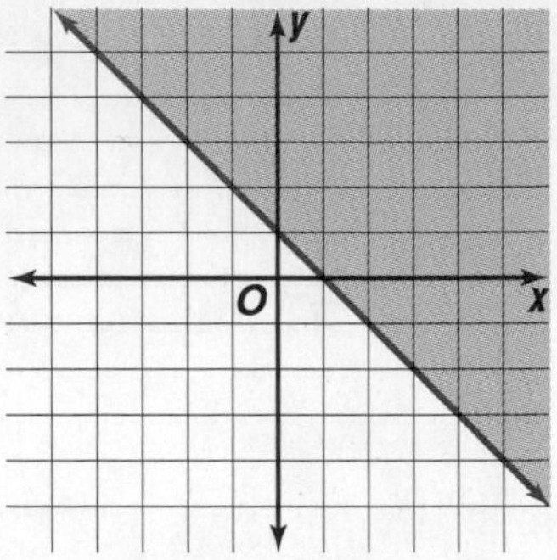

4. $y < 3x + 3$

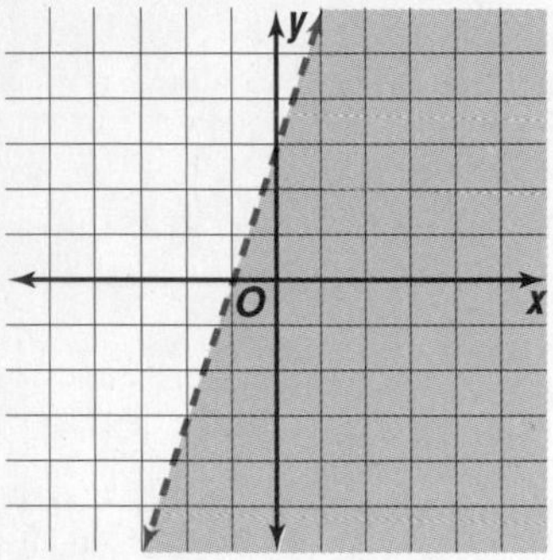

5. $x + y \leq -4$

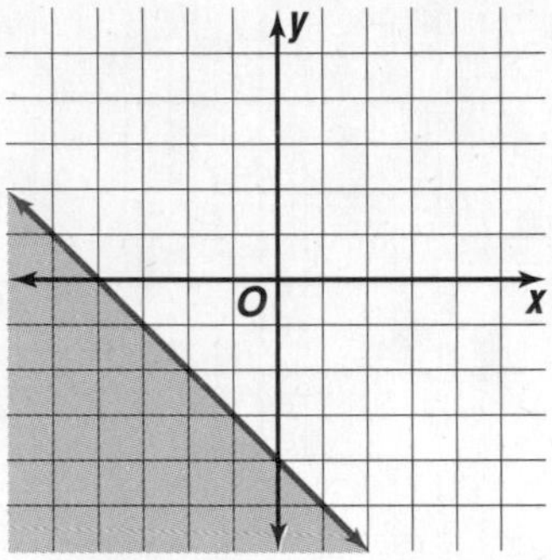

6. $2x + y > 2$

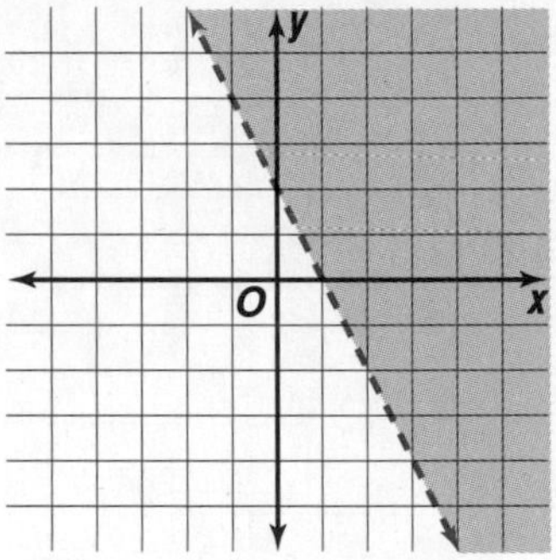

7. $2x - y \geq 10$

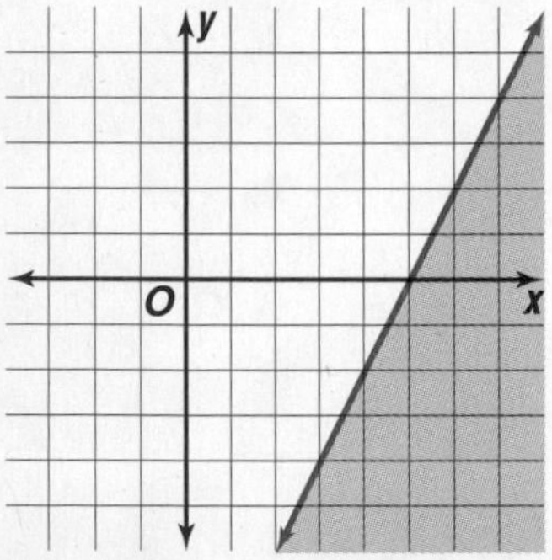

8. $-3x + y > 9$

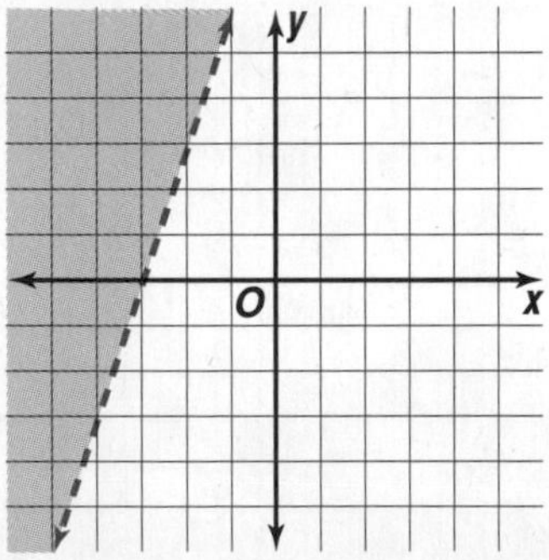

9. $x + 2y \leq -6$

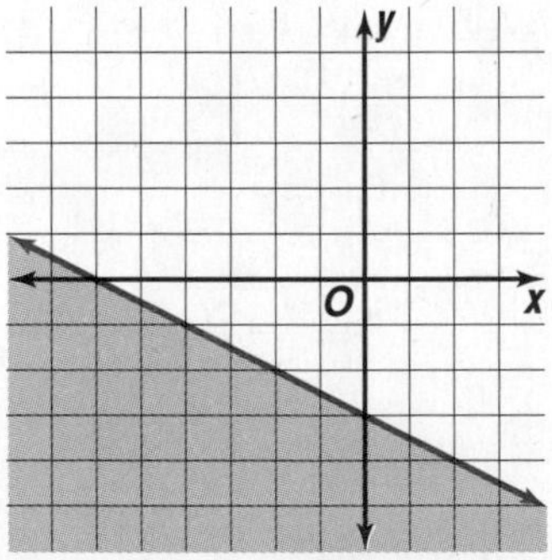

10. $x - 4y < 8$

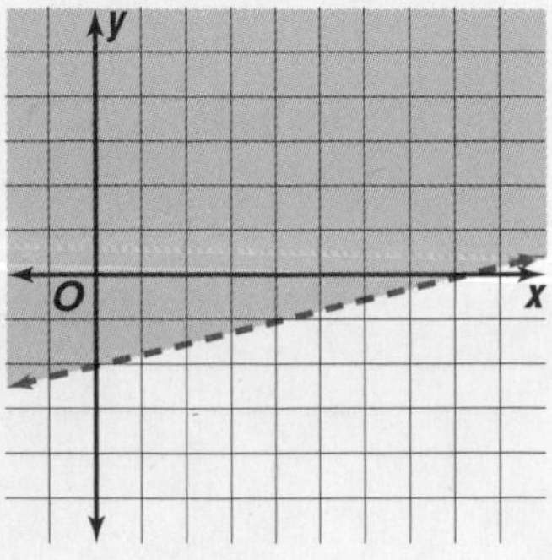

11. $2x + 2y \geq 6$

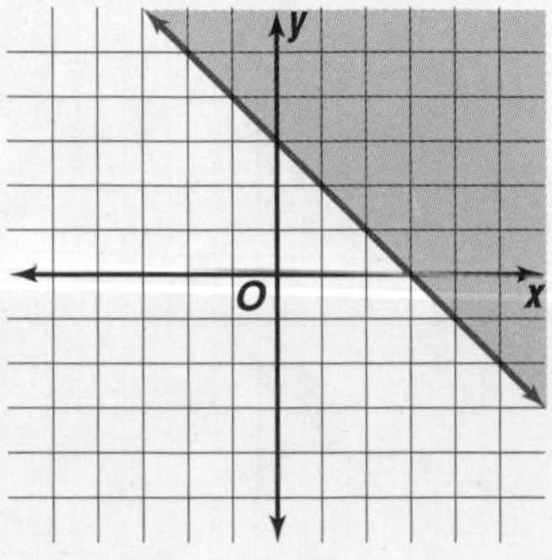

12. $-4x + 2y \leq 12$

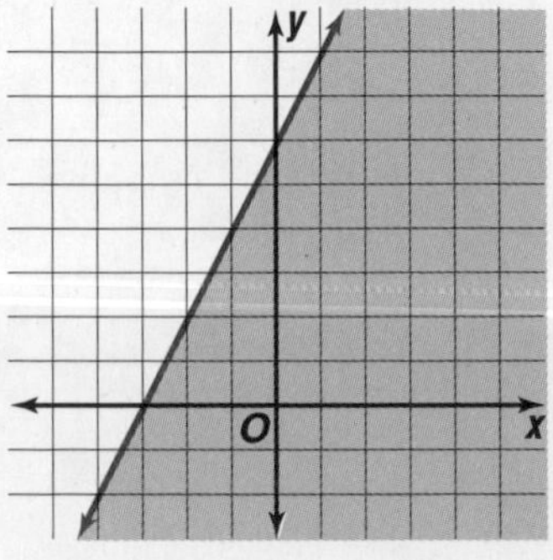

NAME ______________________ DATE __________ PERIOD ______

Practice

Student Edition
Pages 550–553

Graphing Systems of Equations

Solve each system of equations by graphing.

1. $y = 3x$
$y = -x + 4$

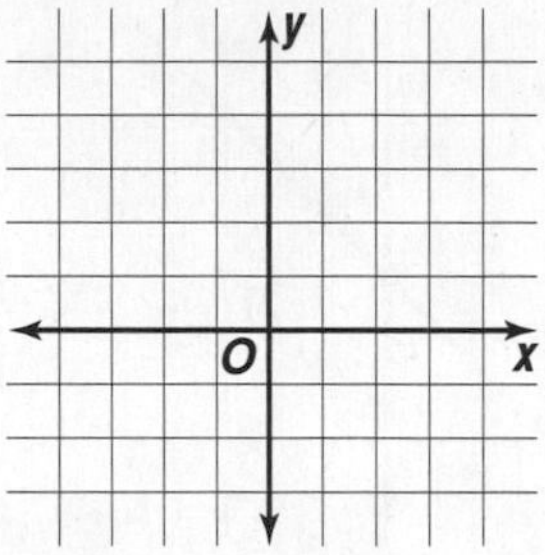

2. $y = x - 4$
$y = 2x - 3$

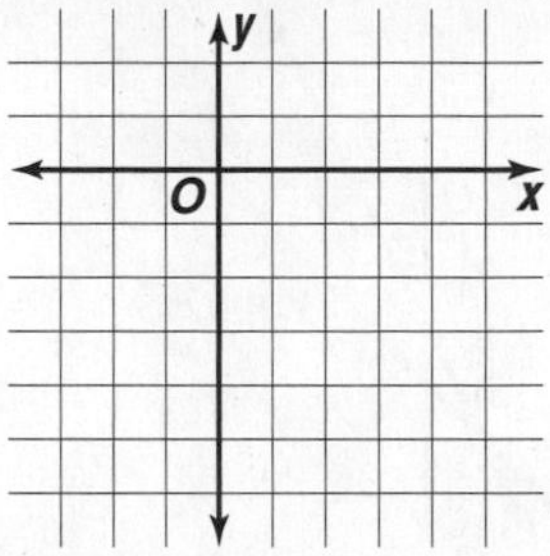

3. $x = -3$
$y = x + 6$

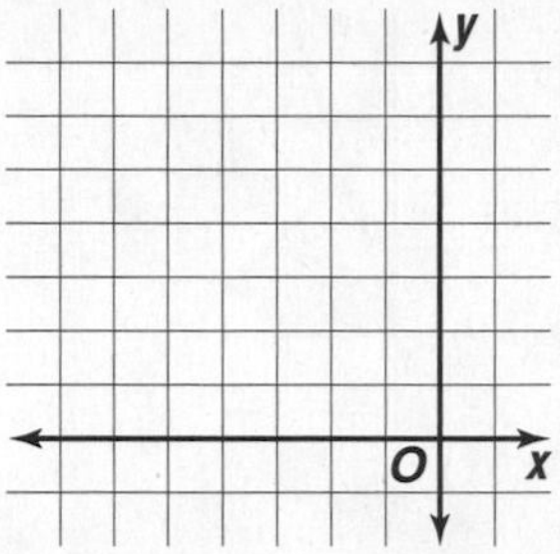

4. $x - y = 1$
$y = 5$

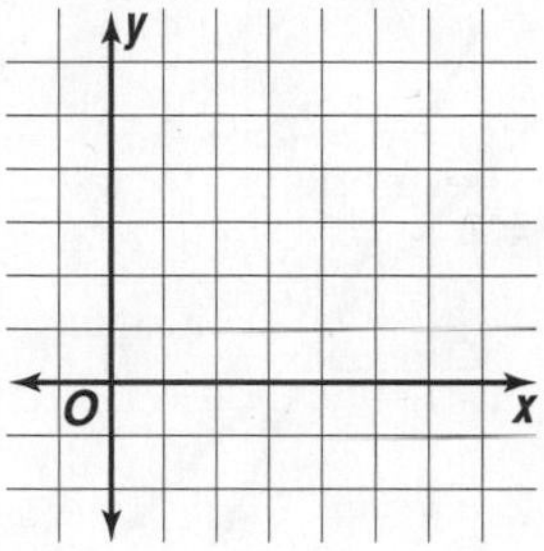

5. $x + y = -1$
$x - y = 3$

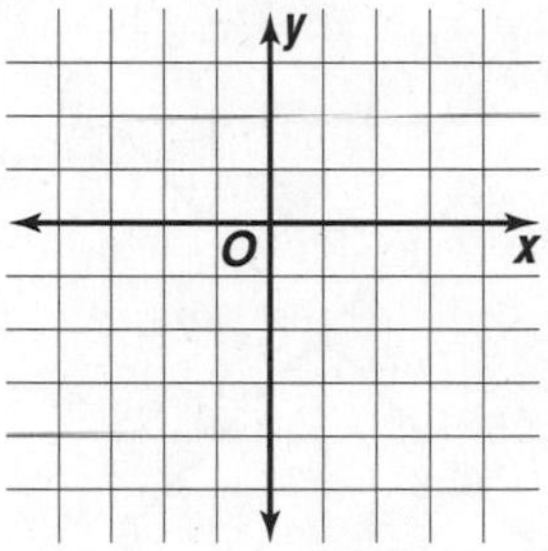

6. $x + y = 2$
$y = -2x + 4$

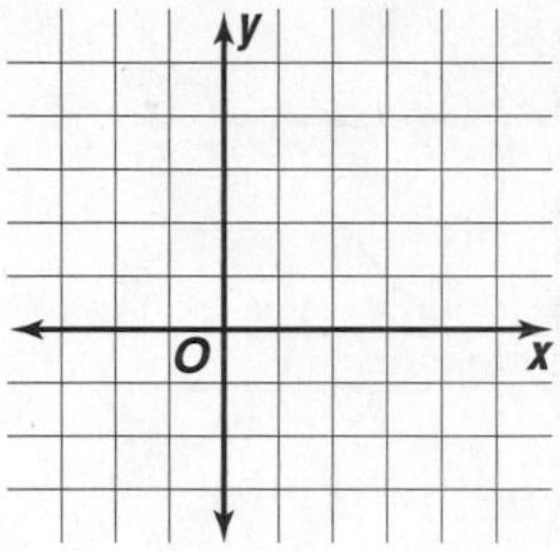

7. $y = x + 3$
$y = -x - 5$

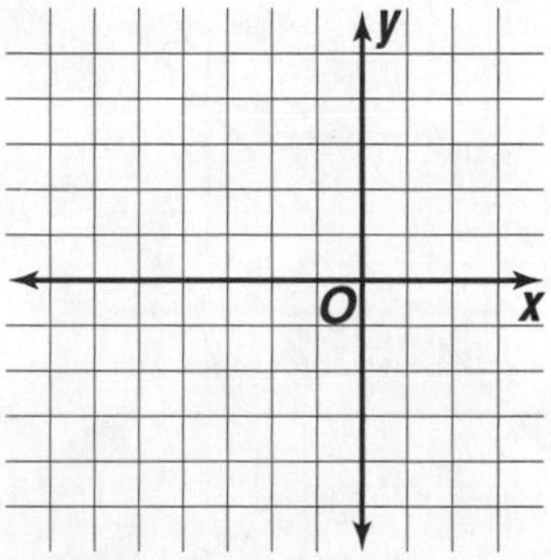

8. $-x + y = 2$
$-2x + y = 7$

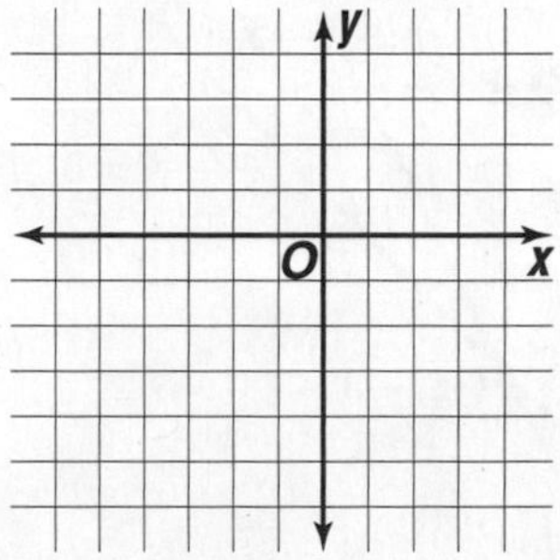

9. $y = x + 6$
$y = 2$

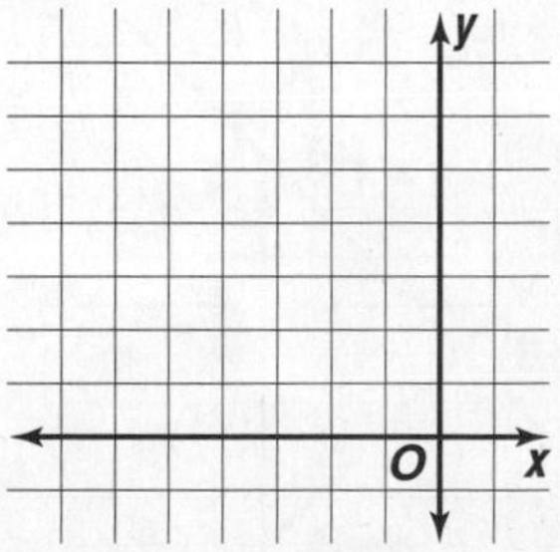

10. $x - y = 4$
$y = -2x + 2$

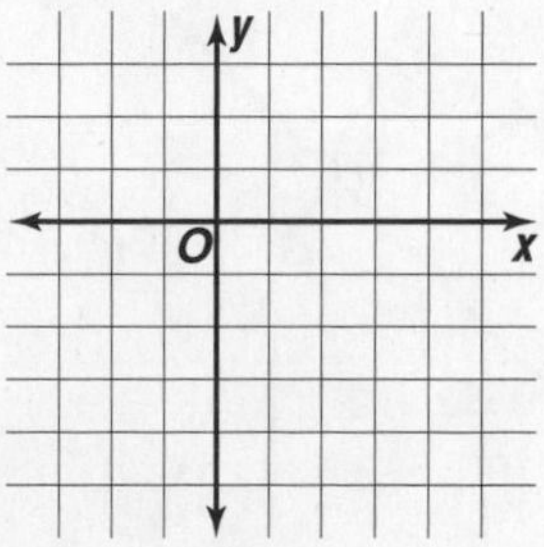

11. $y = x + 2$
$3x + y = 10$

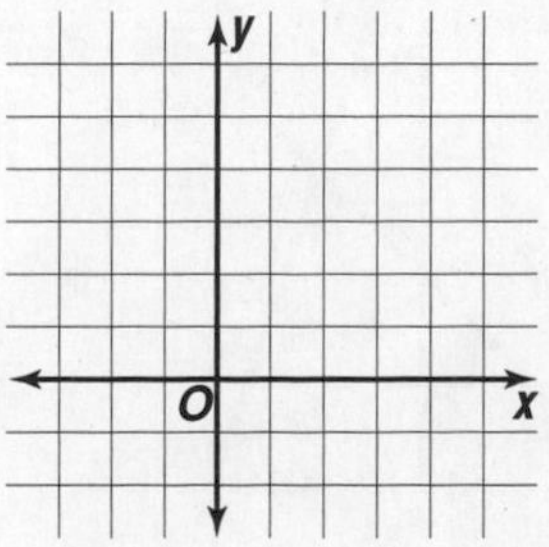

12. $y = x + 2$
$2x + y = -1$

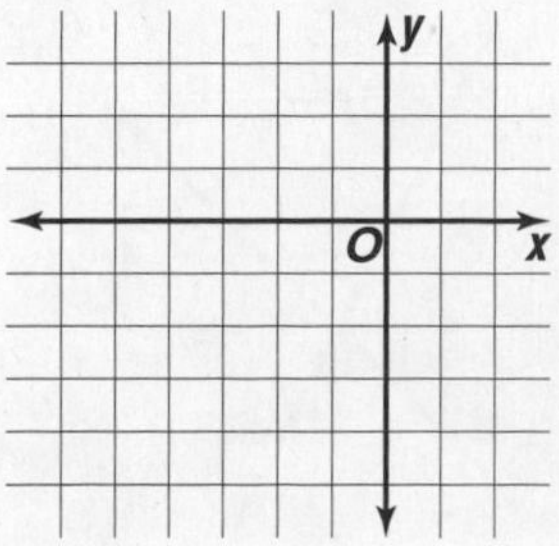

NAME ______________________ DATE __________ PERIOD ______

13–1 Practice

Student Edition
Pages 550–553

Graphing Systems of Equations

Solve each system of equations by graphing.

1. $y = 3x$
$y = -x + 4$ **(1, 3)**

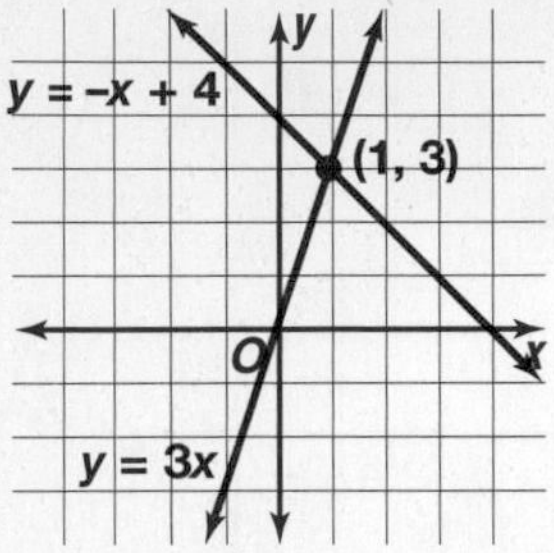

2. $y = x - 4$
$y = 2x - 3$ **(−1, −5)**

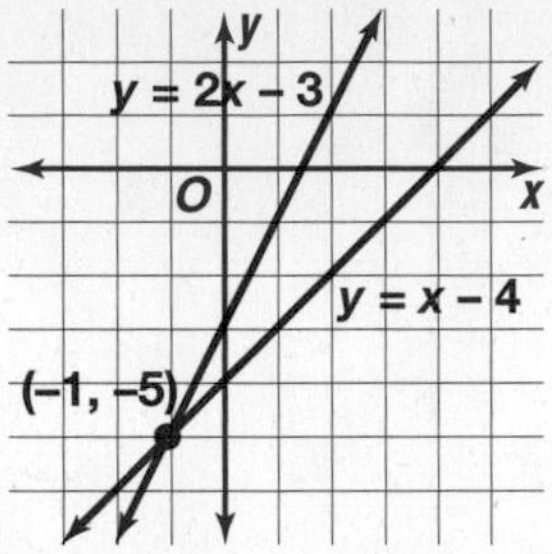

3. $x = -3$
$y = x + 6$ **(−3, 3)**

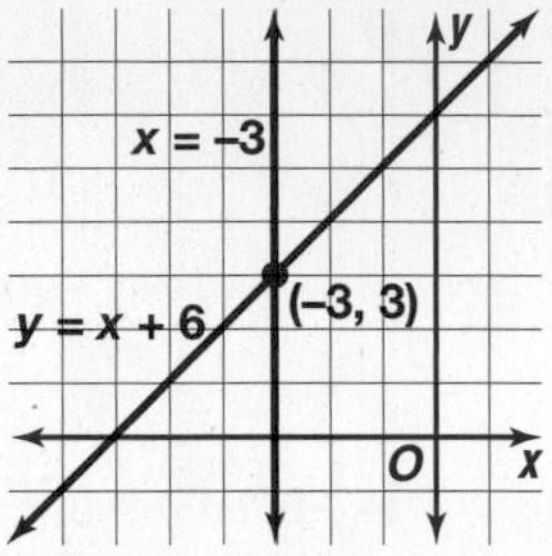

4. $x - y = 1$
$y = 5$ **(6, 5)**

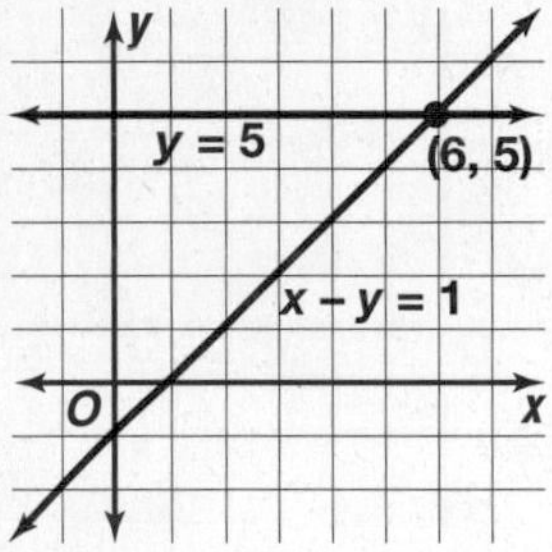

5. $x + y = -1$
$x - y = 3$ **(1, −2)**

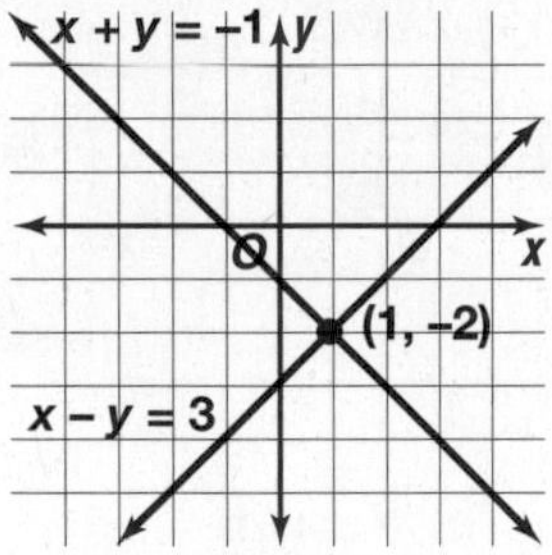

6. $x + y = 2$
$y = -2x + 4$ **(2, 0)**

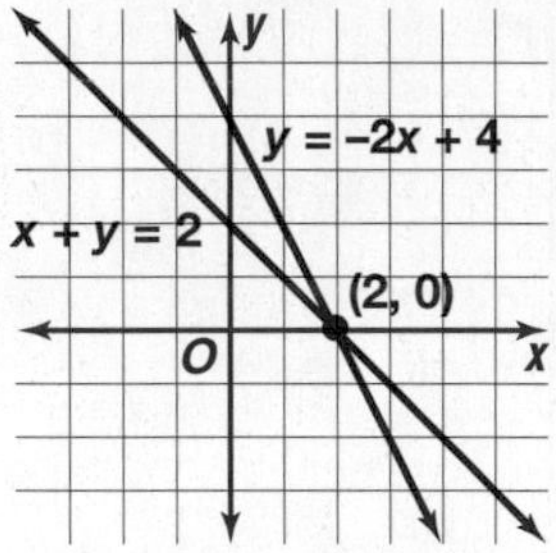

7. $y = x + 3$
$y = -x - 5$ **(−4, −1)**

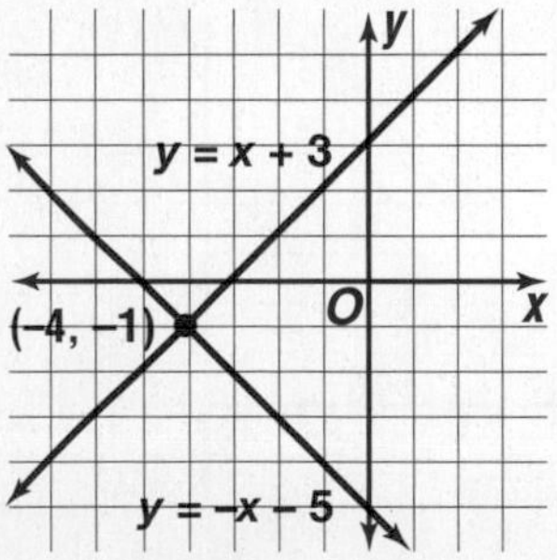

8. $-x + y = 2$
$-2x + y = 7$ **(−5, −3)**

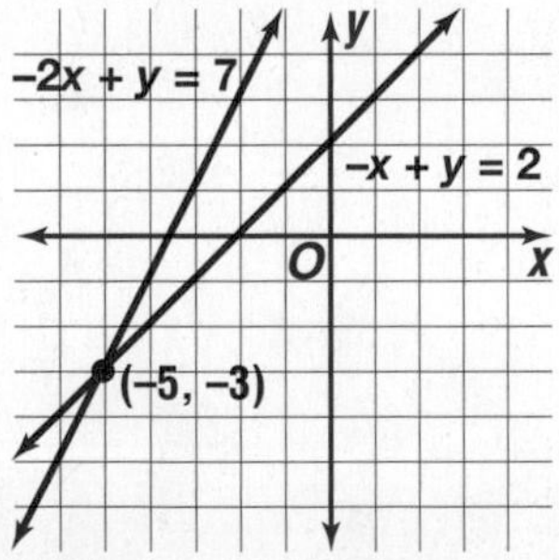

9. $y = x + 6$
$y = 2$ **(−4, 2)**

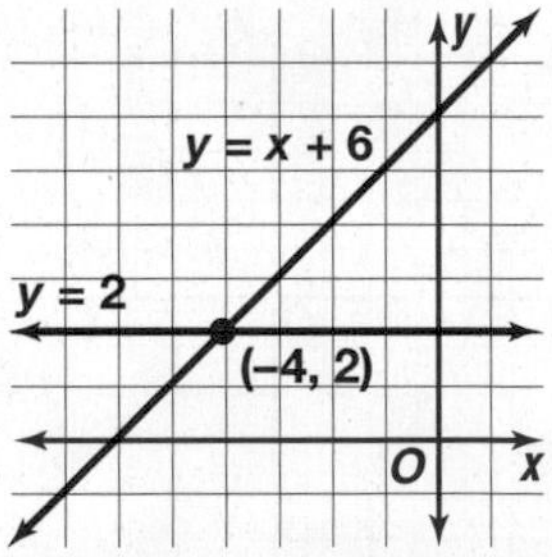

10. $x - y = 4$
$y = -2x + 2$ **(2, −2)**

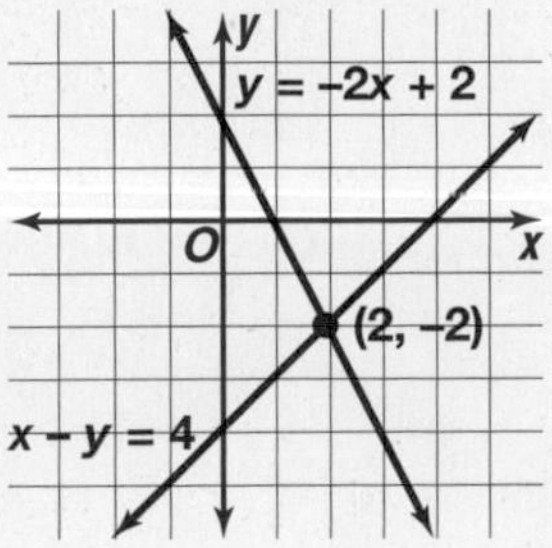

11. $y = x + 2$
$3x + y = 10$ **(2, 4)**

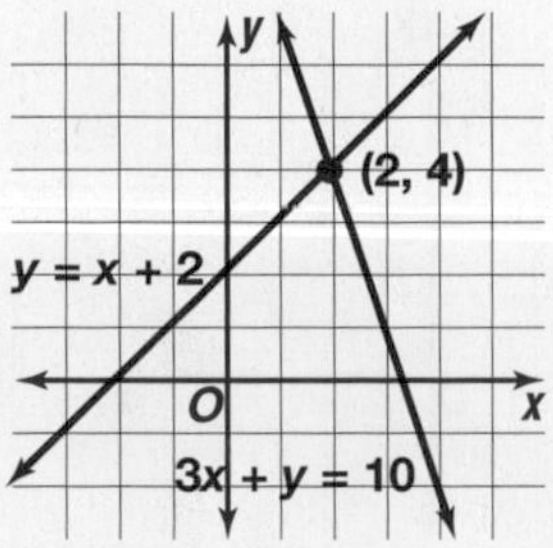

12. $y = x + 2$
$2x + y = -1$ **(−1, 1)**

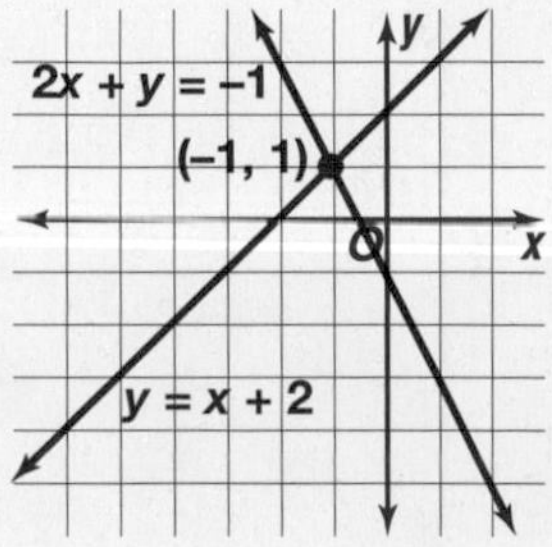

NAME ______________________ DATE ________ PERIOD ______

Practice

Student Edition
Pages 554–559

Solutions of Systems of Equations

***State whether each system is* consistent and independent, consistent and dependent, *or* inconsistent.**

1.

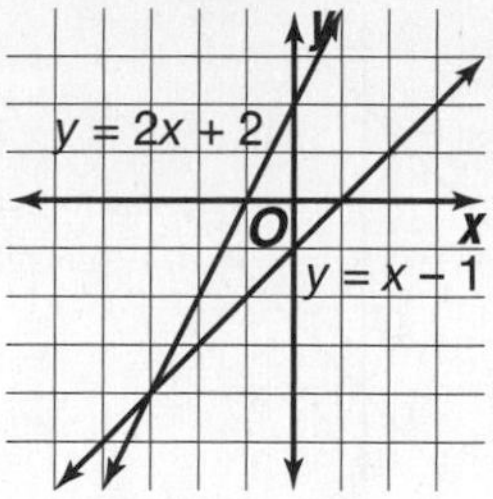

2.

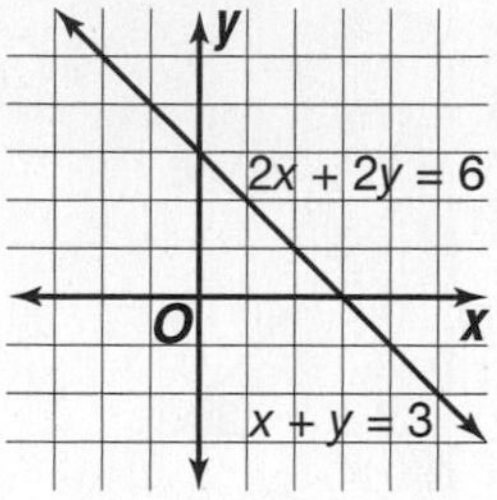

3.

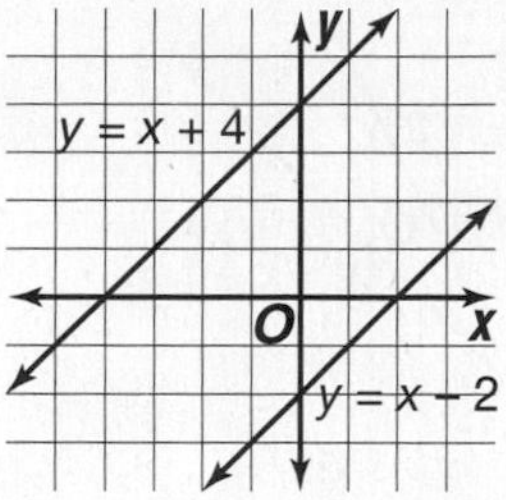

4.

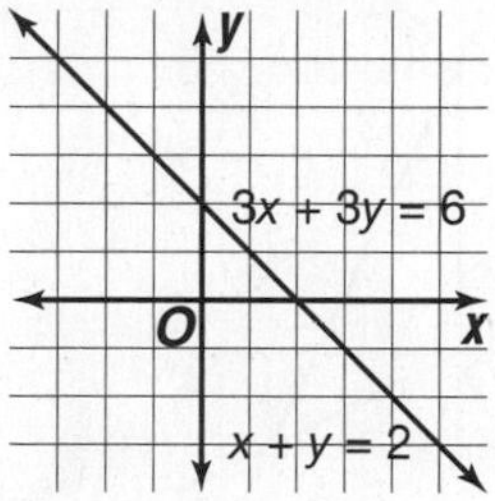

5.

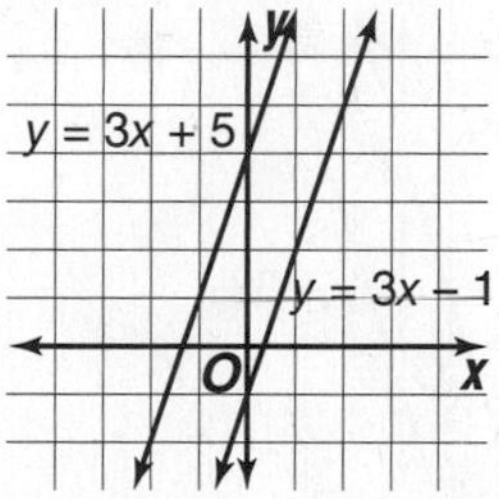

6.

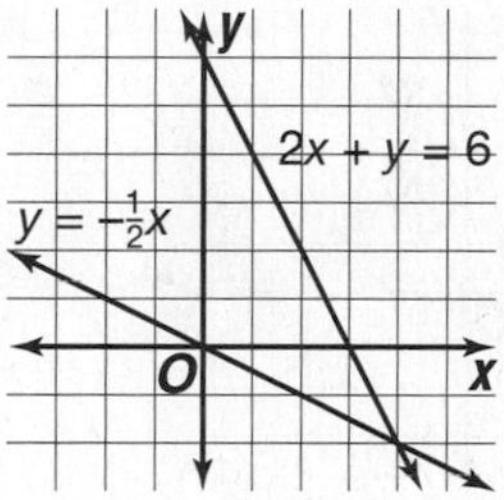

Determine whether each system of equations has* one solution, no *solution, or* infinitely many *solutions by graphing. If the system has one solution, name it.

7. $2x + y = 4$
$4x + 2y = 8$

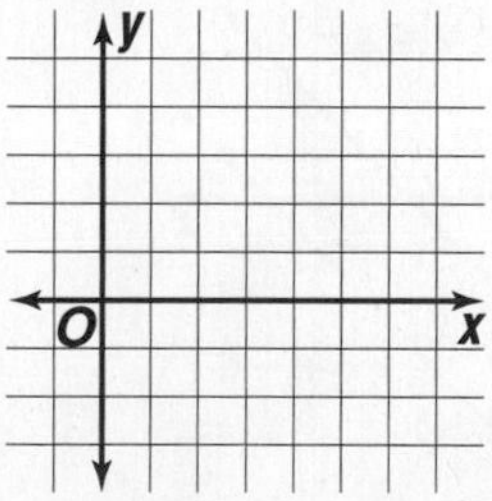

8. $y = x - 1$
$x + y = 3$

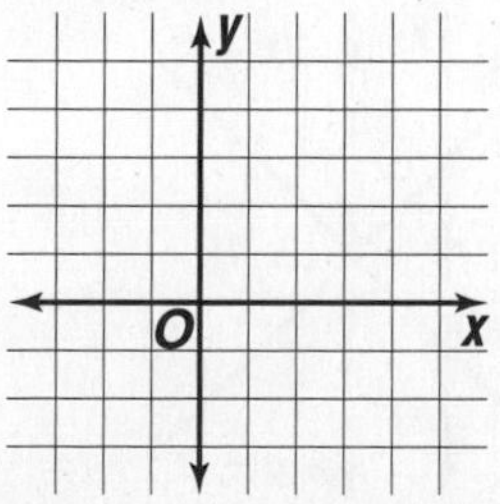

9. $y = x - 2$
$y = x - 5$

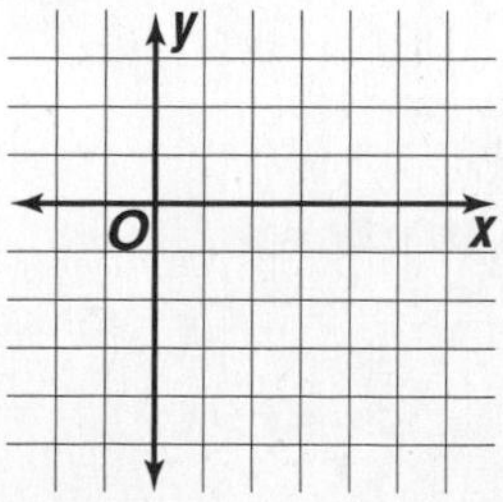

10. $y = 2x$
$y = 2x + 3$

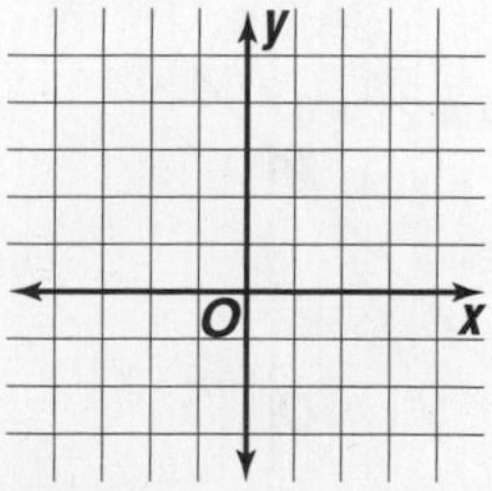

11. $y = x + 5$
$-x + y = 5$

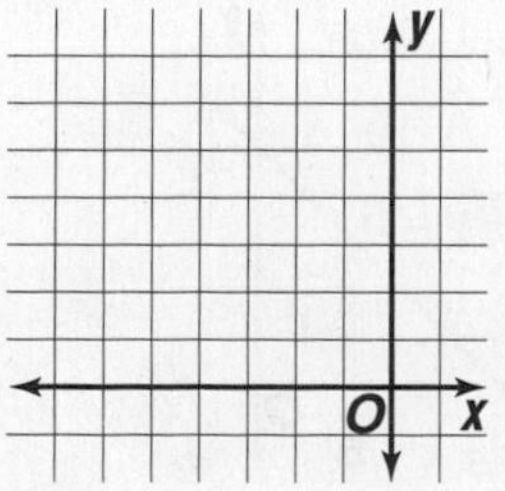

12. $x - y = -5$
$y = 2x + 6$

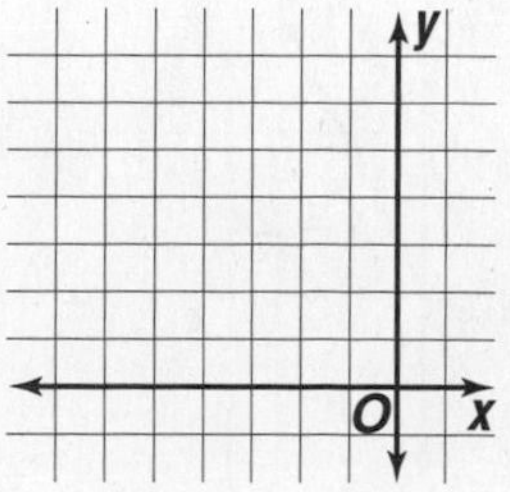

NAME ______________________ DATE ________ PERIOD ______

13–2 Practice

Student Edition
Pages 554–559

Solutions of Systems of Equations

***State whether each system is* consistent and independent, consistent and dependent, *or* inconsistent.**

1.

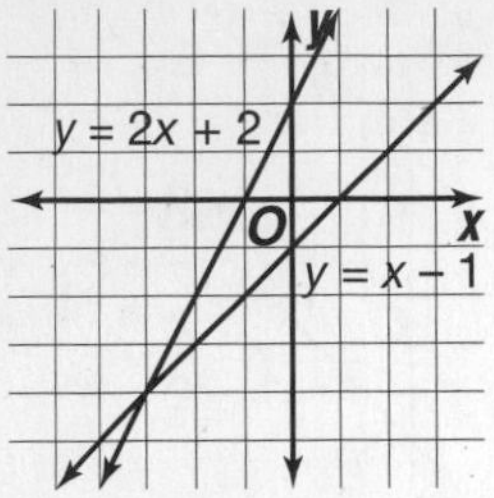

consistent and independent

2.

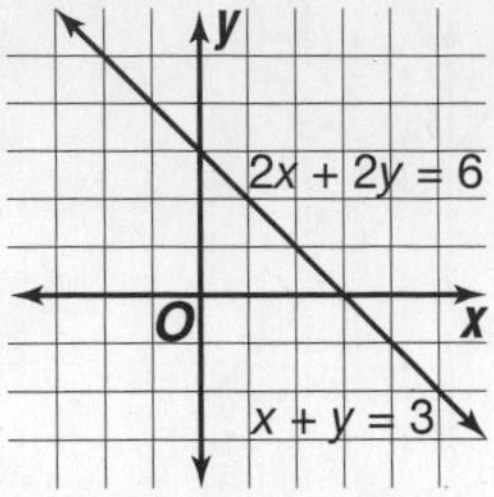

consistent and dependent

3.

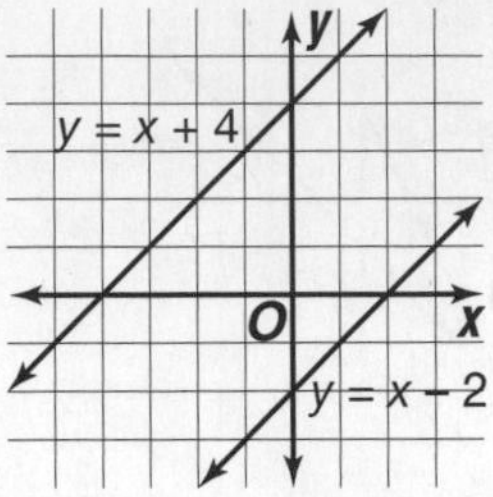

inconsistent

4.

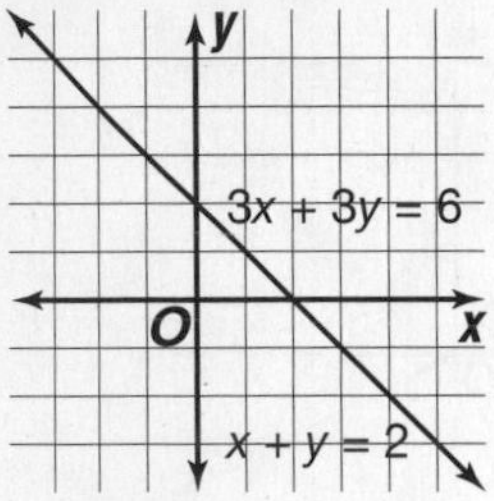

consistent and dependent

5.

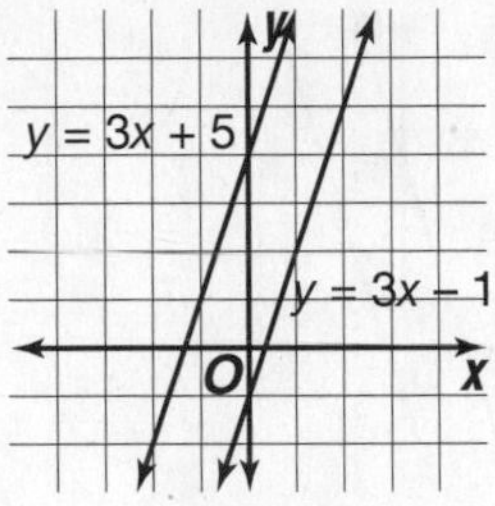

inconsistent

6.

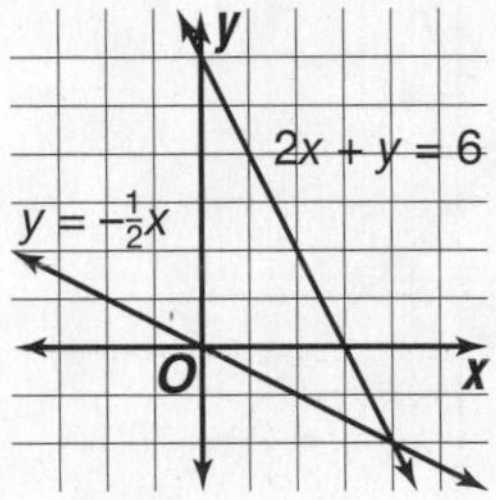

consistent and independent

Determine whether each system of equations has* one solution, no solution, *or* infinitely many *solutions by graphing. If the system has one solution, name it.

7. $2x + y = 4$
$4x + 2y = 8$ **infinitely many**

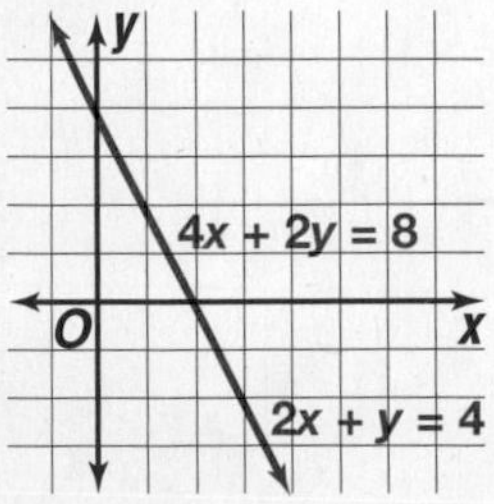

8. $y = x - 1$
$x + y = 3$ **(2, 1)**

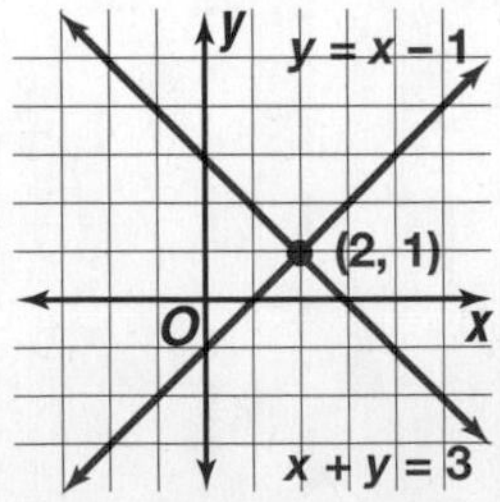

9. $y = x - 2$
$y = x - 5$ **no solution**

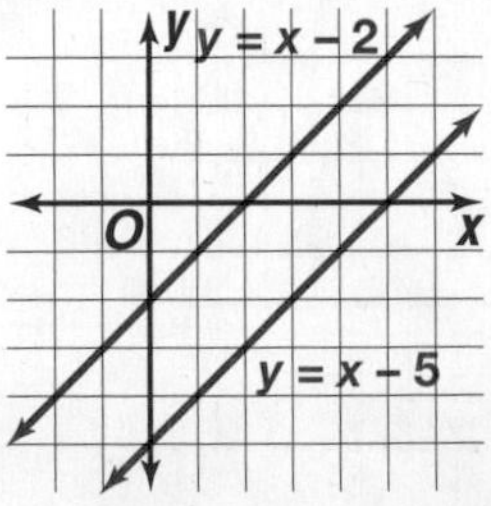

10. $y = 2x$
$y = 2x + 3$ **no solution**

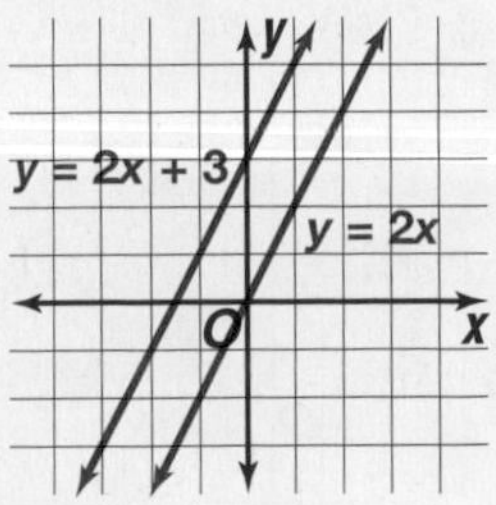

11. $y = x + 5$
$-x + y = 5$ **infinitely many**

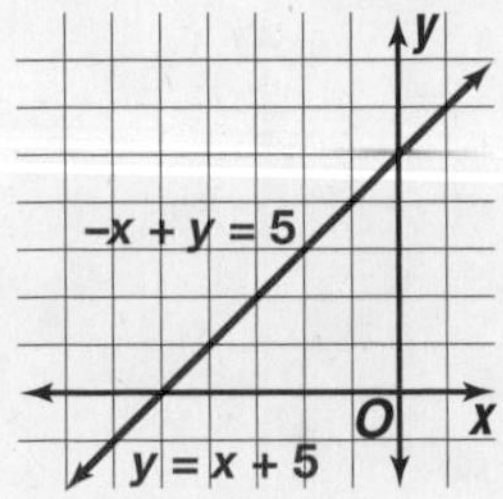

12. $x - y = -5$
$y = 2x + 6$ **(−1, 4)**

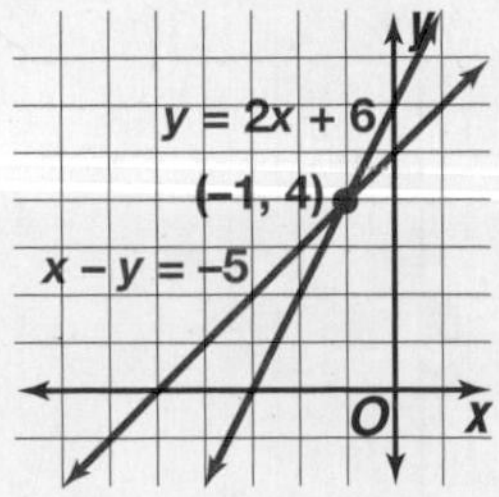

NAME ______________________ DATE __________ PERIOD ______

Practice

Student Edition
Pages 560–565

Substitution

Use substitution to solve each system of equations.

1. $y = x + 8$
$x + y = 2$

2. $y = 2x$
$5x - y = 9$

3. $y = x + 2$
$3x + 3y = 6$

4. $x = 3y$
$2x + 4y = 10$

5. $x = y + 9$
$x + y = -7$

6. $y = 2x + 1$
$2x - y = 3$

7. $x = 3y$
$2x + 3y = 15$

8. $x - 2y = 4$
$3x = 6y + 12$

9. $x = 5y - 2$
$2x + 2y = 4$

10. $4y + 2x = 24$
$x = 3y + 2$

11. $y = 3x + 8$
$4x + 2y = 6$

12. $x = 3y + 10$
$2x + 2y = -12$

13. $x + 2y = -4$
$-2x - 3y = 9$

14. $5x + 2y = 7$
$4x + y = 8$

15. $x = 2y + 11$
$3x + 2y = 9$

16. $x - 2y = -7$
$5x - 7y = -8$

17. $6x - 4y = -5$
$2x + y = 3$

18. $x + 3y = 10$
$4x - 5y = 6$

NAME ______________________ DATE __________ PERIOD ______

Practice

Student Edition
Pages 560–565

Substitution

Use substitution to solve each system of equations.

1. $y = x + 8$
$x + y = 2$

(−3, 5)

2. $y = 2x$
$5x - y = 9$

(3, 6)

3. $y = x + 2$
$3x + 3y = 6$

(0, 2)

4. $x = 3y$
$2x + 4y = 10$

(3, 1)

5. $x = y + 9$
$x + y = -7$

(1, −8)

6. $y = 2x + 1$
$2x - y = 3$

no solution

7. $x = 3y$
$2x + 3y = 15$

$\left(5, \frac{5}{3}\right)$

8. $x - 2y = 4$
$3x = 6y + 12$

infinitely many

9. $x = 5y - 2$
$2x + 2y = 4$

$\left(\frac{4}{3}, \frac{2}{3}\right)$

10. $4y + 2x = 24$
$x = 3y + 2$

(8, 2)

11. $y = 3x + 8$
$4x + 2y = 6$

(−1, 5)

12. $x = 3y + 10$
$2x + 2y = -12$

(−2, −4)

13. $x + 2y = -4$
$-2x - 3y = 9$

(−6, 1)

14. $5x + 2y = 7$
$4x + y = 8$

(3, −4)

15. $x = 2y + 11$
$3x + 2y = 9$

(5, −3)

16. $x - 2y = -7$
$5x - 7y = -8$

(11, 9)

17. $6x - 4y = -5$
$2x + y = 3$

$\left(\frac{1}{2}, 2\right)$

18. $x + 3y = 10$
$4x - 5y = 6$

(4, 2)

NAME ______________________ DATE ________ PERIOD ______

Practice

Student Edition
Pages 566–571

Elimination Using Addition and Subtraction

Use elimination to solve each system of equations.

1. $x + y = 4$
$x - y = -6$

2. $x - y = 7$
$x + y = 1$

3. $3x + y = 12$
$x + y = 8$

4. $x + 5y = -12$
$x + 2y = -9$

5. $x + 2y = 9$
$3x - 2y = 3$

6. $4x + 2y = 2$
$-4x - 3y = 3$

7. $4x - 3y = 10$
$2x - 3y = 2$

8. $2x + 5y = 1$
$2x + 10y = 10$

9. $3y = x + 4$
$2x + 3y = 19$

10. $2x = y - 4$
$2x + 6y = 3$

11. $4y = 2x + 8$
$5x - 4y = 22$

12. $2x + y = 6$
$2x - 2y = -12$

13. $-3x - y = 24$
$3x - 2y = 3$

14. $2x + 3y = 8$
$y = 2x + 8$

15. $-7x = y - 4$
$5x - y = 8$

16. $3x + 5y = 7$
$4x + 5y = 1$

17. $6x - 3y = 3$
$6x - 5y = -3$

18. $y = 2x + 4$
$2x - 4y = 8$

13–4

NAME ______________________ DATE __________ PERIOD ______

Practice

Student Edition
Pages 566–571

Elimination Using Addition and Subtraction

Use elimination to solve each system of equations.

1. $x + y = 4$
$x - y = -6$

(−1, 5)

2. $x - y = 7$
$x + y = 1$

(4, −3)

3. $3x + y = 12$
$x + y = 8$

(2, 6)

4. $x + 5y = -12$
$x + 2y = -9$

(−7, −1)

5. $x + 2y = 9$
$3x - 2y = 3$

(3, 3)

6. $4x + 2y = 2$
$-4x - 3y = 3$

(3, −5)

7. $4x - 3y = 10$
$2x - 3y = 2$

(4, 2)

8. $2x + 5y = 1$
$2x + 10y = 10$

$\left(-4, \frac{9}{5}\right)$

9. $3y = x + 4$
$2x + 3y = 19$

(5, 3)

10. $2x = y - 4$
$2x + 6y = 3$

$\left(-\frac{3}{2}, 1\right)$

11. $4y = 2x + 8$
$5x - 4y = 22$

(10, 7)

12. $2x + y = 6$
$2x - 2y = -12$

(0, 6)

13. $-3x - y = 24$
$3x - 2y = 3$

(−5, −9)

14. $2x + 3y = 8$
$y = 2x + 8$

(−2, 4)

15. $-7x = y - 4$
$5x - y = 8$

(1, −3)

16. $3x + 5y = 7$
$4x + 5y = 1$

(−6, 5)

17. $6x - 3y = 3$
$6x - 5y = -3$

(2, 3)

18. $y = 2x + 4$
$2x - 4y = 8$

(−4, −4)

NAME ______________________ DATE __________ PERIOD ______

13-5 Practice

Student Edition
Pages 572–577

Elimination Using Multiplication

Use elimination to solve each system of equations.

1. $x + 3y = 6$
$2x - 7y = -1$

2. $9x + 3y = 12$
$2x + y = 5$

3. $3x - y = 14$
$5x + 4y = 12$

4. $3x - 3y = -3$
$2x - y = -5$

5. $3x + y = 2$
$6x + 2y = 4$

6. $5x - y = 16$
$-4x - 3y = 10$

7. $5x + 2y = 24$
$10x - 5y = -15$

8. $3x + 4y = 6$
$7x + 8y = 10$

9. $2x - 3y = 5$
$3x + 9y = 21$

10. $3x + 2y = 11$
$6x + 3y = 13$

11. $6x - 2y = 4$
$2x - 5y = -3$

12. $-7x - 3y = -5$
$5x + 6y = 19$

13. $5x - 10y = -3$
$-3x - 5y = 15$

14. $2x + 3y = 2$
$6x + 6y = 5$

15. $2x + 4y = 6$
$3x + 6y = 12$

16. $3x + 3y = 9$
$5x + 4y = 10$

17. $2x - 7y = 5$
$3x - 6y = 12$

18. $2x - 4y = 18$
$-5x - 6y = 3$

NAME ______________________________ DATE __________ PERIOD ______

Practice

Elimination Using Multiplication

Use elimination to solve each system of equations.

1. $x + 3y = 6$
$2x - 7y = -1$

(3, 1)

2. $9x + 3y = 12$
$2x + y = 5$

(−1, 7)

3. $3x - y = 14$
$5x + 4y = 12$

(4, −2)

4. $3x - 3y = -3$
$2x - y = -5$

(−4, −3)

5. $3x + y = 2$
$6x + 2y = 4$

infinitely many

6. $5x - y = 16$
$-4x - 3y = 10$

(2, −6)

7. $5x + 2y = 24$
$10x - 5y = -15$

(2, 7)

8. $3x + 4y = 6$
$7x + 8y = 10$

(−2, 3)

9. $2x - 3y = 5$
$3x + 9y = 21$

(4, 1)

10. $3x + 2y = 11$
$6x + 3y = 13$

$\left(-\frac{7}{3}, 9\right)$

11. $6x - 2y = 4$
$2x - 5y = -3$

(1, 1)

12. $-7x - 3y = -5$
$5x + 6y = 19$

(−1, 4)

13. $5x - 10y = -3$
$-3x - 5y = 15$

$\left(-3, -\frac{6}{5}\right)$

14. $2x + 3y = 2$
$6x + 6y = 5$

$\left(\frac{1}{2}, \frac{1}{3}\right)$

15. $2x + 4y = 6$
$3x + 6y = 12$

no solution

16. $3x + 3y = 9$
$5x + 4y = 10$

(−2, 5)

17. $2x - 7y = 5$
$3x - 6y = 12$

(6, 1)

18. $2x - 4y = 18$
$-5x - 6y = 3$

(3, −3)

13–6

NAME ______________________ DATE __________ PERIOD __________

Practice

Student Edition
Pages 580–585

Solving Quadratic-Linear Systems of Equations

Solve each system of equations by graphing.

1. $y = x^2 + 2$
$y = x + 4$

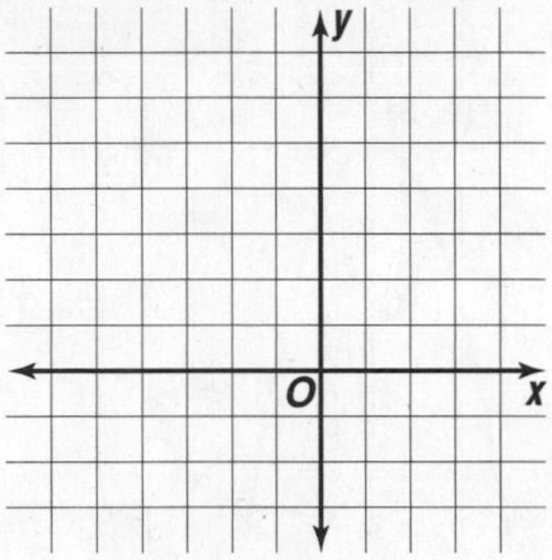

2. $y = x^2 - 1$
$y = x - 2$

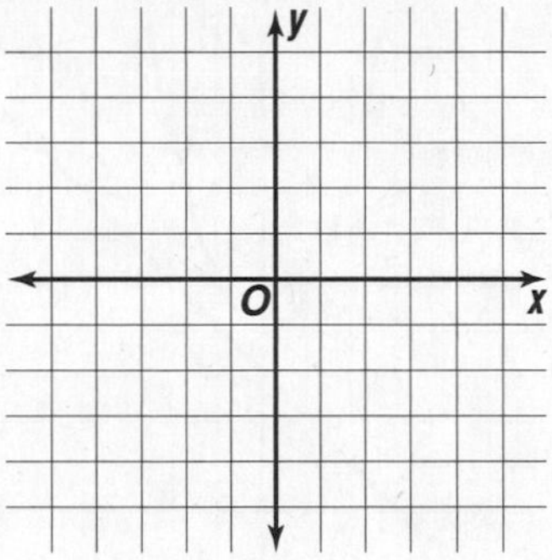

3. $y = -x^2 + 3$
$y = 3$

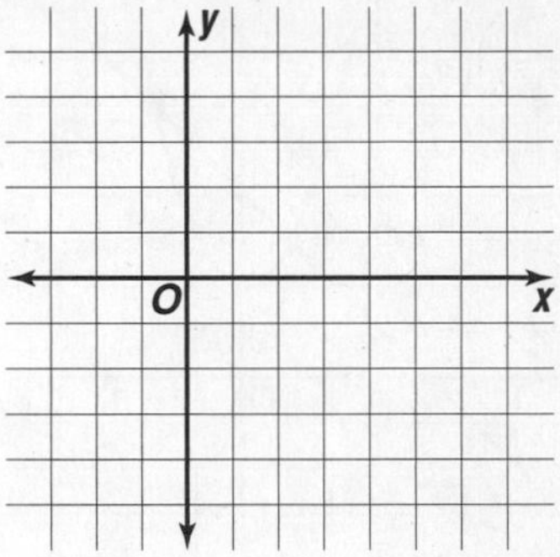

4. $y = x^2 + 1$
$y = -x - 1$

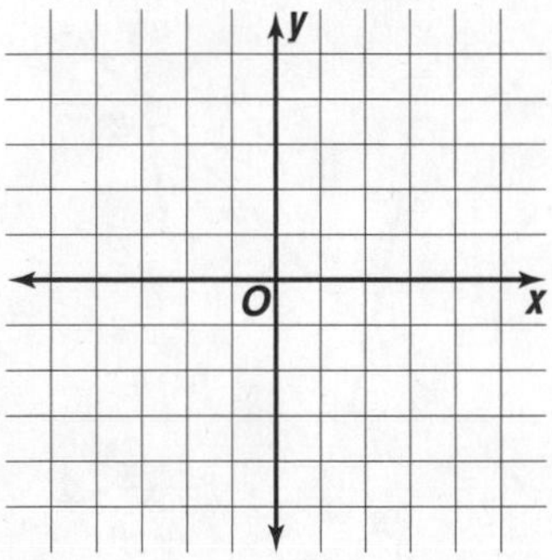

5. $y = -x^2$
$y = -2x + 1$

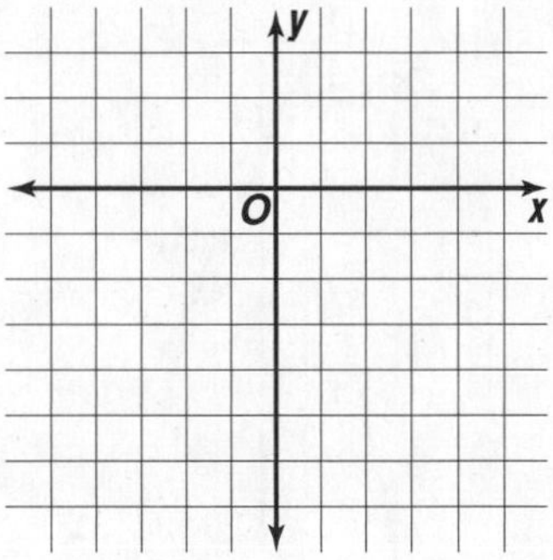

6. $y = x^2 - 2$
$y = x + 4$

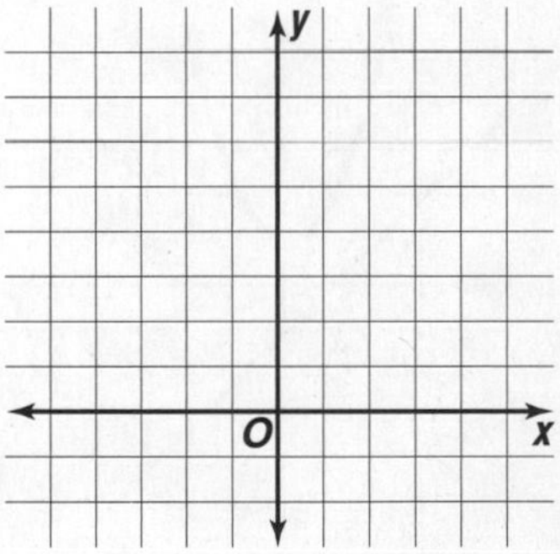

Use substitution to solve each system of equations.

7. $y = -x^2 + 1$
$y = x - 1$

8. $y = x^2 + 2$
$y = -4$

9. $y = x^2 - 5$
$x = -3$

10. $y = -6x^2 + 1$
$y = x + 1$

11. $y = 2x^2 + 3$
$y = x + 2$

12. $y = x^2 + x - 4$
$y = x - 3$

NAME ________________ DATE ________ PERIOD ______

Practice

Student Edition
Pages 580–585

Solving Quadratic-Linear Systems of Equations

Solve each system of equations by graphing.

1. $y = x^2 + 2$
$y = x + 4$

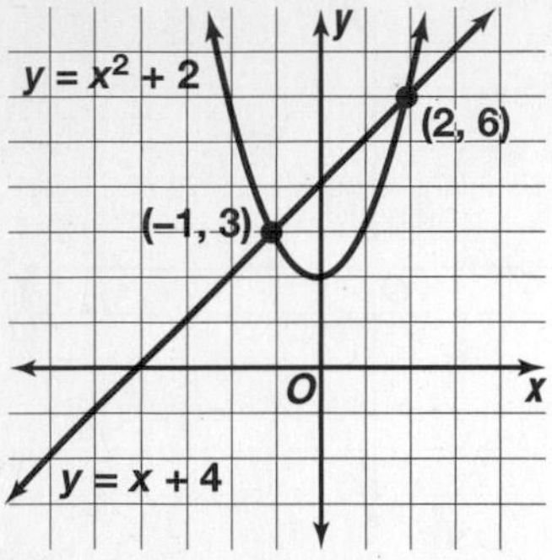

(−1, 3), (2, 6)

2. $y = x^2 - 1$
$y = x - 2$

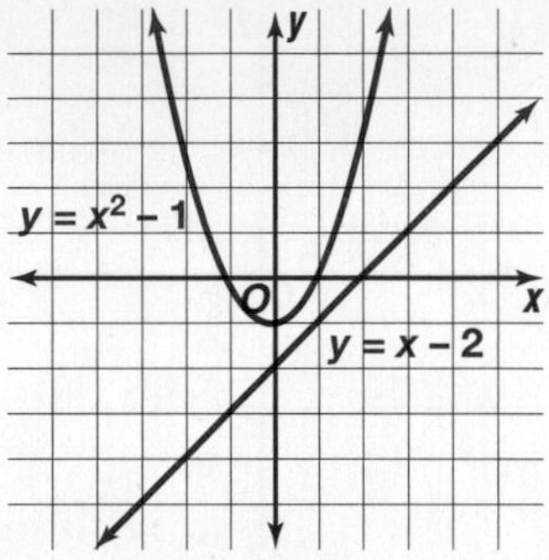

no solution

3. $y = -x^2 + 3$
$y = 3$

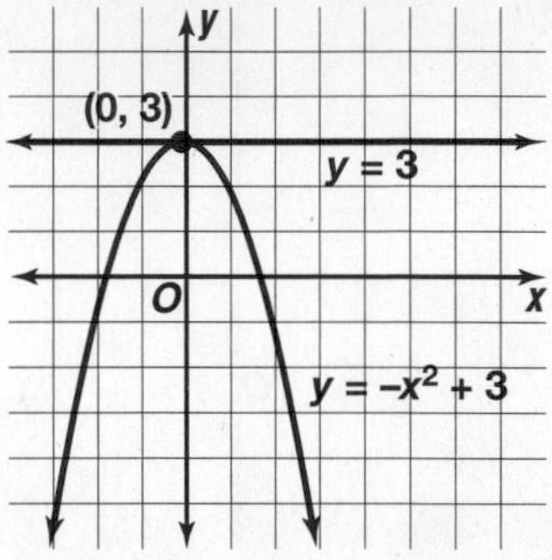

(0, 3)

4. $y = x^2 + 1$
$y = -x - 1$

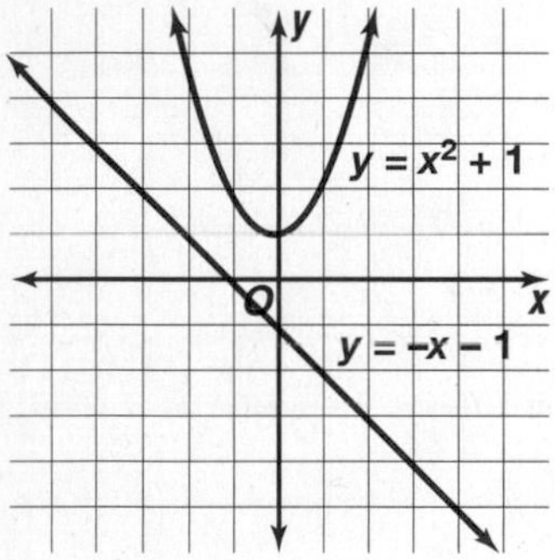

no solution

5. $y = -x^2$
$y = -2x + 1$

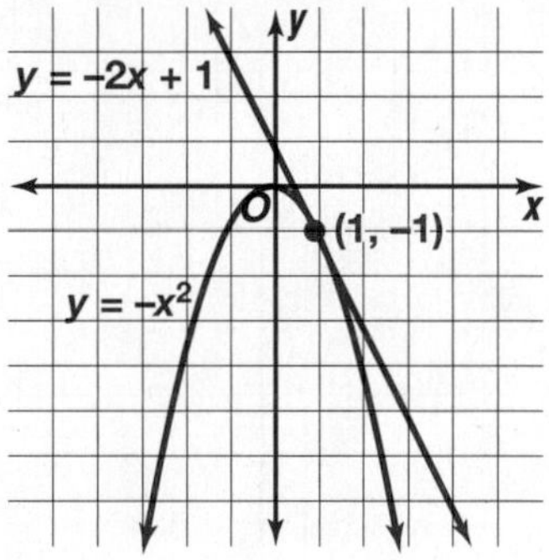

(1, −1)

6. $y = x^2 - 2$
$y = x + 4$

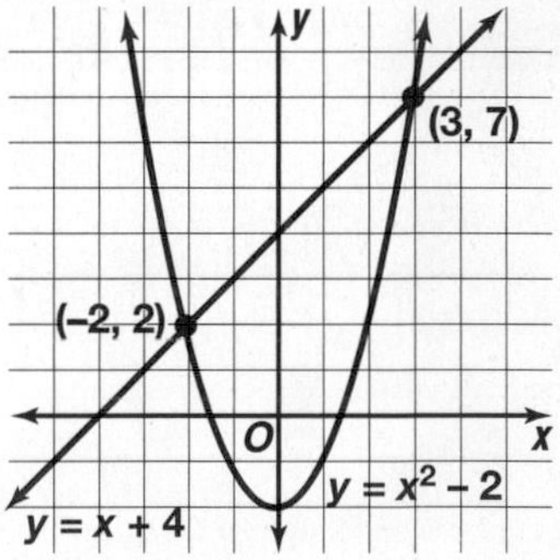

(−2, 2), (3, 7)

Use substitution to solve each system of equations.

7. $y = -x^2 + 1$
$y = x - 1$

(−2, −3), (1, 0)

8. $y = x^2 + 2$
$y = -4$

no solution

9. $y = x^2 - 5$
$x = -3$

(−3, 4)

10. $y = -6x^2 + 1$
$y = x + 1$

(0, 1), $\left(-\frac{1}{6}, \frac{5}{6}\right)$

11. $y = 2x^2 + 3$
$y = x + 2$

no solution

12. $y = x^2 + x - 4$
$y = x - 3$

(−1, −4), (1, −2)

NAME ________________________ DATE ________ PERIOD ______

Practice

Graphing Systems of Inequalities

Solve each system of inequalities by graphing. If the system does not have a solution, write no solution.

1. $x \leq 2$
$y \geq -1$

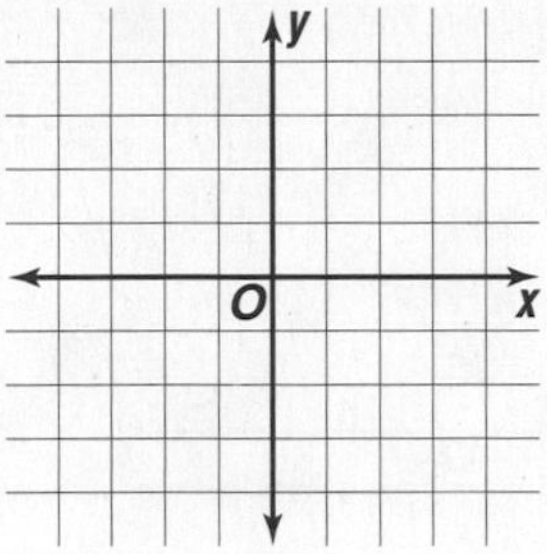

2. $x > 2$
$y > x + 1$

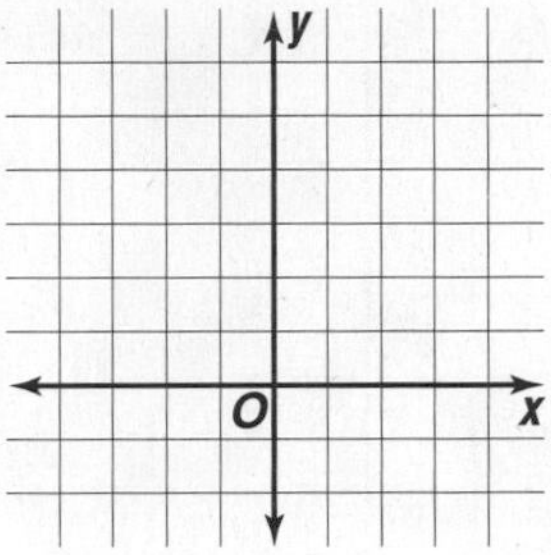

3. $x \geq 3$
$y > x + 2$

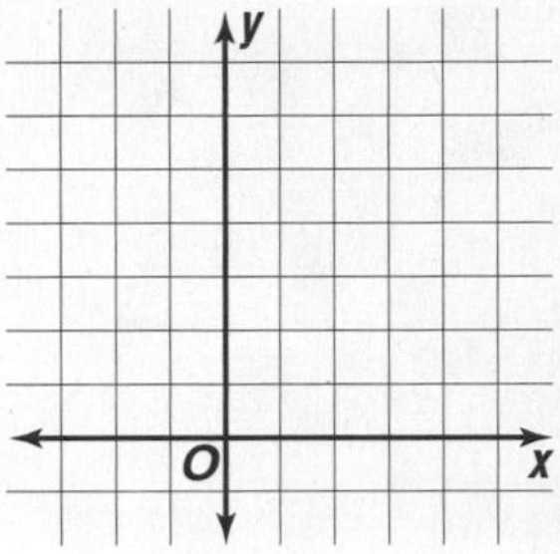

4. $x + y < 1$
$y > x + 3$

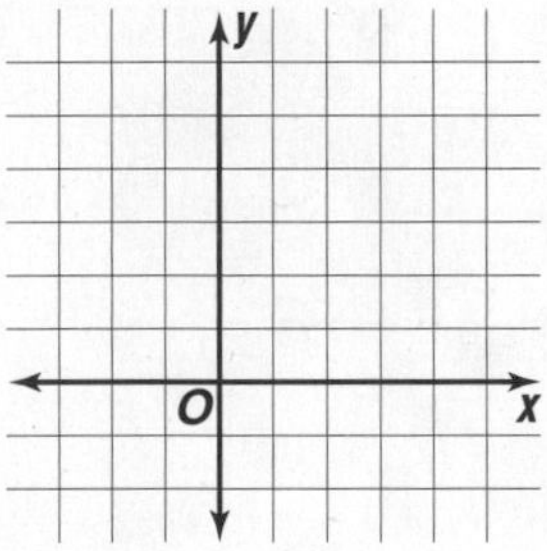

5. $2y \geq x + 4$
$x - 2y \geq 1$

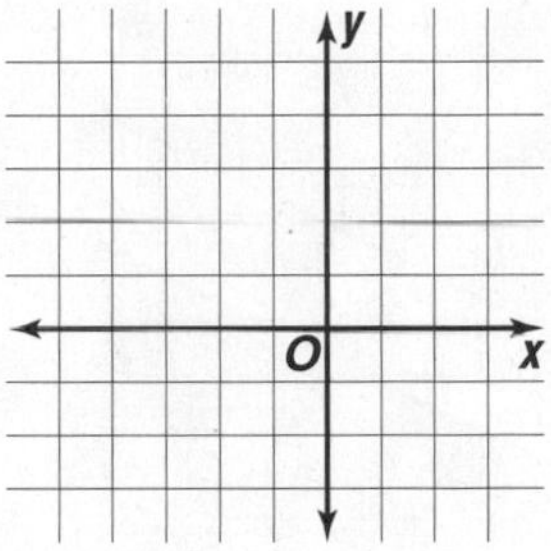

6. $y \leq x + 4$
$x - y \leq 3$

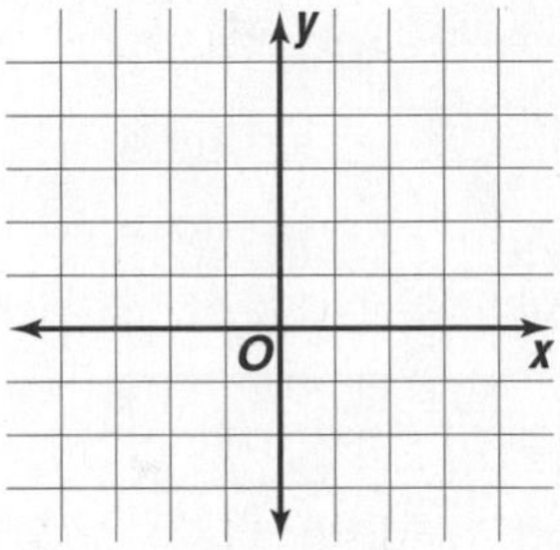

7. $x + y < 2$
$y > x + 4$

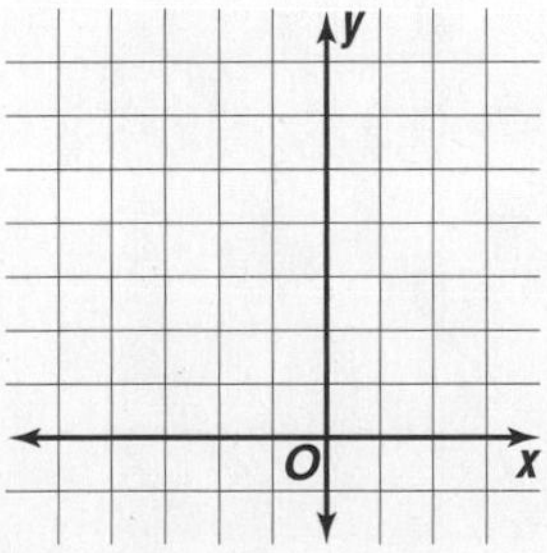

8. $x - y < -4$
$y \leq x - 3$

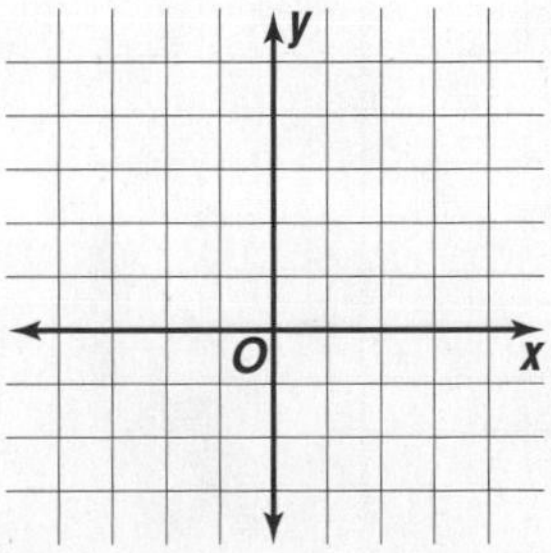

9. $y \geq x + 2$
$y \leq 2x + 2$

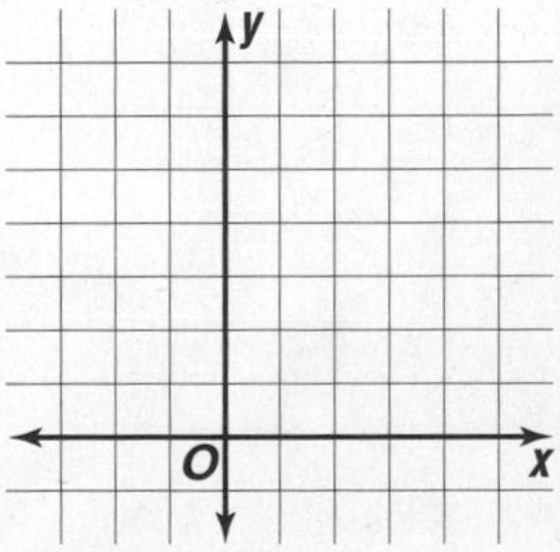

10. $x - y < -5$
$y < -x + 1$

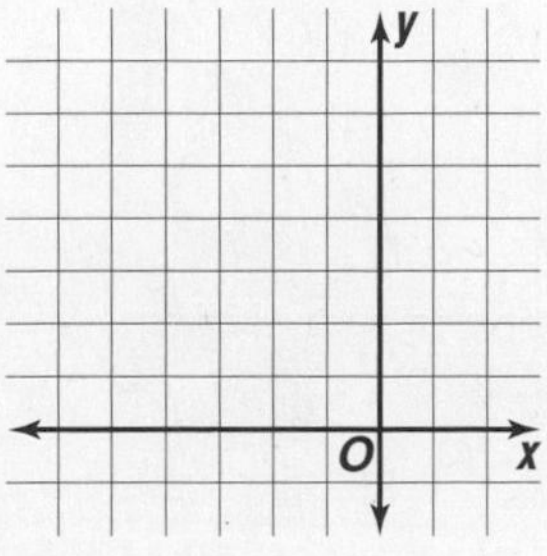

11. $y < x + 2$
$x + y \geq -4$

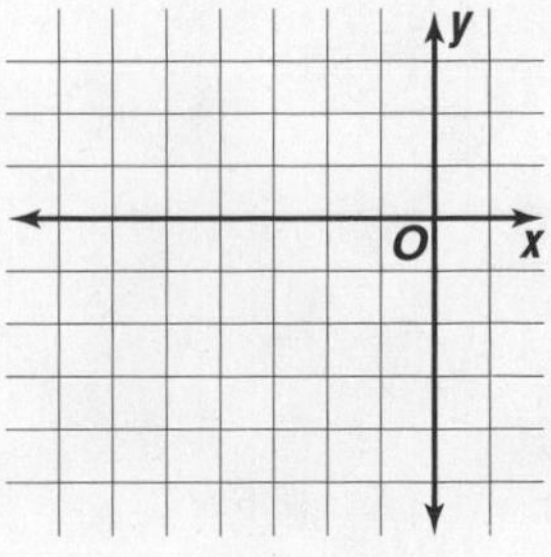

12. $x + 2y > 5$
$x - y > 1$

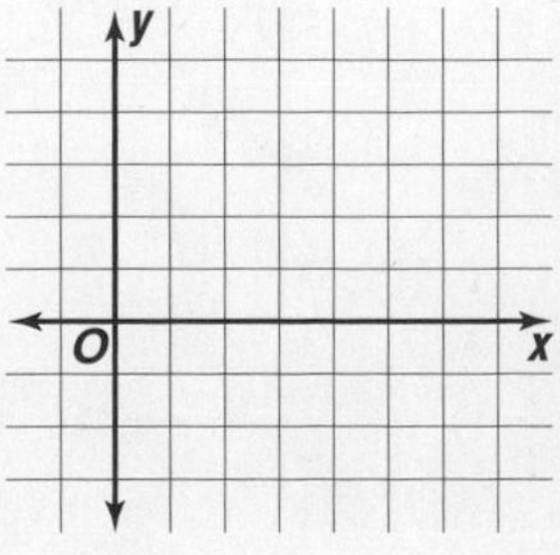

13–7

NAME ______________________ DATE __________ PERIOD ______

Practice

Student Edition
Pages 586–591

Graphing Systems of Inequalities

***Solve each system of inequalities by graphing. If the system does not have a solution, write* no solution.**

1. $x \leq 2$
$y \geq -1$

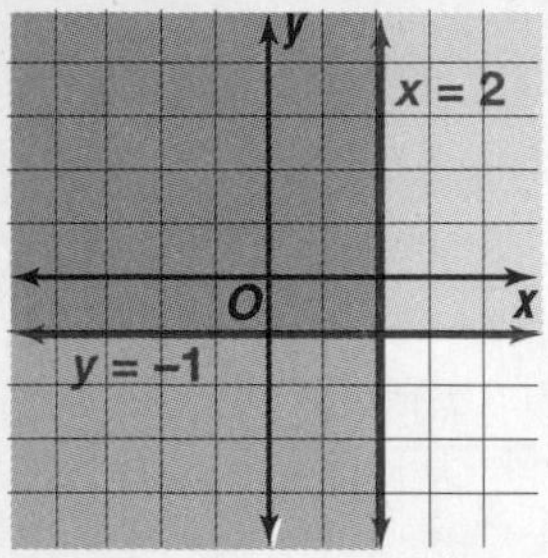

2. $x > 2$
$y > x + 1$

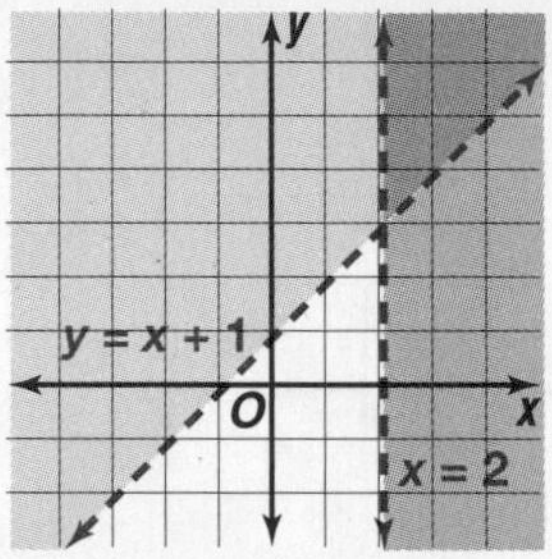

3. $x \geq 3$
$y > x + 2$

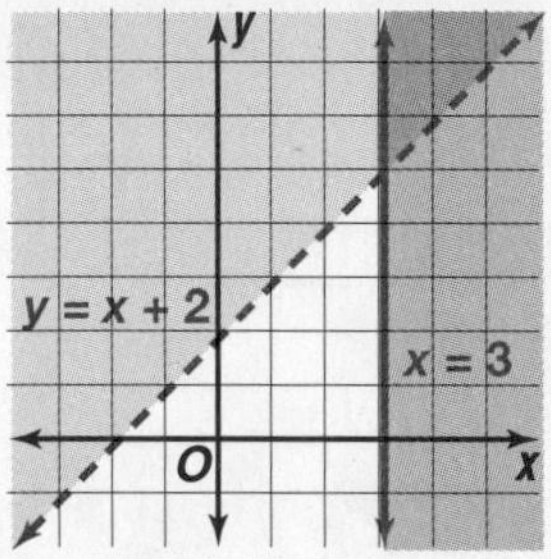

4. $x + y < 1$
$y > x + 3$

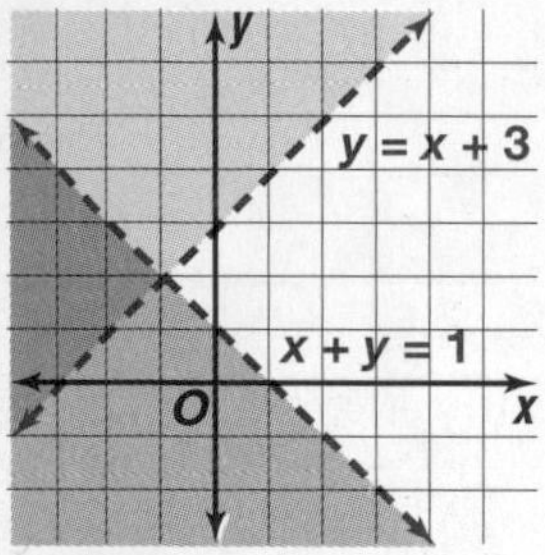

5. $2y \geq x + 4$ **no solution**
$x - 2y \geq 1$

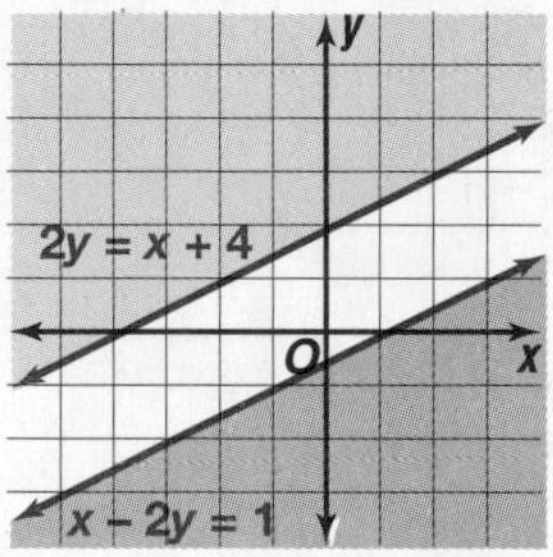

6. $y \leq x + 4$
$x - y \leq 3$

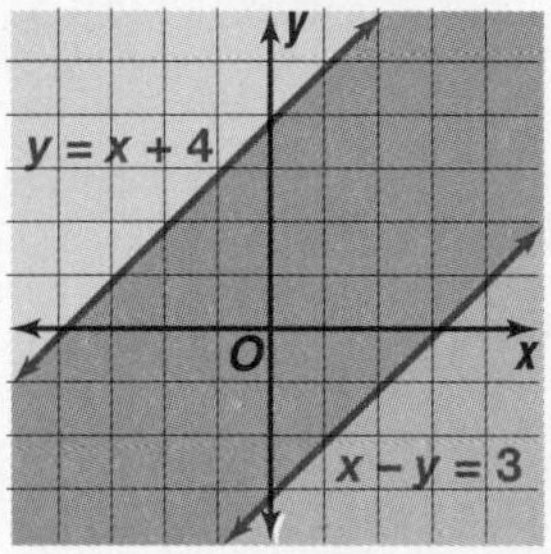

7. $x + y < 2$
$y > x + 4$

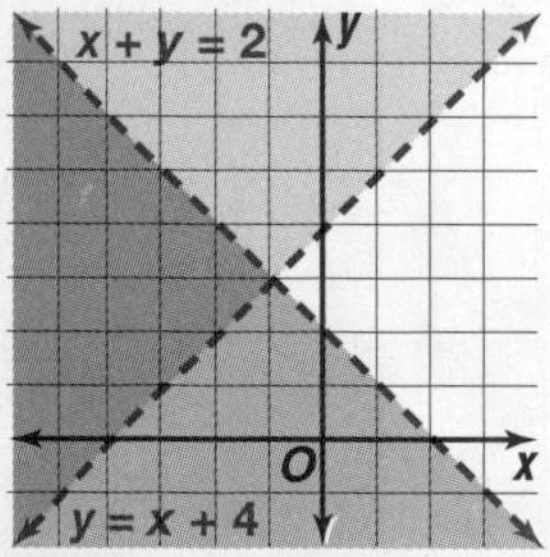

8. $x - y < -4$ **no solution**
$y \leq x - 3$

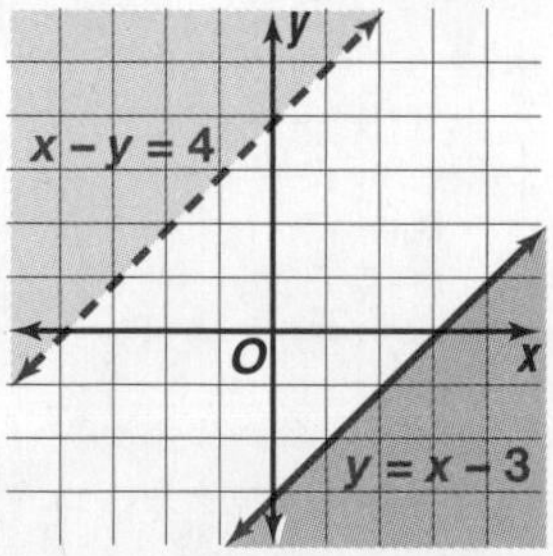

9. $y \geq x + 2$
$y \leq 2x + 2$

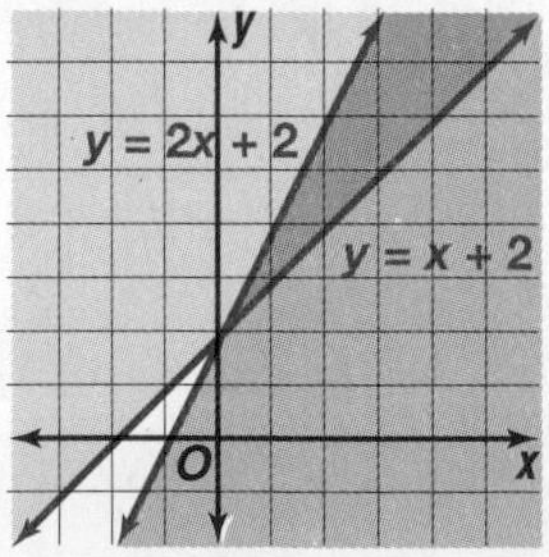

10. $x - y < -5$
$y < -x + 1$

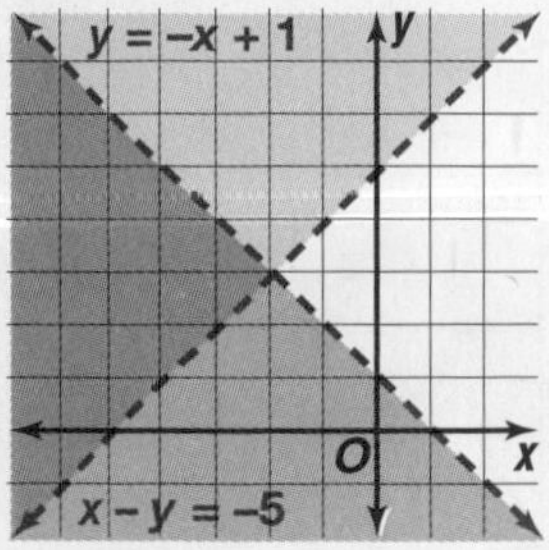

11. $y < x + 2$
$x + y \geq -4$

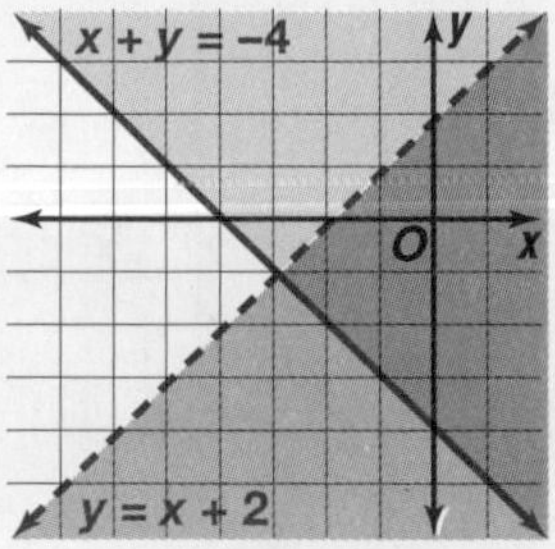

12. $x + 2y > 5$
$x - y > 1$

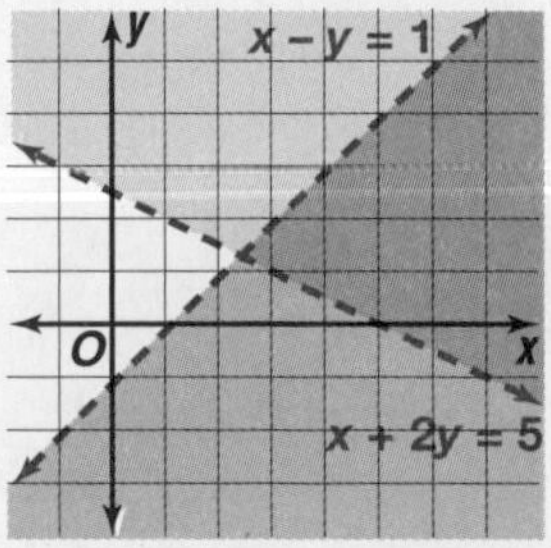

NAME ______________________ DATE ________ PERIOD ______

14-1 Practice

Student Edition
Pages 600–605

The Real Numbers

Name the set or sets of numbers to which each real number belongs. Let N = natural numbers, W = whole numbers, Z = integers, Q = rational numbers, and I = irrational numbers.

1. $\sqrt{19}$ **2.** -8 **3.** $1.737337...$ **4.** $0.\overline{4}$

5. $-\frac{5}{6}$ **6.** $\sqrt{64}$ **7.** $-\frac{28}{7}$ **8.** $-\sqrt{144}$

9. $0.414114111...$ **10.** $\frac{1}{3}$ **11.** 13 **12.** 0.75

Find an approximation, to the nearest tenth, for each square root. Then graph the square root on a number line.

13. $\sqrt{6}$

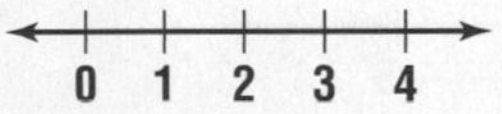

14. $\sqrt{11}$

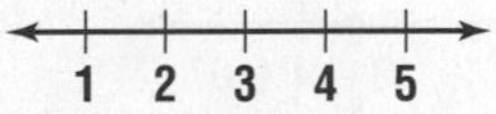

15. $-\sqrt{24}$

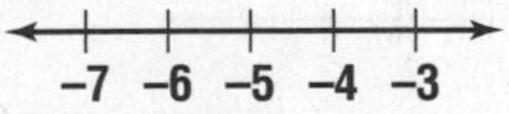

16. $\sqrt{30}$

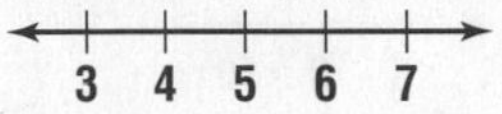

17. $-\sqrt{38}$

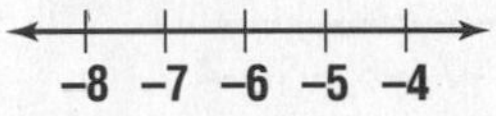

18. $\sqrt{51}$

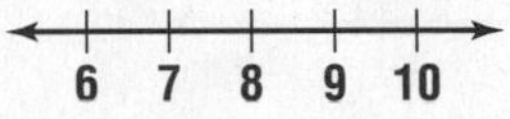

19. $-\sqrt{65}$

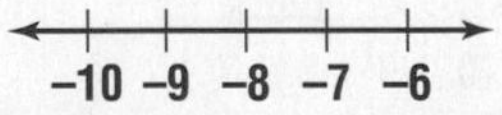

20. $\sqrt{72}$

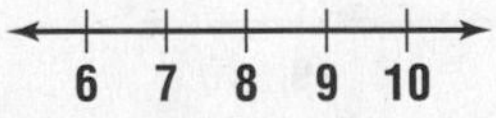

21. $-\sqrt{89}$

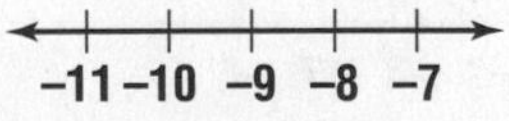

22. $\sqrt{118}$

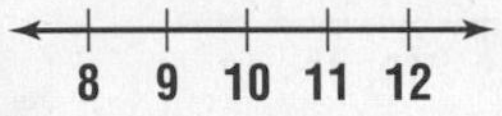

23. $-\sqrt{131}$

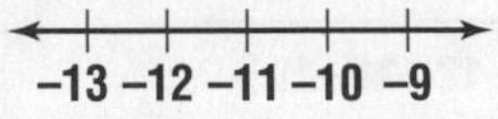

24. $\sqrt{104}$

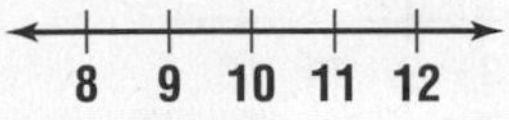

Determine whether each number is rational or irrational. If it is irrational, find two consecutive integers between which its graph lies on the number line.

25. $\sqrt{28}$ **26.** $-\sqrt{9}$ **27.** $\sqrt{56}$

28. $-\sqrt{14}$ **29.** $\sqrt{36}$ **30.** $\sqrt{99}$

31. $-\sqrt{73}$ **32.** $\sqrt{196}$ **33.** $\sqrt{77}$

34. $-\sqrt{100}$ **35.** $\sqrt{88}$ **36.** $-\sqrt{46}$

NAME ______________________ DATE __________ PERIOD ______

Practice

Student Edition
Pages 600–605

The Real Numbers

Name the set or sets of numbers to which each real number belongs. Let N = natural numbers, W = whole numbers, Z = integers, Q = rational numbers, and I = irrational numbers.

1. $\sqrt{19}$ **I**
2. -8 **Z, Q**
3. 1.737337... **I**
4. $0.\overline{4}$ **Q**
5. $-\frac{5}{6}$ **Q**
6. $\sqrt{64}$ **N, W, Z, Q**
7. $-\frac{28}{7}$ **Z, Q**
8. $-\sqrt{144}$ **Z, Q**
9. 0.414114111... **I**
10. $\frac{1}{3}$ **Q**
11. 13 **N, W, Z, Q**
12. 0.75 **Q**

Find an approximation, to the nearest tenth, for each square root. Then graph the square root on a number line.

13. $\sqrt{6}$ **2.4**

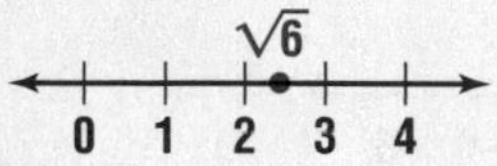

14. $\sqrt{11}$ **3.3**

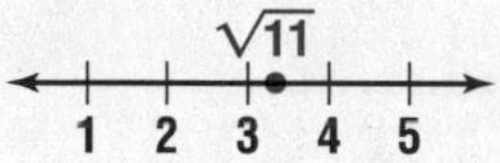

15. $-\sqrt{24}$ **−4.9**

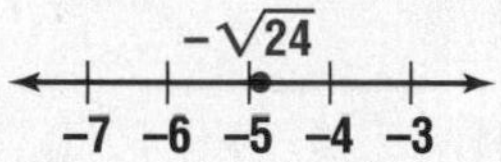

16. $\sqrt{30}$ **5.5**

17. $-\sqrt{38}$ **−6.2**

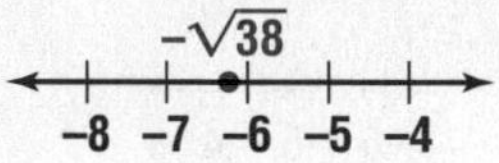

18. $\sqrt{51}$ **7.1**

19. $-\sqrt{65}$ **−8.1**

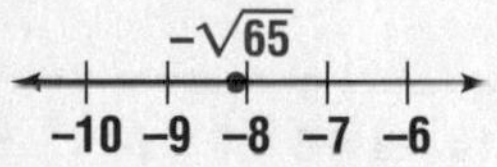

20. $\sqrt{72}$ **8.5**

21. $-\sqrt{89}$ **−9.4**

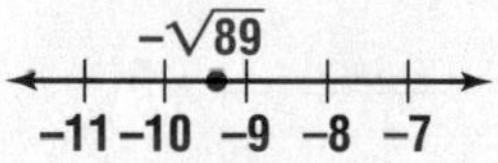

22. $\sqrt{118}$ **10.9**

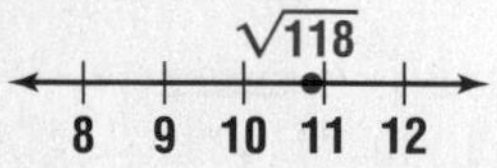

23. $-\sqrt{131}$ **−11.4**

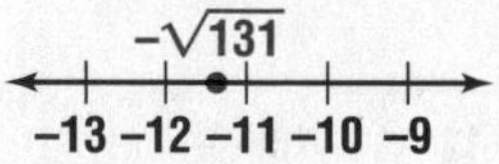

24. $\sqrt{104}$ **10.2**

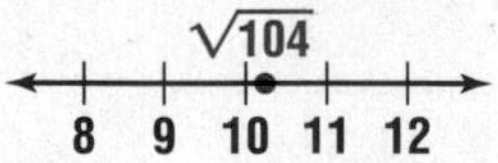

Determine whether each number is rational or irrational. If it is irrational, find two consecutive integers between which its graph lies on the number line.

25. $\sqrt{28}$ **irrational; 5 and 6**
26. $-\sqrt{9}$ **rational**
27. $\sqrt{56}$ **irrational; 7 and 8**
28. $-\sqrt{14}$ **irrational; −4 and −3**
29. $\sqrt{36}$ **rational**
30. $\sqrt{99}$ **irrational; 9 and 10**
31. $-\sqrt{73}$ **irrational; −9 and −8**
32. $\sqrt{196}$ **rational**
33. $\sqrt{77}$ **irrational; 8 and 9**
34. $-\sqrt{100}$ **rational**
35. $\sqrt{88}$ **irrational; 9 and 10**
36. $-\sqrt{46}$ **irrational; −7 and −6**

NAME ______________________ DATE __________ PERIOD ______

Practice

Student Edition
Pages 606–611

The Distance Formula

Find the distance between each pair of points. Round to the nearest tenth, if necessary.

1. $X(4, 2)$, $Y(8, 6)$

2. $Q(-3, 8)$, $R(2, -4)$

3. $A(0, -3)$, $B(-6, 5)$

4. $M(-9, -5)$, $N(-4, 1)$

5. $J(6, 2)$, $K(-7, 5)$

6. $S(-2, 4)$, $T(-3, 8)$

7. $V(-1, -2)$, $W(-9, -7)$

8. $O(5, 2)$, $P(7, -4)$

9. $G(3, 4)$, $H(-2, 1)$

Find the value of a if the points are the indicated distance apart.

10. $C(1, 1)$, $D(a, 7)$; $d = 10$

11. $Y(a, 3)$, $Z(5, -1)$; $d = 5$

12. $F(3, -2)$, $G(-9, a)$; $d = 13$

13. $W(-2, a)$, $X(7, -4)$; $d = \sqrt{85}$

14. $B(a, -6)$, $C(8, -3)$; $d = \sqrt{34}$

15. $T(2, 2)$, $U(a, -4)$; $d = \sqrt{72}$

NAME ______________________ DATE __________ PERIOD ______

Practice

Student Edition
Pages 606–611

The Distance Formula

Find the distance between each pair of points. Round to the nearest tenth, if necessary.

1. $X(4, 2)$, $Y(8, 6)$
   $\sqrt{32}$ or 5.7

2. $Q(-3, 8)$, $R(2, -4)$
   13

3. $A(0, -3)$, $B(-6, 5)$
   10

4. $M(-9, -5)$, $N(-4, 1)$
   $\sqrt{61}$ or 7.8

5. $J(6, 2)$, $K(-7, 5)$
   $\sqrt{178}$ or 13.3

6. $S(-2, 4)$, $T(-3, 8)$
   $\sqrt{17}$ or 4.1

7. $V(-1, -2)$, $W(-9, -7)$
   $\sqrt{89}$ or 9.4

8. $O(5, 2)$, $P(7, -4)$
   $\sqrt{40}$ or 6.3

9. $G(3, 4)$, $H(-2, 1)$
   $\sqrt{34}$ or 5.8

Find the value of a if the points are the indicated distance apart.

10. $C(1, 1)$, $D(a, 7)$; $d = 10$
    9 or −7

11. $Y(a, 3)$, $Z(5, -1)$; $d = 5$
    8 or 2

12. $F(3, -2)$, $G(-9, a)$; $d = 13$
    −7 or 3

13. $W(-2, a)$, $X(7, -4)$; $d = \sqrt{85}$
    −6 or −2

14. $B(a, -6)$, $C(8, -3)$; $d = \sqrt{34}$
    13 or 3

15. $T(2, 2)$, $U(a, -4)$; $d = \sqrt{72}$
    8 or −4

NAME ______________________ DATE __________ PERIOD ______

14-3 Practice

Student Edition
Pages 614–619

Simplifying Radical Expressions

Simplify each expression. Leave in radical form.

1. $\sqrt{28}$

2. $\sqrt{48}$

3. $\sqrt{72}$

4. $\sqrt{90}$

5. $\sqrt{175}$

6. $\sqrt{245}$

7. $\sqrt{7} \cdot \sqrt{14}$

8. $\sqrt{2} \cdot \sqrt{10}$

9. $\sqrt{10} \cdot \sqrt{60}$

10. $\frac{\sqrt{48}}{\sqrt{2}}$

11. $\frac{\sqrt{54}}{\sqrt{3}}$

12. $\frac{\sqrt{96}}{\sqrt{8}}$

13. $\frac{\sqrt{20}}{\sqrt{3}}$

14. $\frac{\sqrt{2}}{\sqrt{10}}$

15. $\frac{\sqrt{8}}{\sqrt{6}}$

16. $\frac{5}{4 - \sqrt{7}}$

17. $\frac{4}{3 + \sqrt{2}}$

18. $\frac{3}{3 - \sqrt{3}}$

Simplify each expression. Use absolute value symbols if necessary.

19. $\sqrt{50x^2}$

20. $\sqrt{27ab^3}$

21. $\sqrt{49c^6d^4}$

22. $\sqrt{63x^2y^5z^2}$

23. $\sqrt{56m^2n^4p^3}$

24. $\sqrt{108r^2s^3t^6}$

14–3

NAME ______________________ DATE __________ PERIOD __________

Practice

Student Edition
Pages 614–619

Simplifying Radical Expressions

Simplify each expression. Leave in radical form.

1. $\sqrt{28}$

   $2\sqrt{7}$

2. $\sqrt{48}$

   $4\sqrt{3}$

3. $\sqrt{72}$

   $6\sqrt{2}$

4. $\sqrt{90}$

   $3\sqrt{10}$

5. $\sqrt{175}$

   $5\sqrt{7}$

6. $\sqrt{245}$

   $7\sqrt{5}$

7. $\sqrt{7} \cdot \sqrt{14}$

   $7\sqrt{2}$

8. $\sqrt{2} \cdot \sqrt{10}$

   $2\sqrt{5}$

9. $\sqrt{10} \cdot \sqrt{60}$

   $10\sqrt{6}$

10. $\frac{\sqrt{48}}{\sqrt{2}}$

    $2\sqrt{6}$

11. $\frac{\sqrt{54}}{\sqrt{3}}$

    $3\sqrt{2}$

12. $\frac{\sqrt{96}}{\sqrt{8}}$

    $2\sqrt{3}$

13. $\frac{\sqrt{20}}{\sqrt{3}}$

    $\frac{2\sqrt{15}}{3}$

14. $\frac{\sqrt{2}}{\sqrt{10}}$

    $\frac{\sqrt{5}}{5}$

15. $\frac{\sqrt{8}}{\sqrt{6}}$

    $\frac{2\sqrt{3}}{3}$

16. $\frac{5}{4 - \sqrt{7}}$

    $\frac{20 + 5\sqrt{7}}{9}$

17. $\frac{4}{3 + \sqrt{2}}$

    $\frac{12 - 4\sqrt{2}}{7}$

18. $\frac{3}{3 - \sqrt{3}}$

    $\frac{3 + \sqrt{3}}{2}$

Simplify each expression. Use absolute value symbols if necessary.

19. $\sqrt{50x^2}$

    $5|x|\sqrt{2}$

20. $\sqrt{27ab^3}$

    $3|b|\sqrt{3ab}$

21. $\sqrt{49c^6d^4}$

    $7|c^3|d^2$

22. $\sqrt{63x^2y^5z^2}$

    $3|xz|y^2\sqrt{7y}$

23. $\sqrt{56m^2n^4p^3}$

    $2|mp|n^2\sqrt{14p}$

24. $\sqrt{108r^2s^3t^6}$

    $6|rt^3|s\sqrt{3s}$

NAME ______________________________ DATE __________ PERIOD _____

Practice

Student Edition
Pages 620–623

Adding and Subtracting Radical Expressions

Simplify each expression.

1. $3\sqrt{7} + 4\sqrt{7}$
2. $9\sqrt{2} - 4\sqrt{2}$
3. $-5\sqrt{17} + 12\sqrt{17}$
4. $7\sqrt{3} - 3\sqrt{3}$
5. $-8\sqrt{5} + 2\sqrt{5}$
6. $-7\sqrt{11} - 2\sqrt{11}$
7. $13\sqrt{10} - 5\sqrt{10}$
8. $-6\sqrt{7} + 4\sqrt{7}$
9. $3\sqrt{7} + \sqrt{3}$
10. $2\sqrt{6} + 4\sqrt{6} + 5\sqrt{6}$
11. $5\sqrt{3} + 4\sqrt{3} - 7\sqrt{3}$
12. $3\sqrt{2} - 2\sqrt{2} + 5\sqrt{2}$
13. $11\sqrt{5} - 3\sqrt{5} - 2\sqrt{5}$
14. $6\sqrt{13} + 3\sqrt{13} - 12\sqrt{13}$
15. $4\sqrt{10} - 3\sqrt{10} - 5\sqrt{10}$
16. $4\sqrt{6} - 2\sqrt{6} + 3\sqrt{6}$
17. $7\sqrt{7} + 4\sqrt{3} - 5\sqrt{7}$
18. $-9\sqrt{2} + 4\sqrt{6} + 2\sqrt{2}$
19. $\sqrt{12} + 2\sqrt{27}$
20. $5\sqrt{63} - \sqrt{28}$
21. $-4\sqrt{96} + 6\sqrt{24}$
22. $-3\sqrt{45} + 3\sqrt{180}$
23. $-4\sqrt{56} + 3\sqrt{126}$
24. $2\sqrt{72} - 3\sqrt{50}$
25. $7\sqrt{32} + 3\sqrt{75}$
26. $\sqrt{32} + \sqrt{8} + \sqrt{18}$
27. $2\sqrt{20} - \sqrt{80} + \sqrt{45}$

NAME ______________________ DATE __________ PERIOD ______

Practice

Student Edition
Pages 620–623

Adding and Subtracting Radical Expressions

Simplify each expression.

1. $3\sqrt{7} + 4\sqrt{7}$
$7\sqrt{7}$

2. $9\sqrt{2} - 4\sqrt{2}$
$5\sqrt{2}$

3. $-5\sqrt{17} + 12\sqrt{17}$
$7\sqrt{17}$

4. $7\sqrt{3} - 3\sqrt{3}$
$4\sqrt{3}$

5. $-8\sqrt{5} + 2\sqrt{5}$
$-6\sqrt{5}$

6. $-7\sqrt{11} - 2\sqrt{11}$
$-9\sqrt{11}$

7. $13\sqrt{10} - 5\sqrt{10}$
$8\sqrt{10}$

8. $-6\sqrt{7} + 4\sqrt{7}$
$-2\sqrt{7}$

9. $3\sqrt{7} + \sqrt{3}$
in simplest form

10. $2\sqrt{6} + 4\sqrt{6} + 5\sqrt{6}$
$11\sqrt{6}$

11. $5\sqrt{3} + 4\sqrt{3} - 7\sqrt{3}$
$2\sqrt{3}$

12. $3\sqrt{2} - 2\sqrt{2} + 5\sqrt{2}$
$6\sqrt{2}$

13. $11\sqrt{5} - 3\sqrt{5} - 2\sqrt{5}$
$6\sqrt{5}$

14. $6\sqrt{13} + 3\sqrt{13} - 12\sqrt{13}$
$-3\sqrt{13}$

15. $4\sqrt{10} - 3\sqrt{10} - 5\sqrt{10}$
$-4\sqrt{10}$

16. $4\sqrt{6} - 2\sqrt{6} + 3\sqrt{6}$
$5\sqrt{6}$

17. $7\sqrt{7} + 4\sqrt{3} - 5\sqrt{7}$
$2\sqrt{7} + 4\sqrt{3}$

18. $-9\sqrt{2} + 4\sqrt{6} + 2\sqrt{2}$
$-7\sqrt{2} + 4\sqrt{6}$

19. $\sqrt{12} + 2\sqrt{27}$
$8\sqrt{3}$

20. $5\sqrt{63} - \sqrt{28}$
$13\sqrt{7}$

21. $-4\sqrt{96} + 6\sqrt{24}$
$-4\sqrt{6}$

22. $-3\sqrt{45} + 3\sqrt{180}$
$9\sqrt{5}$

23. $-4\sqrt{56} + 3\sqrt{126}$
$\sqrt{14}$

24. $2\sqrt{72} - 3\sqrt{50}$
$-3\sqrt{2}$

25. $7\sqrt{32} + 3\sqrt{75}$
$28\sqrt{2} + 15\sqrt{3}$

26. $\sqrt{32} + \sqrt{8} + \sqrt{18}$
$9\sqrt{2}$

27. $2\sqrt{20} - \sqrt{80} + \sqrt{45}$
$3\sqrt{5}$

14–5

NAME ______________________ DATE __________ PERIOD ______

Practice

Student Edition
Pages 624–629

Solving Radical Equations

Solve each equation. Check your solution.

1. $\sqrt{x} - 6 = 3$
2. $\sqrt{k} + 7 = 20$
3. $\sqrt{p + 3} = 3$
4. $\sqrt{n + 11} = 5$
5. $\sqrt{w - 2} - 1 = 6$
6. $\sqrt{y - 5} + 9 = 14$
7. $\sqrt{2r + 1} - 10 = -1$
8. $\sqrt{3h - 11} + 2 = 9$
9. $\sqrt{a + 4} = a - 8$
10. $\sqrt{z - 3} + 5 = z$
11. $\sqrt{3b + 9} + 3 = b$
12. $\sqrt{5f - 5} + 1 = f$
13. $\sqrt{8 + 2c} = c - 8$
14. $\sqrt{3s - 6} = s - 2$
15. $\sqrt{4h + 4} + h = 7$
16. $\sqrt{5m + 4} = m + 2$
17. $\sqrt{2y - 7} - y = -5$
18. $\sqrt{3k + 4} + k = 8$

NAME ______________________ DATE __________ PERIOD ______

Practice

Solving Radical Equations

Solve each equation. Check your solution.

1. $\sqrt{x} - 6 = 3$

   81

2. $\sqrt{k} + 7 = 20$

   169

3. $\sqrt{p + 3} = 3$

   6

4. $\sqrt{n + 11} = 5$

   14

5. $\sqrt{w - 2} - 1 = 6$

   51

6. $\sqrt{y - 5} + 9 = 14$

   30

7. $\sqrt{2r + 1} - 10 = -1$

   40

8. $\sqrt{3h - 11} + 2 = 9$

   20

9. $\sqrt{a + 4} = a - 8$

   12

10. $\sqrt{z - 3} + 5 = z$

    7

11. $\sqrt{3b + 9} + 3 = b$

    9

12. $\sqrt{5f - 5} + 1 = f$

    6 and 1

13. $\sqrt{8 + 2c} = c - 8$

    14

14. $\sqrt{3s - 6} = s - 2$

    5 and 2

15. $\sqrt{4h + 4} + h = 7$

    3

16. $\sqrt{5m + 4} = m + 2$

    1 and 0

17. $\sqrt{2y - 7} - y = -5$

    8

18. $\sqrt{3k + 4} + k = 8$

    4

NAME ______________________ DATE ____________ PERIOD ________

Practice

Student Edition
Pages 638–643

Simplifying Rational Expressions

Find the excluded value(s) for each rational expression.

1. $\frac{2n}{n-4}$

2. $\frac{6}{x+3}$

3. $\frac{3b}{b(b+9)}$

4. $\frac{y+2}{y^2-4}$

5. $\frac{4x+6}{(x+6)(x-5)}$

6. $\frac{2a-2}{a^2-3a-28}$

Simplify each rational expression.

7. $\frac{6}{15}$

8. $\frac{12m}{18m^3}$

9. $\frac{16x^2y}{36xy^3}$

10. $\frac{25ab}{30b^2}$

11. $\frac{-8y^4z}{20y^6z^2}$

12. $\frac{5(x-1)}{8(x-1)}$

13. $\frac{y(y+7)}{9(y+7)}$

14. $\frac{x^2-4x}{3(x-4)}$

15. $\frac{x^2+2x}{5x+10}$

16. $\frac{x^2+5x}{(x+5)(x-7)}$

17. $\frac{x^2-6x}{x^2-4x-12}$

18. $\frac{(x+4)(x+4)}{(x+4)(x-2)}$

19. $\frac{b^2+6b+9}{b^2-2b-15}$

20. $\frac{y^2-36}{y^2+9y+18}$

21. $\frac{x^2-16}{x^2+x-12}$

22. $\frac{y^2+4y+4}{y^2-4}$

23. $\frac{a^2+3a}{a^2-3a-18}$

24. $\frac{y^2+7y+10}{y^2+5y}$

25. $\frac{x^2+4x+3}{x^2+3x+2}$

26. $\frac{x^2-6x+8}{x^2+x-6}$

27. $\frac{9-x^2}{x^2+6x-27}$

NAME ______________________ DATE __________ PERIOD ______

Practice

Student Edition
Pages 638–643

Simplifying Rational Expressions

Find the excluded value(s) for each rational expression.

1. $\frac{2n}{n-4}$ **4**

2. $\frac{6}{x+3}$ **−3**

3. $\frac{3b}{b(b+9)}$ **0, −9**

4. $\frac{y+2}{y^2-4}$ **2, −2**

5. $\frac{4x+6}{(x+6)(x-5)}$ **−6, 5**

6. $\frac{2a-2}{a^2-3a-28}$ **7, −4**

Simplify each rational expression.

7. $\frac{6}{15}$ $\mathbf{\frac{2}{5}}$

8. $\frac{12m}{18m^3}$ $\mathbf{\frac{2}{3m^2}}$

9. $\frac{16x^2y}{36xy^3}$ $\mathbf{\frac{4x}{9y^2}}$

10. $\frac{25ab}{30b^2}$ $\mathbf{\frac{5a}{6b}}$

11. $\frac{-8y^4z}{20y^6z^2}$ $\mathbf{\frac{-2}{5y^2z}}$

12. $\frac{5(x-1)}{8(x-1)}$ $\mathbf{\frac{5}{8}}$

13. $\frac{y(y+7)}{9(y+7)}$ $\mathbf{\frac{y}{9}}$

14. $\frac{x^2-4x}{3(x-4)}$ $\mathbf{\frac{x}{3}}$

15. $\frac{x^2+2x}{5x+10}$ $\mathbf{\frac{x}{5}}$

16. $\frac{x^2+5x}{(x+5)(x-7)}$ $\mathbf{\frac{x}{x-7}}$

17. $\frac{x^2-6x}{x^2-4x-12}$ $\mathbf{\frac{x}{x+2}}$

18. $\frac{(x+4)(x+4)}{(x+4)(x-2)}$ $\mathbf{\frac{x+4}{x-2}}$

19. $\frac{b^2+6b+9}{b^2-2b-15}$ $\mathbf{\frac{b+3}{b-5}}$

20. $\frac{y^2-36}{y^2+9y+18}$ $\mathbf{\frac{y-6}{y+3}}$

21. $\frac{x^2-16}{x^2+x-12}$ $\mathbf{\frac{x-4}{x-3}}$

22. $\frac{y^2+4y+4}{y^2-4}$ $\mathbf{\frac{y+2}{y-2}}$

23. $\frac{a^2+3a}{a^2-3a-18}$ $\mathbf{\frac{a}{a-6}}$

24. $\frac{y^2+7y+10}{y^2+5y}$ $\mathbf{\frac{y+2}{y}}$

25. $\frac{x^2+4x+3}{x^2+3x+2}$ $\mathbf{\frac{x+3}{x+2}}$

26. $\frac{x^2-6x+8}{x^2+x-6}$ $\mathbf{\frac{x-4}{x+3}}$

27. $\frac{9-x^2}{x^2+6x-27}$ $\mathbf{\frac{-(x+3)}{x+9}}$

15–2

NAME ______________________ DATE __________ PERIOD ______

Practice

Student Edition
Pages 644–649

Multiplying and Dividing Rational Expressions

Find each product.

1. $\frac{3x^2}{2y} \cdot \frac{y^2}{9}$

2. $\frac{4a^2b}{6b^2c} \cdot \frac{3ab}{2c}$

3. $\frac{7n}{n-2} \cdot \frac{3(n-2)}{28}$

4. $\frac{2}{m(m+3)} \cdot \frac{3m+9}{6}$

5. $\frac{4y+8}{y^2-2y} \cdot \frac{y-2}{y+2}$

6. $\frac{x^2-49}{x^2+5x} \cdot \frac{x+5}{x+7}$

7. $\frac{5x+25}{x^2-5x+6} \cdot \frac{x-3}{x+5}$

8. $\frac{a+5}{3a+6} \cdot \frac{3a^2+6a}{a^2+2a-15}$

9. $\frac{x^2+8x+12}{4x-12} \cdot \frac{2x-6}{x^2+4x-12}$

10. $\frac{2n^2-10n}{n^2-9n+20} \cdot \frac{n^2-8n+16}{4n^2}$

Find each quotient.

11. $\frac{4a^3}{b^2c} \div \frac{2a}{bc}$

12. $\frac{15x^2y^2}{3} \div 3xy$

13. $\frac{3y+9}{y+2} \div (y+3)$

14. $\frac{8n^3}{n-4} \div \frac{4n}{n-4}$

15. $\frac{6x^2y}{3y} \div 2xy$

16. $\frac{b^2-81}{b} \div (b+9)$

17. $\frac{6x^2+36x}{4x} \div \frac{4x+24}{2x^2}$

18. $\frac{y^2+5y-14}{9y} \div \frac{y^2-8y+12}{3y^2}$

19. $\frac{x^2-2x-15}{x-2} \div \frac{x^2-10x+25}{2-x}$

20. $\frac{y^2-8y+7}{5y^2} \div \frac{7-y}{10y}$

NAME ______________________ DATE __________ PERIOD _____

Practice

Multiplying and Dividing Rational Expressions

Find each product.

1. $\frac{3x^2}{2y} \cdot \frac{y^2}{9}$ $\mathbf{\frac{x^2y}{6}}$

2. $\frac{4a^2b}{6b^2c} \cdot \frac{3ab}{2c}$ $\mathbf{\frac{a^3}{c^2}}$

3. $\frac{7n}{n-2} \cdot \frac{3(n-2)}{28}$ $\mathbf{\frac{3n}{4}}$

4. $\frac{2}{m(m+3)} \cdot \frac{3m+9}{6}$ $\mathbf{\frac{1}{m}}$

5. $\frac{4y+8}{y^2-2y} \cdot \frac{y-2}{y+2}$ $\mathbf{\frac{4}{y}}$

6. $\frac{x^2-49}{x^2+5x} \cdot \frac{x+5}{x+7}$ $\mathbf{\frac{x-7}{x}}$

7. $\frac{5x+25}{x^2-5x+6} \cdot \frac{x-3}{x+5}$ $\mathbf{\frac{5}{x-2}}$

8. $\frac{a+5}{3a+6} \cdot \frac{3a^2+6a}{a^2+2a-15}$ $\mathbf{\frac{a}{a-3}}$

9. $\frac{x^2+8x+12}{4x-12} \cdot \frac{2x-6}{x^2+4x-12}$ $\mathbf{\frac{x+2}{2(x-2)}}$

10. $\frac{2n^2-10n}{n^2-9n+20} \cdot \frac{n^2-8n+16}{4n^2}$ $\mathbf{\frac{n-4}{2n}}$

Find each quotient.

11. $\frac{4a^3}{b^2c} \div \frac{2a}{bc}$ $\mathbf{\frac{2a^2}{b}}$

12. $\frac{15x^2y^2}{3} \div 3xy$ $\mathbf{\frac{5xy}{3}}$

13. $\frac{3y+9}{y+2} \div (y+3)$ $\mathbf{\frac{3}{y+2}}$

14. $\frac{8n^3}{n-4} \div \frac{4n}{n-4}$ $\mathbf{2n^2}$

15. $\frac{6x^2y}{3y} \div 2xy$ $\mathbf{\frac{x}{y}}$

16. $\frac{b^2-81}{b} \div (b+9)$ $\mathbf{\frac{b-9}{b}}$

17. $\frac{6x^2+36x}{4x} \div \frac{4x+24}{2x^2}$ $\mathbf{\frac{3x^2}{4}}$

18. $\frac{y^2+5y-14}{9y} \div \frac{y^2-8y+12}{3y^2}$ $\mathbf{\frac{y(y+7)}{3(y-6)}}$

19. $\frac{x^2-2x-15}{x-2} \div \frac{x^2-10x+25}{2-x}$ $\mathbf{\frac{-(x+3)}{x-5}}$

20. $\frac{y^2-8y+7}{5y^2} \div \frac{7-y}{10y}$ $\mathbf{\frac{-2(y-1)}{y}}$

NAME ______________________ DATE __________ PERIOD ______

Practice

Student Edition
Pages 650–655

Dividing Polynomials

Find each quotient.

1. $(4x - 2) \div (2x - 1)$

2. $(y^2 + 5y) \div (y + 5)$

3. $(9a^2 + 6a) \div (3a + 2)$

4. $(8n^3 - 4n^2) \div (4n - 2)$

5. $(x^2 - 9x + 18) \div (x - 6)$

6. $(b^2 - b - 20) \div (b - 5)$

7. $(y^2 + 4y + 4) \div (y + 2)$

8. $(m^2 - 5m - 6) \div (m + 1)$

9. $(b^2 + 11b + 30) \div (b + 4)$

10. $(x^2 - 6x + 9) \div (x - 2)$

11. $(r^2 - 4) \div (r + 3)$

12. $(4x^2 + 6x + 5) \div (2x - 2)$

13. $(3n^2 - 11n + 8) \div (n - 3)$

14. $(6y^2 + 5y - 3) \div (3y + 1)$

15. $(s^3 - 1) \div (s - 1)$

16. $(a^3 + 4a + 16) \div (a + 2)$

17. $(m^3 - 9) \div (m - 2)$

18. $(x^3 - 7x - 8) \div (x + 1)$

NAME ______________________ DATE __________ PERIOD ______

Practice

Student Edition
Pages 650–655

Dividing Polynomials

Find each quotient.

1. $(4x - 2) \div (2x - 1)$

2

2. $(y^2 + 5y) \div (y + 5)$

y

3. $(9a^2 + 6a) \div (3a + 2)$

3*a*

4. $(8n^3 - 4n^2) \div (4n - 2)$

$\mathbf{2n^2}$

5. $(x^2 - 9x + 18) \div (x - 6)$

$x - 3$

6. $(b^2 - b - 20) \div (b - 5)$

$b + 4$

7. $(y^2 + 4y + 4) \div (y + 2)$

$y + 2$

8. $(m^2 - 5m - 6) \div (m + 1)$

$m - 6$

9. $(b^2 + 11b + 30) \div (b + 4)$

$b + 7 + \frac{2}{b + 4}$

10. $(x^2 - 6x + 9) \div (x - 2)$

$x - 4 + \frac{1}{x - 2}$

11. $(r^2 - 4) \div (r + 3)$

$r - 3 + \frac{5}{r + 3}$

12. $(4x^2 + 6x + 5) \div (2x - 2)$

$2x + 5 + \frac{15}{2x - 2}$

13. $(3n^2 - 11n + 8) \div (n - 3)$

$3n - 2 + \frac{2}{n - 3}$

14. $(6y^2 + 5y - 3) \div (3y + 1)$

$2y + 1 + \frac{-4}{3y + 1}$

15. $(s^3 - 1) \div (s - 1)$

$s^2 + s + 1$

16. $(a^3 + 4a + 16) \div (a + 2)$

$a^2 - 2a + 8$

17. $(m^3 - 9) \div (m - 2)$

$m^2 + 2m + 4 + \frac{-1}{m - 2}$

18. $(x^3 - 7x - 8) \div (x + 1)$

$x^2 - x - 6 + \frac{-2}{x + 1}$

15–4

NAME ______________________ DATE __________ PERIOD ______

Practice

Student Edition
Pages 656–661

Combining Rational Expressions with Like Denominators

Find each sum or difference. Write in simplest form.

1. $\frac{8}{n} + \frac{4}{n}$

2. $\frac{3x}{9} + \frac{4x}{9}$

3. $\frac{7}{2k} - \frac{5}{2k}$

4. $\frac{6n}{n} - \frac{3n}{n}$

5. $\frac{-5a}{2} + \frac{4a}{2}$

6. $\frac{2y}{3} + \frac{y}{3}$

7. $\frac{9x}{11} - \frac{8x}{11}$

8. $\frac{6p}{5} - \frac{p}{5}$

9. $\frac{9}{16q} + \frac{3}{16q}$

10. $\frac{4t}{9} - \frac{t}{9}$

11. $\frac{1}{4m} - \frac{3}{4m}$

12. $\frac{-2}{10x} + \frac{6}{10x}$

13. $\frac{6s}{7} + \frac{8s}{7}$

14. $\frac{8}{3y} - \frac{2}{3y}$

15. $\frac{4}{x - 7} - \frac{2}{x - 7}$

16. $\frac{-2}{x + 3} + \frac{3}{x + 3}$

17. $\frac{5}{y - 4} - \frac{8}{y - 4}$

18. $\frac{3m}{m + 2} - \frac{m}{m + 2}$

19. $\frac{3n}{n - 1} + \frac{2}{n - 1}$

20. $\frac{5a}{a + 4} - \frac{7}{a + 4}$

21. $\frac{4g}{g + 3} + \frac{12}{g + 3}$

22. $\frac{2r + 2}{r - 5} - \frac{r - 4}{r - 5}$

23. $\frac{s - 3}{s + 1} + \frac{4s + 8}{s + 1}$

24. $\frac{-11b}{5b + 3} + \frac{12b - 2}{5b + 3}$

25. $\frac{15y}{4y - 2} - \frac{3y + 6}{4y - 2}$

26. $\frac{5c + 3}{2c + 1} + \frac{9c + 4}{2c + 1}$

27. $\frac{2x + 3}{3x + 4} - \frac{8x + 11}{3x + 4}$

15–4

NAME ______________________ DATE __________ PERIOD ________

Practice

Student Edition
Pages 656–661

Combining Rational Expressions with Like Denominators

Find each sum or difference. Write in simplest form.

1. $\frac{8}{n} + \frac{4}{n}$ $\mathbf{\frac{12}{n}}$

2. $\frac{3x}{9} + \frac{4x}{9}$ $\mathbf{\frac{7x}{9}}$

3. $\frac{7}{2k} - \frac{5}{2k}$ $\mathbf{\frac{1}{k}}$

4. $\frac{6n}{n} - \frac{3n}{n}$ **3**

5. $\frac{-5a}{2} + \frac{4a}{2}$ $\mathbf{-\frac{a}{2}}$

6. $\frac{2y}{3} + \frac{y}{3}$ $\mathbf{y}$

7. $\frac{9x}{11} - \frac{8x}{11}$ $\mathbf{\frac{x}{11}}$

8. $\frac{6p}{5} - \frac{p}{5}$ $\mathbf{p}$

9. $\frac{9}{16q} + \frac{3}{16q}$ $\mathbf{\frac{3}{4q}}$

10. $\frac{4t}{9} - \frac{t}{9}$ $\mathbf{\frac{t}{3}}$

11. $\frac{1}{4m} - \frac{3}{4m}$ $\mathbf{-\frac{1}{2m}}$

12. $\frac{-2}{10x} + \frac{6}{10x}$ $\mathbf{\frac{2}{5x}}$

13. $\frac{6s}{7} + \frac{8s}{7}$ $\mathbf{2s}$

14. $\frac{8}{3y} - \frac{2}{3y}$ $\mathbf{\frac{2}{y}}$

15. $\frac{4}{x-7} - \frac{2}{x-7}$ $\mathbf{\frac{2}{x-7}}$

16. $\frac{-2}{x+3} + \frac{3}{x+3}$ $\mathbf{\frac{1}{x+3}}$

17. $\frac{5}{y-4} - \frac{8}{y-4}$ $\mathbf{-\frac{3}{y-4}}$

18. $\frac{3m}{m+2} - \frac{m}{m+2}$ $\mathbf{\frac{2m}{m+2}}$

19. $\frac{3n}{n-1} + \frac{2}{n-1}$ $\mathbf{\frac{3n+2}{n-1}}$

20. $\frac{5a}{a+4} - \frac{7}{a+4}$ $\mathbf{\frac{5a-7}{a+4}}$

21. $\frac{4g}{g+3} + \frac{12}{g+3}$ **4**

22. $\frac{2r+2}{r-5} - \frac{r-4}{r-5}$ $\mathbf{\frac{r+6}{r-5}}$

23. $\frac{s-3}{s+1} + \frac{4s+8}{s+1}$ **5**

24. $\frac{-11b}{5b+3} + \frac{12b-2}{5b+3}$ $\mathbf{\frac{b-2}{5b+3}}$

25. $\frac{15y}{4y-2} - \frac{3y+6}{4y-2}$ **3**

26. $\frac{5c+3}{2c+1} + \frac{9c+4}{2c+1}$ **7**

27. $\frac{2x+3}{3x+4} - \frac{8x+11}{3x+4}$ **−2**

NAME ______________________ DATE __________ PERIOD ______

Practice

Combining Rational Expressions with Unlike Denominators

Find the LCM for each pair of expressions.

1. $4ab$, $18b$

2. $6x^2y$, $9xy$

3. $10a^2$, $12ab^2$

4. $y + 2$, $y^2 - 4$

5. $x^2 - 9$, $x^2 + 5x + 6$

6. $x^2 - 3x - 4$, $2x^2 - 2x - 8$

Write each pair of expressions with the same LCD.

7. $\frac{4}{b}, \frac{5}{ab}$

8. $\frac{5}{6c^2}, \frac{3}{8c}$

9. $\frac{6}{7x^2y}, \frac{4}{5xy}$

10. $\frac{3}{r + 4}, \frac{7}{2r + 8}$

11. $\frac{x}{x - 2}, \frac{x + 1}{x - 5}$

12. $\frac{3}{y - 4}, \frac{2y}{y^2 - 16}$

Find each sum or difference. Write in simplest form.

13. $\frac{2k}{8} + \frac{3k}{16}$

14. $\frac{n}{2} - \frac{n}{7}$

15. $\frac{7}{3b} - \frac{3}{b}$

16. $\frac{5}{x} + \frac{3}{y}$

17. $\frac{2}{m^2n} - \frac{6}{mn}$

18. $\frac{c}{4c} + \frac{8}{c}$

19. $\frac{1}{6a} - \frac{2}{9a^2}$

20. $\frac{2}{3ab} + \frac{3b}{4ab}$

21. $\frac{p}{4p^2q} + \frac{3}{5pq}$

22. $\frac{2x}{3xy^2} - \frac{2}{5xy}$

23. $\frac{2s}{s^2 - 4} + \frac{4}{s + 2}$

24. $\frac{b}{b^2 - 9} - \frac{5}{b - 3}$

25. $\frac{-5}{2r + 3} + \frac{7}{6r + 9}$

26. $\frac{6}{y + 2} + \frac{3}{y}$

27. $\frac{x}{x - 3} - \frac{2}{x - 4}$

NAME ______________________ DATE __________ PERIOD ______

15–5 Practice

Student Edition
Pages 662–667

Combining Rational Expressions with Unlike Denominators

Find the LCM for each pair of expressions.

1. $4ab$, $18b$
   $36ab$

2. $6x^2y$, $9xy$
   $18x^2y$

3. $10a^2$, $12ab^2$
   $60a^2b^2$

4. $y + 2$, $y^2 - 4$
   $(y + 2)(y - 2)$

5. $x^2 - 9$, $x^2 + 5x + 6$
   $(x + 2)(x + 3)(x - 3)$

6. $x^2 - 3x - 4$, $2x^2 - 2x - 8$
   $(x + 1)(x - 4)(2x + 2)$

Write each pair of expressions with the same LCD.

7. $\frac{4}{b}, \frac{5}{ab}$
   $\frac{4a}{ab}, \frac{5}{ab}$

8. $\frac{5}{6c^2}, \frac{3}{8c}$
   $\frac{20}{24c^2}, \frac{9c}{24c^2}$

9. $\frac{6}{7x^2y}, \frac{4}{5xy}$
   $\frac{30}{35x^2y}, \frac{28x}{35x^2y}$

10. $\frac{3}{r + 4}, \frac{7}{2r + 8}$
    $\frac{6}{2(r + 4)}, \frac{7}{2(r + 4)}$

11. $\frac{x}{x - 2}, \frac{x + 1}{x - 5}$
    $\frac{x(x - 5)}{(x - 2)(x - 5)}, \frac{(x + 1)(x - 2)}{(x - 2)(x - 5)}$

12. $\frac{3}{y - 4}, \frac{2y}{y^2 - 16}$
    $\frac{3(y + 4)}{y^2 - 16}, \frac{2y}{y^2 - 16}$

Find each sum or difference. Write in simplest form.

13. $\frac{2k}{8} + \frac{3k}{16}$ **$\frac{7k}{16}$**

14. $\frac{n}{2} - \frac{n}{7}$ **$\frac{5n}{14}$**

15. $\frac{7}{3b} - \frac{3}{b}$ **$-\frac{2}{3b}$**

16. $\frac{5}{x} + \frac{3}{y}$ **$\frac{5y + 3x}{xy}$**

17. $\frac{2}{m^2n} - \frac{6}{mn}$ **$\frac{2 - 6m}{m^2n}$**

18. $\frac{c}{4c} + \frac{8}{c}$ **$\frac{c + 32}{4c}$**

19. $\frac{1}{6a} - \frac{2}{9a^2}$ **$\frac{3a - 4}{18a^2}$**

20. $\frac{2}{3ab} + \frac{3b}{4ab}$ **$\frac{8 + 9b}{12ab}$**

21. $\frac{p}{4p^2q} + \frac{3}{5pq}$ **$\frac{17p}{20p^2q}$**

22. $\frac{2x}{3xy^2} - \frac{2}{5xy}$ **$\frac{10x - 6y}{15xy^2}$**

23. $\frac{2s}{s^2 - 4} + \frac{4}{s + 2}$ **$\frac{6s - 8}{s^2 - 4}$**

24. $\frac{b}{b^2 - 9} - \frac{5}{b - 3}$ **$\frac{-4b - 15}{b^2 - 9}$**

25. $\frac{-5}{2r + 3} + \frac{7}{6r + 9}$
    $\frac{-8}{3(2r + 3)}$

26. $\frac{6}{y + 2} + \frac{3}{y}$
    $\frac{9y + 6}{y(y + 2)}$

27. $\frac{x}{x - 3} - \frac{2}{x - 4}$
    $\frac{x^2 - 6x + 6}{(x - 3)(x - 4)}$

15–6

NAME ______________________ DATE __________ PERIOD ______

Practice

Student Edition
Pages 668–673

Solving Rational Equations

Solve each equation. Check your solution.

1. $\frac{c}{2} + \frac{c}{2} = \frac{1}{2}$

2. $\frac{3b}{5} - \frac{1}{5} = \frac{b}{5}$

3. $\frac{8}{a} = \frac{12}{a} + 5$

4. $\frac{7}{b} - 2 = \frac{3}{b}$

5. $\frac{7}{9t} - \frac{5}{6t} = \frac{1}{3}$

6. $\frac{4}{5x} + \frac{1}{4x} = \frac{3}{4}$

7. $\frac{3x}{4} - \frac{2x}{3} = \frac{1}{4}$

8. $\frac{s+7}{6} - 2 = \frac{s}{4}$

9. $\frac{n-3}{2} = \frac{n}{5} + 3$

10. $\frac{y+6}{3} - \frac{y+12}{7} = 2$

11. $\frac{11}{p-2} - \frac{2}{p-2} = -8$

12. $\frac{x+5}{2x} + \frac{x+3}{3x} = \frac{1}{3}$

13. $\frac{2}{n} - \frac{3}{n+1} = \frac{3}{n+1}$

14. $\frac{6}{y-3} - \frac{5}{y} = \frac{3}{y}$

15. $\frac{6}{s} + \frac{3s}{s-2} - 2 = 3$

16. $\frac{5}{k} + \frac{k-2}{k+1} = 1$

17. $\frac{r+2}{r} - \frac{r+2}{r-5} = -\frac{3}{r-5}$

18. $\frac{2c}{c+3} - \frac{4}{2c+6} = 4$

19. $\frac{3b}{b+2} + \frac{3}{3b+6} = 2$

20. $\frac{2m}{m+3} - \frac{4}{m-3} = 2$

21. $\frac{y}{y+2} + \frac{3}{y-2} = \frac{y}{y-2}$

Practice

Solving Rational Equations

Solve each equation. Check your solution.

1. $\frac{c}{2} + \frac{c}{2} = \frac{1}{2}$ $\mathbf{\frac{1}{2}}$

2. $\frac{3b}{5} - \frac{1}{5} = \frac{b}{5}$ $\mathbf{\frac{1}{2}}$

3. $\frac{8}{a} = \frac{12}{a} + 5$ $\mathbf{-\frac{4}{5}}$

4. $\frac{7}{b} - 2 = \frac{3}{b}$ **2**

5. $\frac{7}{9t} - \frac{5}{6t} = \frac{1}{3}$ $\mathbf{-\frac{1}{6}}$

6. $\frac{4}{5x} + \frac{1}{4x} = \frac{3}{4}$ $\mathbf{\frac{7}{5}}$

7. $\frac{3x}{4} - \frac{2x}{3} = \frac{1}{4}$ **3**

8. $\frac{s+7}{6} - 2 = \frac{s}{4}$ **−10**

9. $\frac{n-3}{2} = \frac{n}{5} + 3$ **15**

10. $\frac{y+6}{3} - \frac{y+12}{7} = 2$ **9**

11. $\frac{11}{p-2} - \frac{2}{p-2} = -8$ $\mathbf{\frac{7}{8}}$

12. $\frac{x+5}{2x} + \frac{x+3}{3x} = \frac{1}{3}$ **−7**

13. $\frac{2}{n} - \frac{3}{n+1} = \frac{3}{n+1}$ $\mathbf{\frac{1}{2}}$

14. $\frac{6}{y-3} - \frac{5}{y} = \frac{3}{y}$ **12**

15. $\frac{6}{s} + \frac{3s}{s-2} - 2 = 3$ **1**

16. $\frac{5}{k} + \frac{k-2}{k+1} = 1$ $\mathbf{-\frac{5}{2}}$

17. $\frac{r+2}{r} - \frac{r+2}{r-5} = -\frac{3}{r-5}$ **−5**

18. $\frac{2c}{c+3} - \frac{4}{2c+6} = 4$ **−7**

19. $\frac{3b}{b+2} + \frac{3}{3b+6} = 2$ **3**

20. $\frac{2m}{m+3} - \frac{4}{m-3} = 2$ $\mathbf{\frac{3}{5}}$

21. $\frac{y}{y+2} + \frac{3}{y-2} = \frac{y}{y-2}$ **6**